ADVANCED MODULAR MATHEMATICS

Mechanics
3 & 4

A and AS level

The Uni　　　*London modular mathematics syllabus*

Graham Smithers

for

NATIONAL
EXTENSION
COLLEGE

510 SMI

CollinsEducational

An Imprint of HarperCollinsPublishe

D0234780

Published by Collins Educational
An imprint of HarperCollins*Publishers*
77-85 Fulham Palace Road
Hammersmith
London W6 8JB

© National Extension College Trust Ltd 1995
First published 1995
ISBN 0 00 322401 5

This book was written by Graham Smithers for the National Extension College Trust Ltd.

All rights reserved. No part of this publication may be reproduced, stored in a retrieval system or transmitted in any form or by any means, electronic, mechanical, photocopying or otherwise, without the prior permission of the publishers.

Designed by Derek Lee
Cover design and implementation by Derek Lee
Page layout by Mary Bishop
Project editor, Hugh Hillyard-Parker

The author and publishers thank Pat Perkins and Clive Morris for their comments on this book.

Printed and bound in the UK by Scotprint Ltd, Musselburgh

The National Extension College is an educational trust and a registered charity with a distinguished body of trustees. It is an independent, self-financing organisation.

Since it was established in 1963, NEC has pioneered the development of flexible learning for adults. NEC is actively developing innovative materials and systems for distance-learning options from basic skills and general education to degree and professional training.

For further details of NEC resources that support *Advanced Modular Mathematics*, and other NEC courses, contact NEC Customer Services:

National Extension College Trust Ltd
18 Brooklands Avenue
Cambridge CB2 2HN
Telephone 01223 316644, Fax 01223 313586

CONTENTS

M3/M4

Advanced Modular Mathematics

FOREWORD This book is one of a series covering the University of London Examination and Assessment Council's modular 'A' level Mathematics syllabus. It covers all the subject material for Mechanics 3 and 4 (Modules M3 and M4). Sections 1–4 focus on the topics needed for M3, while Sections 5–9 move on to the more advanced topics of Module M4.

While this series of text books has been structured to match the University of London (ULEAC) syllabuses, we hope that the informal style of the text and approach to important concepts will encourage other readers, whose final examinations are from other examination Boards, to use the books for extra reading and practice.

This book is meant to be *used*: read the text, study the worked examples and work through the exercises, which will give you practice in the basic skills you need for maths at this level. There are many books for advanced mathematics, which include many more exercises: use this book to direct your studies, making use of as many other resources as you can. This book will act as a bridge between your new syllabus and the many older books that can still give even more practice in advanced mathematics.

Exercises are given at the end of each section; these range from the basic to exam-type questions. Many exercises, and worked examples, are based on *applications* of the mathematics in this book. We have given answers to all problems, so that you can check your work.

The National Extension College has more experience of flexible-learning materials than any other body (see p. ii). This series is a distillation of that experience: *Advanced Modular Mathematics* helps to put you in control of your own learning.

Permissions

We are grateful to the University of London Examinations and Assessment Council for permission to reproduce questions from past examination papers in the Exercises at the end of the following sections.

Section 3: Exercise 10 (M3 Specimen paper, Q5); 20 (M3 Specimen paper, Q3)

Section 4: Exercise 12 (6386, M3 June 1993, Q2); Exercise 13 (6386, M3 June 1993, Q3)

Section 5: Exercise 1 (M4 Specimen paper, Q1); Exercise 9 (M4 Specimen paper, Q5); Exercise 14 (6387, M4 January 1993, Q2); Exercise 20 (6387, M4 January 1994, Q2)

Section 6: Exercise 8 (6386, M3 June 1992, Q2); Exercise 12 (6386, M3 January 1993, Q1)

Section 7: Exercise 12 (M4 Specimen paper, Q7)

Section 8: Exercise 16 (M4 Specimen paper, Q4)

The University of London Examinations and Assessment Council accepts no responsibility whatsoever for the accuracy or method of working in the answers given, which are entirely the responsibility of the author.

Moments of inertia of a rigid body

Emma is looking at the grandfather clock in the hall and is trying to set up a mathematical model for the swing of the pendulum.

She has already studied Module M2 and so she could model the pendulum as a particle on the end of a light rod. So, applying her knowledge of motion in a vertical circle, she could set up the equations of motion and thus get a solution. But this isn't a very realistic model because the pendulum itself has weight and the 'bob' on the end is certainly not a particle, it is more likely to be a solid circular disc. If, then, she modelled the pendulum as a uniform circular disc attached to the end of a uniform rod, how could she set up the equations of motion? In particular, how could she obtain the kinetic energy of the system?

In order to write down the kinetic energy of a rigid body, we need to know its *moment of inertia* about a particular axis. (In Emma's case, she would need to know the moment of inertia about a line perpendicular to the face of the clock and through the point of suspension.) In this section we will see how to work out the moment of inertia for assorted rigid bodies about different axes.

When you've finished this section you should be able to:

● write down the moment of inertia of a uniform circular ring about a line through its centre and perpendicular to its plane
● use integration to find moments of inertia formulae for uniform circular discs, uniform rods and uniform heavy spheres
● use the theorems of parallel axes and perpendicular axes, so enabling you to move from one axis to another
● use these results to work out the moment of inertia of a composite body, e.g. Emma and her pendulum.

Introducing moments of inertia

Imagine a light rod of length a with a particle of mass m attached to the end. The rod is then made to move in a horizontal circle, with angular velocity ω, about a fixed vertical axis through the other end of the rod.

Figure 1.1

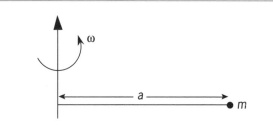

The kinetic energy of the particle is $\frac{1}{2}m(a\omega)^2 = \frac{1}{2}ma^2\omega^2$.

Now let us imagine a whole series of particles, of masses $m_1, m_2 \dots$, attached to the rod and at distance $a_1, a_2, \dots$ from the axis of rotation. The kinetic energy of this system is:

$$\frac{1}{2}(m_1a_1^2 + m_2a_2^2 + \dots)\,\omega^2$$

The expression inside the bracket is called the **moment of inertia (MI) of the system about the given axis of rotation**.

For a continuous distribution of matter (for example a uniform rod), the finding of its MI will involve some integration. (The procedure is similar to that which was used in Module M2 for finding the centre of mass of uniform rigid bodies.)

Finding moments of inertia

To obtain the standard results, we need to remember that:

$$MI = \Sigma ma^2 = \int \text{Mass} \times (\text{Distance})^2$$

where each particle of mass m is at a distance a from the axis being considered.

Example

Find the moment of inertia of a uniform circular ring, of mass M and radius a, about an axis through its centre and perpendicular to its plane.

Solution

Each particle of the ring is at the same distance a from the axis.

$\therefore$ $MI = \Sigma ma^2 = a^2 \Sigma m = Ma^2$

Example Prove that the moment of inertia of a uniform rod, mass M, length $2a$, about an axis through its centre perpendicular to its length is $\frac{1}{3}Ma^2$.

Solution Consider a small element of the rod of length dx where the distance from the centre of the rod is x.

Figure 1.2

axis
x
dx
rod
centre of rod

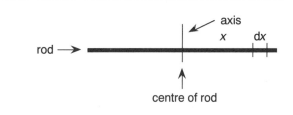

If the mass per unit length of the rod is ρ, then:

$$\text{MI} = \int_{-a}^{a} (\rho \, dx)x^2 = \int_{-a}^{a} \rho x^2 \, dx = \left[\rho \frac{x^3}{3}\right]_{-a}^{a} = \frac{2}{3}\rho a^3$$

But $M = 2a\rho$ $\quad \therefore$ $\text{MI} = \frac{1}{3}Ma^2$

[In order to be strictly correct, we ought to have taken the small length of rod as δx. Then the moment of inertia of the rod about the given axis would be the limit of $\Sigma(\rho\,\delta x)x^2$ as $\delta x \to 0$

i.e. $\quad \text{MI} = \int_{-a}^{a} (\rho \, dx)x^2$, as before.

However this strict approach is not necessary and the immediate use of dx is both quicker and 'acceptable' in proofs.]

Example Prove that the moment of inertia of a uniform circular disc, mass M, and radius r, about an axis through its centre perpendicular to its plane is $\frac{1}{2}Mr^2$.

Solution The disc can be considered as being made up of a series of concentric rings. If one of these rings has radius x, then its mass may be taken as $2\pi x\rho$ dx

Figure 1.3

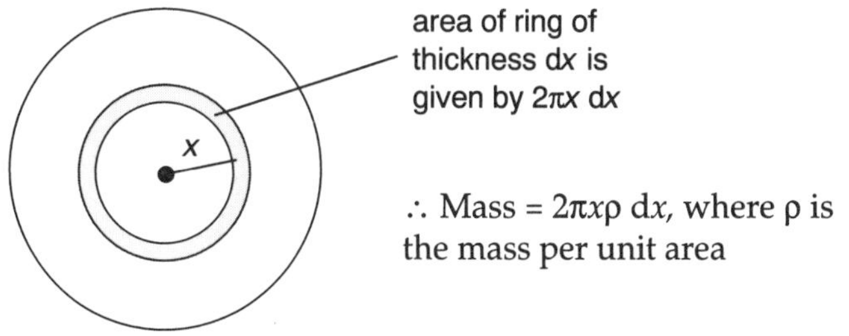

area of ring of
thickness dx is
given by 2πx dx
x
∴ Mass = 2πxρ dx, where ρ is
the mass per unit area

∴ For the whole disc we have:

$$\text{MI} = \int_0^r (2\pi x \rho \, dx) \, x^2 = 2\pi\rho \int_0^r x^3 \, dx = 2\pi\rho \left[\frac{x^4}{4}\right]_0^r = \frac{1}{2}\pi\rho r^4$$

But $M = \pi r^2 \rho$ ∴ $\text{MI} = \frac{1}{2}Mr^2$

Example

Prove that the moment of inertia of a uniform solid sphere, mass M, radius r, about a diameter is $\frac{2}{5}Mr^2$.

Solution

The sphere can be considered as being made up of a series of circular discs perpendicular to the axis, of which a typical one has its centre at a distance x from the centre of the sphere and thickness dx.

Figure 1.4

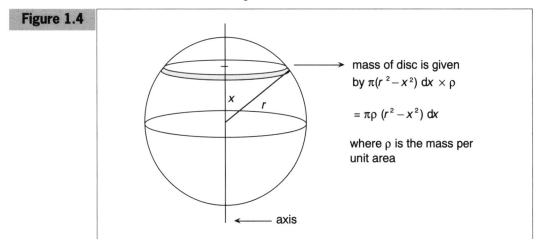

mass of disc is given by $\pi(r^2 - x^2) \, dx \times \rho$

$= \pi\rho \, (r^2 - x^2) \, dx$

where ρ is the mass per unit area

axis

The moment of inertia of this disc about the given axis is:

$$\frac{1}{2}\left(\pi\rho \, (r^2 - x^2) \, dx\right)(r^2 - x^2) \quad \text{or} \quad \frac{1}{2}\pi\rho \left(r^2 - x^2\right)^2 dx$$

(using the result in the previous example).

∴ For the whole sphere we have:

$$\text{MI} = \int_{-r}^r \frac{1}{2}\pi\rho \, (r^2 - x^2)^2 \, dx \ = \frac{1}{2}\pi\rho \int_{-r}^r \left[r^4 - 2r^2x^2 + x^4\right] dx$$

$$= \frac{1}{2}\pi\rho \left[r^4 x - \frac{2r^2x^3}{3} + \frac{x^5}{5}\right]_{-r}^r$$

$$= \frac{8}{15}\pi\rho r^5$$

But $M = \frac{4}{3}\pi r^3 \rho$ ∴ $\text{MI} = \frac{2}{5}Mr^2$

Examination note

Your syllabus requires that you are able to prove the above three results. We recommend that, before you sit the exam, you completely master these proofs so that you can reproduce them, and work with them, quickly and accurately.

To summarise:

The moment of inertia of

(a) a uniform rod, mass M, length $2a$ about an axis through its centre perpendicular to its length is $\frac{1}{3}Ma^2$

(b) a uniform circular disc, mass M, radius r, about an axis through its centre perpendicular to its plane is $\frac{1}{2}Mr^2$

(c) a uniform solid sphere, mass M, radius r, about a diameter is $\frac{2}{5}Mr^2$.

Fortunately there are two results concerning moment of inertia that make calculations so much easier. You need to be able to use them both.

The theorem of parallel axes: $I_P = I_G + Md^2$

Suppose that we know the moment of inertia of a given body about an axis through its centre of mass G. Let's call it I_G. If we are given another parallel axis through P distance d from G, then the moment of inertia of the body about this new axis is $I_G + Md^2$, where M is the mass of the body:

i.e. $I_P = I_G + Md^2$

Figure 1.5

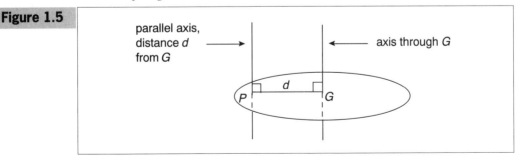

parallel axis, distance d from G axis through G

P d G

Proof of the parallel axes theorem

(This is included for completeness only. You will *not* be asked to reproduce the proof in the examination. You will simply be asked to *use* the result.)

Let us choose our axes, so that the axis through P is the z-axis. If the coordinates of the centre of mass G are $(\bar{x}, \bar{y}, \bar{z})$, then the coordinates of any other point mass m of the body can be written as $(\bar{x} + x', \bar{y} + y', \bar{z} + z')$.

Hence:

- $I_G = \Sigma m\,(x'^2 + y'^2)$, since the axis through G is parallel to the z-axis   ... ①

- $Md^2 = \Sigma m\,(\bar{x}^2 + \bar{y}^2)$, since the axis through P is the z-axis   ... ②

- $\Sigma mx' = \Sigma my' = \Sigma mz' = 0$, using the properties of the centre of mass G ... ③

$$\therefore \quad I_P = \Sigma m\left[(\bar{x} + x')^2 + (\bar{y} + y')^2 \right]$$

$$= \Sigma m(x'^2 + y'^2) \quad + (\bar{x}^2 + \bar{y}^2)\,\Sigma m \quad + 2\bar{x}\,\Sigma mx' \quad + 2\bar{y}\,\Sigma my'$$

$$= I_G \qquad\qquad\quad + Md^2 \qquad\qquad + \quad 0 \qquad\quad + \quad 0\,,$$

using ①, ② and ③ above.

$$\therefore\; I_P = I_G + Md^2, \text{ as required.}$$

The theorem of perpendicular axes: $I_Z = I_X + I_Y$

Suppose that we are given a lamina and two perpendicular axes in the plane of the lamina. Let's call them OX and OY and let the corresponding moments of inertia be I_X and I_Y. If OZ is perpendicular to both of these axes then, the moment of inertia of the lamina about OZ is given by $I_X + I_Y$.

i.e. $I_Z = I_X + I_Y$

Figure 1.6

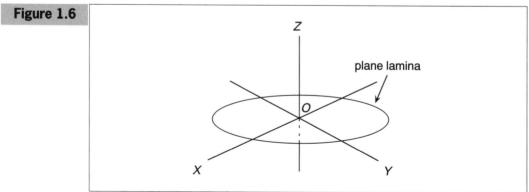

Proof of the perpendicular axis theorem

(Again, this is included for completeness only. You will *not* be asked to reproduce the proof in the examination, but you will need to be able to use the result.)

Take the plane of the lamina as the x–y plane and the perpendicular axis OZ as the z-axis. Since $z = 0$ for all points on the lamina

$$I_X = \Sigma my^2, \quad I_Y = \Sigma mx^2 \text{ and } I_Z = \Sigma m(x^2 + y^2)$$

$\therefore \qquad I_z = I_X + I_Y$, as required.

There are *two important points to remember* about this theorem of perpendicular axes:

● The theorem only works for a *lamina* (whereas the theorem of parallel axes worked for a body).

● The two axes that are added have to be *in the plane of the lamina*.

Let's see how these theorems can be put to good use.

Example Write down the moment of inertia of a uniform rod AB of mass M and length $2a$ about an axis perpendicular to the rod and through its centre. Deduce the moment of inertia of the rod about a parallel axis through the end A.

Solution Look at Figure 1.7.

Figure 1.7

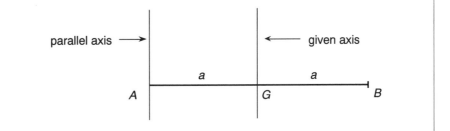

From our first example we have $I_G = \frac{1}{3} Ma^2$

$\therefore$ The parallel axes theorem gives:

$$I_A = I_G + Ma^2 \Rightarrow I_A = \frac{1}{3} Ma^2 + Ma^2$$

$$\Rightarrow I_A = \frac{4}{3} Ma^2.$$

| Example | G is the centre of mass of a body of mass M and points P and Q are such that PGQ is a straight line. Parallel axes are drawn through P and Q perpendicular to the line PQ, and the moments of inertia of the body about these axes are I_P and I_Q respectively. |

If $GP = p$ and $GQ = q$, prove that $I_P = I_Q + M(p^2 - q^2)$

| Solution | Look at Figure 1.8. |

| Figure 1.8 | 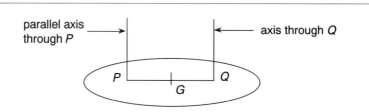 |

parallel axis through P axis through Q

P Q

G

The parallel axes theorem gives:

$$I_P = I_G + Mp^2 \quad \text{and} \quad I_Q = I_G + Mq^2$$

Now eliminate I_G to get the required result,

$$I_P = I_Q + M(p^2 - q^2)$$

It is important to note that $I_P \neq I_Q + M(p + q)^2$, i.e. we cannot use the parallel axes theorem to go directly from Q to P. We can only use the parallel axes theorem if we work *from* G.

| Example | Write down the moment of inertia of a uniform circular disc, mass M, radius r, about an axis through its centre perpendicular to the plane of the disc. Deduce the moment of inertia of this disc about an axis through its centre *in* the plane of the disc. Hence find the moment of inertia of the disc about any tangent in the plane of the disc. |

| Solution | Look at Figure 1.9. |

| Figure 1.9 | |

axis perpendicular to the plane of the disc

G

From our second example we have $I_G = \frac{1}{2}Mr^2$.

If GX and GY are two perpendicular axes in the plane of the disc then, by symmetry, the moment of inertia of the disc about each of these axes will be the same. If we call this common value I and then use the perpendicular axis theorem, we get:

$$I_G = I + I \quad \Rightarrow \quad \tfrac{1}{2}Mr^2 = 2I$$

$$\Rightarrow \quad I = \tfrac{1}{4}Mr^2$$

∴   The moment of inertia of the disc about an axis in the plane of the disc is $\tfrac{1}{4}Mr^2$

If T is any point on the circumference of the disc then, using the parallel axes theorem we have:

Figure 1.10

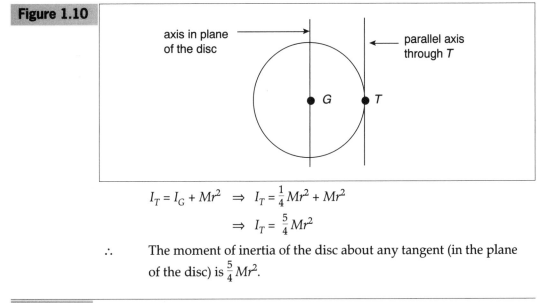

$$I_T = I_G + Mr^2 \quad \Rightarrow \quad I_T = \tfrac{1}{4}Mr^2 + Mr^2$$

$$\Rightarrow \quad I_T = \tfrac{5}{4}Mr^2$$

∴   The moment of inertia of the disc about any tangent (in the plane of the disc) is $\tfrac{5}{4}Mr^2$.

Example   A uniform rectangular lamina has mass M and sides $2a$ and $2b$. Its centre of mass is G. Find the moment of inertia of the rectangular lamina about the following axes:

(a)   through G and parallel to the side of length $2a$

(b)   through G and parallel to the side of length $2b$

(c)   through G and perpendicular to the plane of the lamina

(d)   through V and perpendicular to the plane of the lamina (when V is any vertex of the rectangle).

Solution   (a) Look at Figure 1.11.

Figure 1.11

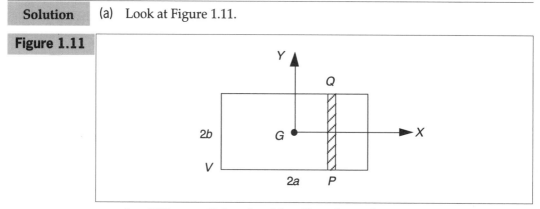

Let GX be parallel to the side of length $2a$. If we take a thin strip PQ perpendicular to GX (see Figure 1.11), then this may be regarded as a uniform rod PQ of length $2b$ and mass m.

∴ Its moment of inertia about GX is $\frac{1}{3}mb^2$.

But the rectangular lamina is the sum of such strips

∴ $I_{GX} = \Sigma \frac{1}{3}mb^2 = \frac{1}{3}b^2\Sigma m = \frac{1}{3}Mb^2$

∴ The moment of inertia about GX is $\frac{1}{3}Mb^2$

(b) Look at Figure 1.12.

Figure 1.12

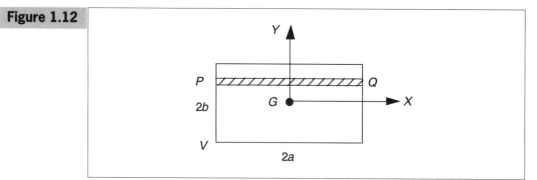

Let GY be parallel to the side of length $2b$. If we take a thin strip PQ perpendicular to GY (see Figure 1.12), then this may be regarded as a uniform rod PQ of length $2a$ of mass m'

∴ Its moment of inertia about GY is $\frac{1}{3}m'a^2$

But the rectangular lamina is the sum of such strips

∴ $I_{GY} = \Sigma \frac{1}{3}m'a^2 = \frac{1}{3}a^2\Sigma m' = \frac{1}{3}Ma^2$

∴ The moment of inertia about GY is $\frac{1}{3}Ma^2$

(c)   The perpendicular axis theorem gives:

$$I_G = I_{GX} + I_{GY} \Rightarrow I_G = \tfrac{1}{3}Mb^2 + \tfrac{1}{3}Ma^2 \Rightarrow I_G = \tfrac{1}{3}M(b^2 + a^2)$$

(d)   The parallel axes theorem gives:

$$I_V = I_G + M(a^2 + b^2) \Rightarrow I_V = \tfrac{1}{3}M(b^2 + a^2) + M(a^2 + b^2)$$

$$\Rightarrow I_V = \tfrac{4}{3}M(a^2 + b^2)$$

Radius of gyration

Since all moments of inertia I can be written in the form mass $\times$ (distance)^2, we often write $I = Mk^2$ and call the length k the **radius of gyration**.

Example   Find the radius of gyration of a uniform solid sphere, mass M, radius r about a diameter.

Solution   From the Example on page 4 we have:

$$\text{MI} = \tfrac{2}{5}Mr^2 \Rightarrow \text{MI} = M\left(r\sqrt{\tfrac{2}{5}}\right)^2 \Rightarrow k = r\sqrt{\tfrac{2}{5}}.$$

$\therefore$ The radius of gyration is $\left(\sqrt{\tfrac{2}{5}}\right)r$.

Composite bodies

We now return to the problem posed in the introduction – Emma and her pendulum. All we need to know is that, to find the moment of inertia of a composite body, you simply add the separate moments of inertia for each body.

Example   Figure 1.13 shows a mathematical model for a pendulum. It consists of a thin uniform rod PQ, of mass $2M$ and length $4a$, attached to the point Q on the surface of a uniform circular disc, of mass $5M$ and radius a, so that PQ produced passes through the centre G of the disc. The pendulum can rotate in a vertical plane about a fixed horizontal axis through P.

Find the moment of inertia of the pendulum about this horizontal axis through P.

Figure 1.13

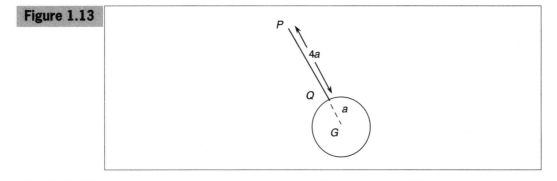

Solution   The moment of inertia of rod PQ about the axis through P (see the Example on page 7) is:

$$\tfrac{4}{3}(2M)(2a)^2, \quad \text{i.e.} \quad \tfrac{32}{3}Ma^2 \qquad\qquad \dots \text{①}$$

The moment of inertia of the circular disc about the parallel axes through G is (see Example on page 3).

$$\tfrac{1}{2}(5M)a^2, \quad \text{i.e.} \quad \tfrac{5}{2}Ma^2$$

∴   Using the parallel axes theorem, the moment of inertia of the circular disc about the parallel axis through P is

$$\tfrac{5}{2}Ma^2 + (5M)(5a)^2, \quad \text{i.e.} \quad 127\tfrac{1}{2}Ma^2 \qquad\qquad \dots \text{②}$$

Now add ① and ② to get the total moment of inertia

$$\text{i.e.} \quad \tfrac{32}{3}Ma^2 + 127\tfrac{1}{2}Ma^2 \;=\; 138\tfrac{1}{6}Ma^2$$

∴   The total moment of inertia about the horizontal axis through P is $138\tfrac{1}{6}Ma^2$

Example   Figure 1.14 shows a uniform rod AB of mass M and length $4a$. Attached to A and B are particles of mass M and $3M$ respectively. Find the moment of inertia of the system about an axis through A perpendicular to the rod AB.

Figure 1.14

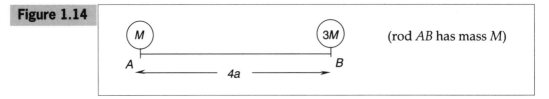

Solution   For the rod AB, the moment of inertia about the axis through A (see the Example on page 6) is $\frac{4}{3}M(2a)^2$, i.e. $5\frac{1}{3}Ma^2$.

The moment of inertia for the particle at B about the axis through A is

$$3M(4a)^2, \quad \text{i.e. } 48\,Ma^2$$

The particle of A has zero moment of inertia about the axis through A since it lies on that axis.

∴   The total moment of inertia about an axis through A perpendicular to AB is

$$5\frac{1}{3}Ma^2 + 48Ma^2, \quad \text{i.e. } 53\frac{1}{3}Ma^2$$

You should now be able to work through Exercises 1–13 on pp. 13–15.

EXERCISES

1 AB is a uniform rod of length $2a$ and mass m. To B is attached a particle of mass $2m$. Find the moment of inertia of the system about an axis through the centre of the rod perpendicular to its length. Find also the moment of inertia about a parallel axis through A.

2 Write down the moment of inertia of a uniform circular disc, mass m, radius r, about an axis through the centre perpendicular to its plane.

A solid cylinder has base radius r and height h. Its mass is M.

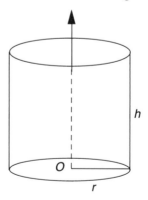

Deduce the moment of inertia of the cylinder about its axis of symmetry.

3 Find the moment of inertia of a circular ring, of mass M and radius a, about an axis through a point on its circumference and perpendicular to its plane.

4 Find the moment of inertia of a square lamina, of mass M and side $2a$, about an axis perpendicular to the plane of the lamina and through one corner.

5 Find the moment of inertia of a circular ring, of mass M and radius a, about a diameter.

6 Find the radius of gyration of a circular ring of radius a about a tangent line in the plane of the ring.

7 Find the radius of gyration of a circular disc of radius a about a tangent line in the plane of the disc.

8 Show that the moment of inertia of a cube, of mass m and edge $2a$, about one of its edges is $\frac{8}{3}ma^2$.

9 Find the radius of gyration for uniform solids of the shapes given below.
   (a) A circular disc of radius r, about a perpendicular axis through a point of the rim
   (b) A brick with edges a, b, c about an axis through the centre parallel to an edge of length a
   (c) A square wire frame, of side $2a$, about a perpendicular axis through one corner.

10 Find the moment of inertia of a uniform square lamina of side $2a$ and mass m about a diagonal.

11

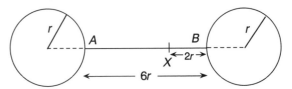

The diagram shows two uniform spheres each of mass $5m$ and radius r, joined by a thin uniform rod AB of length $6r$ and mass $6m$. The points A and B lie on the line joining the centre of the spheres. If $BX = 2r$, find the moment of inertia of the system about an axis through X perpendicular to the rod.

12 A uniform disc, of mass m and radius r, has a particle of mass M attached to a point distance $\frac{1}{2}r$ from the centre of the disc. Find the moment of inertia of the system about an axis through the centre of the disc and perpendicular to its plane.

13

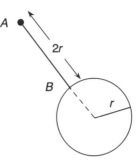

The figure shows a pendulum. It consists of a thin uniform rod AB, of mass $\dfrac{3m}{2}$ and length $2r$, attached to the point B on the surface of a uniform solid sphere, of mass $5m$ and radius r, so that AB produced passes through the centre of the sphere. The pendulum can rotate in a vertical plane about a fixed smooth horizontal axis through A. Show that the moment of inertia of the pendulum about the horizontal axis through A is $49\,mr^2$.

SUMMARY

You should now be able to:

● prove by integration the following three results for moments of inertia:

   (a) uniform rod, mass M, length $2a$, about axis through centre perpendicular to its length: $\dfrac{1}{3}Ma^2$

   (b) uniform circular disc, mass M, radius r, about axis through centre perpendicular to its plane: $\dfrac{1}{2}Mr^2$

   (c) uniform solid sphere, mass M, *radius* r, about diameter: $\dfrac{2}{5}Mr^2$

● use the parallel axes theorem for any body:
   $$I_P = I_G + Md^2$$

● use the perpendicular axes theorem for any lamina:
   $$I_Z = I_X + I_Y$$

   (where X and Y are perpendicular axes in the plane of the lamina)

● understand the term 'radius of gyration' (if $MI = mk^2$, then k is the radius of gyration)

● find the moment of inertia of a composite body about an axis, by adding the separate moments of inertia for each body about that axis.

Rotation of a rigid body about a fixed smooth axis

Suppose I hold a piece of string, to the other end of which is attached an orange.

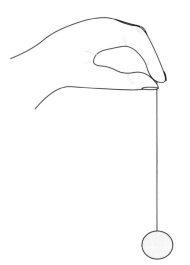

I now swing the orange round so that it moves in a vertical circle, with the string remaining taut throughout.

In Module M2, if we were asked to discuss the motion of this orange, then we would model the situation by regarding it as a particle on the end of a light inelastic string. However, with our knowledge of moments of inertia, we can now make a more realistic model of the situation. We can model it as a solid uniform sphere attached to the end of a uniform heavy rod.

In this section we will see how to tackle more realistic models such as this.

When you've finished this section you should be able to:

- write down the equations of motion for a rigid body moving about a fixed smooth horizontal or vertical axis
- use these equations of motion to find the force on the fixed axis
- write down, and use, the kinetic energy for such a system
- use angular momentum to describe the effect of an impulse on a rigid body which is free to rotate about a fixed axis.

A summary of relevant results previously obtained

It will be helpful if we reminded ourselves about circular motion, as covered in Module M2.

For a particle of mass m moving in a circle of radius r, centre O, and with angular velocity ω, we have the following **velocity diagram**:

Figure 2.1

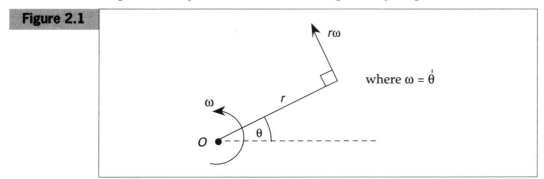

We'll see later that the **momentum diagram** is more relevant and so we have:

Figure 2.2

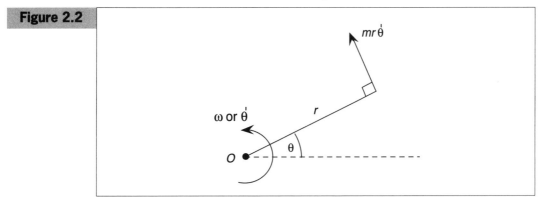

Similarly, for a particle of mass m moving in a circle of radius r, centre O, and with angular velocity ω, we have the following **acceleration diagram**.

Figure 2.3

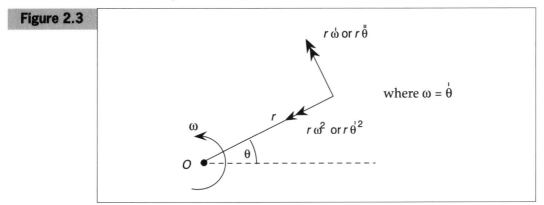

We'll see later that the *mass-acceleration* diagram is more relevant and so we have

Figure 2.4

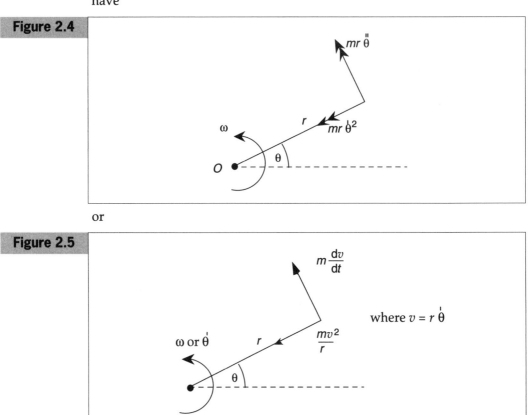

or

Figure 2.5

Motion of a rigid body about a fixed smooth axis

If a rigid body of mass M is rotating about a fixed smooth axis through its centre of mass G, then the *moment* of the mass acceleration of any point mass m about G is given by (see Figure 2.4) $r \times mr\ddot{\theta}$ or $mr^2 \ddot{\theta}$.

Hence the *total* moment of the mass acceleration of the whole body about the axis is $\Sigma mr^2 \ddot{\theta}$. But $\Sigma mr^2 \ddot{\theta} = (\Sigma mr^2)\ddot{\theta} = I_G\ddot{\theta}$, where I_G is the moment of inertia of the body about the fixed axis through G.

And so, **if a rigid body is spinning about a fixed axis through G, the total moment of mass acceleration is as shown in Figure 2.6.**

Figure 2.6

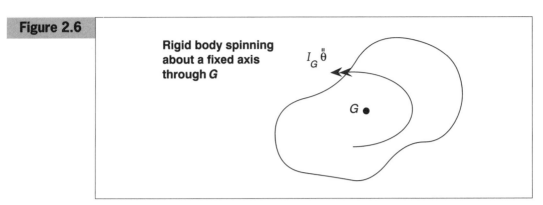

Rigid body spinning about a fixed axis through *G*

If we now allow *G* to move then, calling its mass acceleration components $M\ddot{x}$ and $M\ddot{y}$, we have the mass acceleration system for the body shown in Figure 2.7.

Figure 2.7

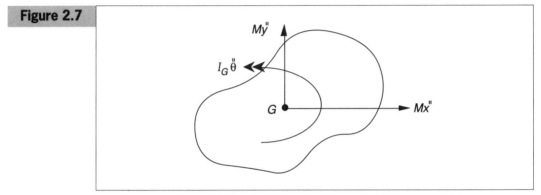

However, we are interested in the case of a rigid body which is spinning about a fixed axis through some point *P*. We therefore replace the mass accelerations $M\ddot{x}$, $M\ddot{y}$ by the equivalent components, shown in Figure 2.4.

And so, **if a rigid body of mass *M* is spinning about a fixed axis through *P*, the total mass acceleration system is as shown in Figure 2.8.**

Figure 2.8

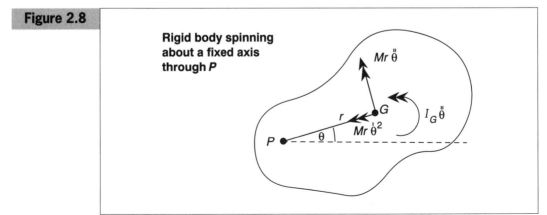

Rigid body spinning about a fixed axis through *P*

Assuming that the axis through P is smooth (so that there is no frictional couple at P, only forces at the axis), and assuming that there are no other external forces acting on the body (other than its weight), then we have the following force diagram.

If a rigid body of mass M is spinning about a fixed smooth axis through P, then the total force system is as shown in Figure 2.9.

Figure 2.9

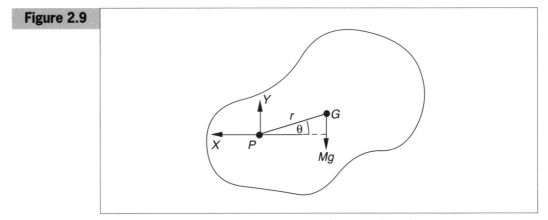

But the systems given in Figures 2.8 and 2.9 are describing the same situation. In particular, if we take moments about P for the mass accelerations and then moments about P for the forces, we get:

$$\overset{\curvearrowleft}{P} : r \times Mr\ddot{\theta} + I_G\ddot{\theta} = -Mg \times r \cos \theta$$

But this can be rewritten as

$$(Mr^2 + I_G)\ddot{\theta} = -Mgr \cos \theta$$

Using the parallel axes theorem (see Section 1, page 5), we see that $Mr^2 + I_G$ is the moment of inertia of the rigid body about the axis through P.

∴   The moments equation above can be written as

$$I_P\ddot{\theta} = -Mgr \cos \theta$$

If a rigid body is spinning about a smooth, fixed axis through P, and if no other forces are acting apart from the weight Mg, then

$$I_P\ddot{\theta} = -Mgr \cos \theta$$

where I_P is the moment of inertia of the rigid body about the axis through P.

This is a most useful result and we shall be returning to it time and time again.

But we can deduce even more because this equation can be integrated. Multiplying both sides by $\dot{\theta}$ we get

$$I_P \ddot{\theta}\, \dot{\theta} = -Mgr \cos \theta\, \dot{\theta}$$

i.e. $\qquad I_P \dfrac{d}{dt}\left(\dfrac{\dot{\theta}^2}{2}\right) = -Mgr \cos \theta\, \dfrac{d\theta}{dt}$

Now integrating both sides with respect to t we get

$$I_P \dfrac{\dot{\theta}^2}{2} = -Mgr \sin \theta + \text{constant}$$

i.e. $\qquad \dfrac{1}{2} I_P\, \dot{\theta}^2 + Mgr \sin \theta = \text{constant}$

This important equation is the statement of **conservation of energy**. $Mgr \sin \theta$ is the potential energy of the rigid body (above some fixed level) and $\dfrac{1}{2}I_P\dot{\theta}^2$ can be shown to be the kinetic energy of the rigid body. And so:

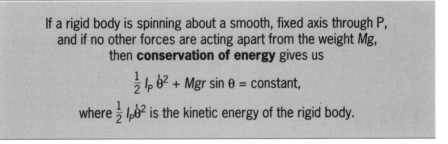

> If a rigid body is spinning about a smooth, fixed axis through P,
> and if no other forces are acting apart from the weight Mg,
> then **conservation of energy** gives us
>
> $$\tfrac{1}{2} I_P\, \dot{\theta}^2 + Mgr \sin \theta = \text{constant},$$
>
> where $\tfrac{1}{2} I_P\dot{\theta}^2$ is the kinetic energy of the rigid body.

The importance of the energy equation is that it allows us to calculate $r\dot{\theta}$. We'll see shortly why this is important.

One more point before proceeding. The integration above *was* rather tricky and I have only added it for completeness. As far as your examination is concerned, you simply need to know, and be able to use, the two previously boxed equations (on page 20 and above).

Returning to the systems given in Figures 2.8 and 2.9, if we need to find the forces X and Y then, instead of taking moments about P, we resolve.

> Resolving horizontally for the forces and
> horizontally for the mass accelerations we get
>
> $$\leftarrow : X = Mr\dot{\theta}^2 \cos \theta + Mr\ddot{\theta} \sin \theta$$
>
> and resolving vertically for the forces and
> vertically for the mass accelerations we get
>
> $$\uparrow : Y - Mg = Mr\ddot{\theta} \cos \theta - Mr\dot{\theta}^2 \sin \theta$$

But in order to find the values of X and Y from these equations, we need to know the values of $\ddot{\theta}$ and $\dot{\theta}$. For $\ddot{\theta}$ we use the moments equation on page 20.

i.e. $I_p\ddot{\theta} = - Mgr \cos \theta$

and for $\dot{\theta}$ we use the energy equation on page 21.

i.e. $\frac{1}{2}I_p\dot{\theta}^2 + Mgr \sin \theta = $ constant.

Thus we can find the forces X and Y.

A summary so far

In tackling problems involving the motion of a rigid body about a fixed smooth axis through P, we need to remember that:

- $I_p\ddot{\theta} = - Mgr \cos \theta$, where I_p is the moment of inertia of the body about the axis through P

- $\frac{1}{2}I_p\dot{\theta}^2 + Mgr \sin \theta = $ constant, where $\frac{1}{2}I_p\dot{\theta}^2$ is the kinetic energy of the body

- the force components X and Y at P are found by resolving, i.e.

$$X = Mr\dot{\theta}^2 \cos \theta + Mr\ddot{\theta} \sin \theta$$

and $Y - Mg = Mr\ddot{\theta} \cos \theta - Mr\dot{\theta}^2 \sin \theta$

Example   A uniform rod AB of length $2a$ and mass M is smoothly hinged at its end A to a fixed point. It is held in a horizontal position and then released.

(a) How fast is the end moving when it passes through the vertical position?

(b) What is the force on the hinge at A at that instant?

Solution   I always like to begin by putting down a general force diagram and a general mass acceleration diagram when the question involves forces.

Figure 2.10

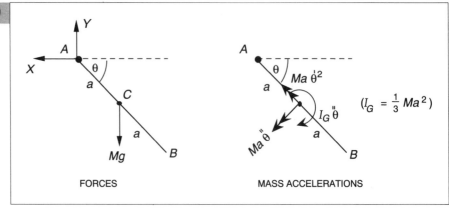

FORCES   MASS ACCELERATIONS

(a) The first question involves speeds and so we need the conservation of energy equation.

The kinetic energy of the rod $= \frac{1}{2}I_A \dot{\theta}^2 = \frac{1}{2}\left(\frac{4}{3}Ma^2\right)\dot{\theta}^2 = \frac{2}{3}Ma^2\dot{\theta}^2$

The potential energy of the rod $= -Mga \sin\theta$ (taking the original level as that of zero PE).

$\therefore \quad \frac{2}{3}Ma^2\dot{\theta}^2 - Mga\sin\theta = \text{constant}$

But initially $\theta = 0$ and $\dot{\theta} = 0$ (because the rod is released from rest)

$\therefore \quad$ Constant $= 0$

$\therefore \quad$ Cancelling down gives us

$$a^2\dot{\theta}^2 = \frac{3ga}{2}\sin\theta.$$

When the rod is vertical $\theta = \frac{\pi}{2} \Rightarrow \sin\theta = 1 \Rightarrow a\dot{\theta} = \sqrt{\frac{3ga}{2}}$

But the speed of B is $2a\dot{\theta}$

$\therefore \quad$ The required speed of B is $2\sqrt{\frac{3ga}{2}}$ i.e. $\sqrt{6ga}$

(b) The second question involves forces so we need to resolve. We get:

$\uparrow : Y - Mg = Ma\dot{\theta}^2 \sin\theta - Ma\ddot{\theta}\cos\theta$

$\leftarrow : X = Ma\dot{\theta}^2 \cos\theta + Ma\ddot{\theta}\sin\theta$

We already know the values of θ and $\dot{\theta}$ and to find $\ddot{\theta}$ we use the moments equation $I_A\ddot{\theta} = Mga\cos\theta$

$\therefore \quad$ When the rod is vertical $\theta = \frac{\pi}{2}$, $a\dot{\theta} = \sqrt{\frac{3ga}{2}}$ and $\ddot{\theta} = 0$

This gives $Y = \frac{5Mg}{2}$ and $X = 0$

$\therefore \quad$ When the rod is vertical, the force at the hinge is vertically upwards and of magnitude $\frac{5Mg}{2}$.

Example

A uniform rod *AB* of length 6*a* and mass *m* can rotate freely in a vertical plane about a fixed axis through *A*, and carries a symmetrically placed solid sphere of mass 5*m* and radius *a* at *B*. When the sphere is in its lowest position its centre is given a horizontal velocity *v*. Show that the rod will describe complete revolutions if 37 v^2 > 1064 *ga*. (This is a model for the situation described in the introduction.)

Solution

The force diagram is given by:

Figure 2.11

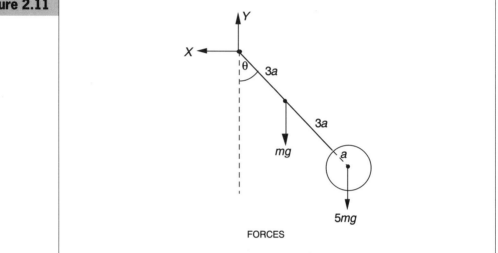

FORCES

The question involves speeds so we use the conservation of energy equation.

Moment of inertia of rod about axis through *A*

$$= \frac{4}{3} m(3a)^2 \quad = 12ma^2$$

Moment of inertia of sphere about axis through *A*

$$= \frac{2}{5}(5m)a^2 + 5m(7a)^2 \quad \text{(using the parallel axes theorem)}$$

$$= 247ma^2$$

∴ Moment of inertia of system about axis through *A* is

$$12ma^2 + 247ma^2 = 259ma^2$$

∴ KE for the system $= \frac{1}{2}(259ma^2)\,\dot{\theta}^2 \quad = \frac{259}{2}ma^2\,\dot{\theta}^2$

and PE for the system $= -mg\,3a\cos\theta - 5mg\,7a\cos\theta = -38mga\cos\theta$

(taking the horizontal through *A* as having zero PE)

∴   Conservation of energy gives

$$\frac{259}{2}\, ma^2\, \dot\theta^2 - 38mga \cos\theta = \text{constant}$$

But initially θ= 0 and $7a\dot\theta = v$

∴   Constant $= \dfrac{259}{2}\, \dfrac{mv^2}{49} - 38\, mga$

$$= \frac{37}{14}\, mv^2 - 38\, mga$$

∴   The energy equation becomes

$$\frac{259}{2}\, ma^2\dot\theta^2 - 38mga \cos\theta = \frac{37}{14}\, mv^2 - 38\, mga$$

But the rod will describe complete revolutions if the speed at the highest point is just zero

∴   putting $\theta = \pi$ and $\dot\theta = 0$, we get

$$38mga = \frac{37mv^2}{14} - 38mga$$

∴ $1064ga = 37v^2$

∴   Complete revolutions are obtained if v exceeds this value,

i.e.   if $37v^2 > 1064ga$

You should now be able to work through Exercises 1–16 on pp. 34–36.

The compound pendulum: small oscillations

If a body hangs in stable equilibrium from a fixed horizontal axis about which it is free to rotate, and is then displaced, it will oscillate as a pendulum. Such a system is called a compound pendulum. We then have the force system shown in Figure 2.12.

THIS BOOK IS THE PROPERTY
OF CORNWALL COLLES

Figure 2.12

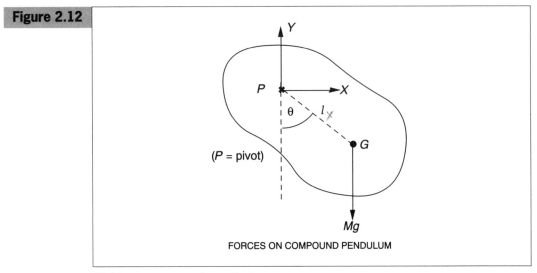

FORCES ON COMPOUND PENDULUM

Taking moments about P gives us

$$P \curvearrowleft \quad : \quad Mgl \sin \theta = -I_p \ddot{\theta}$$

It is important to *note the minus sign here*. (The weight has a clockwise moment but θ is increasing in an anti-clockwise direction.)

If the oscillations are small, then $\sin \theta \approx \theta$

$$\therefore \qquad Mgl\theta = -I_p\ddot{\theta} \quad \text{or} \quad \ddot{\theta} = -\left(\frac{Mgl}{I_p}\right)\theta$$

But the last equation is nothing more than the simple harmonic motion equation $\ddot{\theta} = -\omega^2\theta$, which you met in Module M2. You will recall that the period for such a motion is given by $\dfrac{2\pi}{\omega}$.

$\therefore$ A compound pendulum, performing small oscillations, will have a

period of $2\pi \sqrt{\dfrac{I_p}{Mgl}}$.

There is no need to remember this result precisely, just be able to find it in special cases.

(a) Write down the formula for the period of oscillation of a simple pendulum of length l.

(b) A uniform rod AB of length $2a$ is freely pivoted at A. Find:

(i) its period of small oscillations and

(ii) the length of the equivalent simple pendulum.

| **Solution** | (a) | You will recall from Module M2 that the period of a simple pendulum of length l is $2\pi \sqrt{\dfrac{l}{g}}$. |

(b)   We have the following force diagram:

Figure 2.13

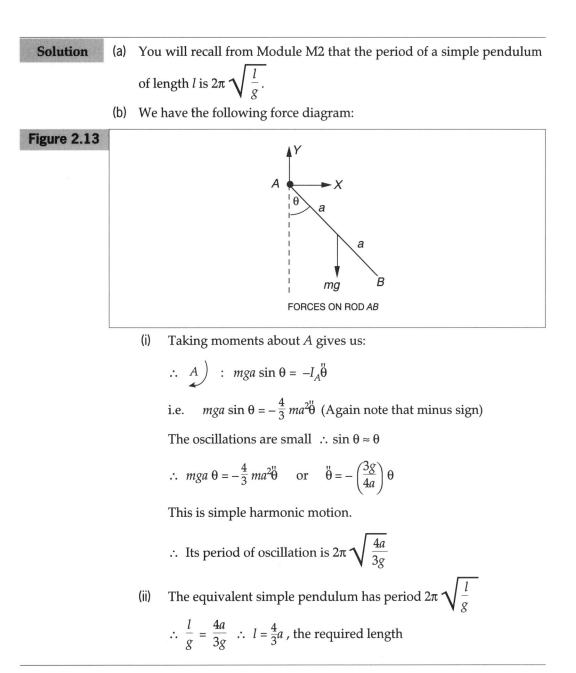

FORCES ON ROD *AB*

(i)   Taking moments about A gives us:

$$\therefore \; A \Big) \quad : \quad mga \sin \theta = -I_A \ddot{\theta}$$

i.e. $mga \sin \theta = -\dfrac{4}{3} ma^2 \ddot{\theta}$ (Again note that minus sign)

The oscillations are small $\therefore \sin \theta \approx \theta$

$$\therefore \; mga\,\theta = -\frac{4}{3} ma^2 \ddot{\theta} \quad \text{or} \quad \ddot{\theta} = -\left(\frac{3g}{4a}\right)\theta$$

This is simple harmonic motion.

$\therefore$ Its period of oscillation is $2\pi \sqrt{\dfrac{4a}{3g}}$

(ii)   The equivalent simple pendulum has period $2\pi \sqrt{\dfrac{l}{g}}$

$$\therefore \; \frac{l}{g} = \frac{4a}{3g} \quad \therefore \; l = \frac{4}{3}a \text{ , the required length}$$

Example

Figure 2.14 shows a pendulum which can rotate in a vertical plane about a fixed smooth horizontal axis through A. The pendulum consists of a thin uniform rod AB, of mass $\frac{3}{2}m$ and length $2r$, attached to a the point B on the surface of a uniform solid sphere, of mass $5m$ and radius r, so that AB produced passes through the centre of the sphere.

Figure 2.14

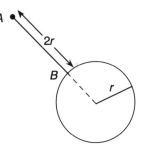

(a) Show that the moment of inertia of the pendulum about the horizontal axis through A is $49\,mr^2$.

(b) Find, in terms of r and g, the period of small oscillations of the pendulum about its position of stable equilibrium.

Solution

(a) The moment of inertia of the system about the horizontal axis through A is:

$$\underbrace{\frac{4}{3}\left(\frac{3m}{2}\right)r^2}_{\text{rod } AB} \ + \ \underbrace{\frac{2}{5}(5m)\,r^2 + (5m)(3r)^2}_{\text{sphere}} = 49\,mr^2, \text{ as required.}$$

(b) When the inclination of AB to the downward vertical is θ, we have:

$$\curvearrowleft A \ : \quad \frac{3m}{2}\,gr\sin\theta + 5mg \times 3r\sin\theta = -(49mr^2)\,\ddot{\theta}$$

Replacing $\sin\theta$ by θ, this equation reduces to

$$\ddot{\theta} = -\left(\frac{33g}{98r}\right)\theta$$

$\therefore$ The period of small oscillations is $2\pi\sqrt{\dfrac{98r}{33g}}$

You should now be able to work through Exercises 17–24 on pp. 37–38.

Impulses on rigid bodies free to rotate about a fixed smooth axis

In just the same way that the mass accelerations of a rigid body can be reduced to the mass acceleration of the centre of mass G, together with a couple $I_G\ddot{\theta}$ about G, the momentum of a rigid body can be similarly reduced. This time we have:

The momentum system for a rigid body of mass M rotating about a smooth fixed axis through P is as shown in Figure 2.15.

Figure 2.15

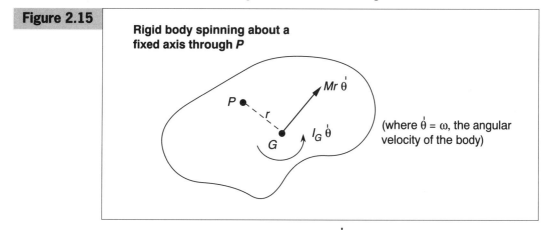

Rigid body spinning about a fixed axis through P

$Mr\dot{\theta}$

P r

$I_G\dot{\theta}$ G

(where $\dot{\theta}$ = ω, the angular velocity of the body)

Note that the momentum component $Mr\dot{\theta}$ is perpendicular to PG and that I_G represents the moment of inertia of the body about a parallel axis through G.

When considering momentum problems in Modules M1 and M2, we used the result that:

Momentum after – Momentum before = Impulse

This will generalise to our situation as follows:

Figure 2.16

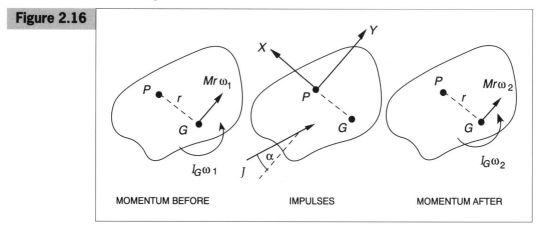

X Y

P r $Mr\omega_1$

G

$I_G\omega_1$ J α

P

G

P $Mr\omega_2$ r

G

$I_G\omega_2$

MOMENTUM BEFORE   IMPULSES   MOMENTUM AFTER

(ω_1 is the angular velocity of the body *before* the impulse; J is the impulse itself and X and Y are the impulsive reactions at the smooth hinge; ω_2 is the angular velocity of the body *after* the impulse.)

Once again we can get three equations from this situation. The first (and most important) is obtained by taking moments about P.

$$\therefore \quad \overset{\curvearrowleft}{P}): (Mr^2\omega_2 + I_G\omega_2) - (Mr^2\omega_1 + I_G\omega_1) = Jd,$$

where d is the perpendicular distance of the line of action of the impulse J from P.

Using the parallel axes theorem (see Section 1), we see that $Mr^2 + I_G$ is the moment of inertia of the rigid body about the axis through P

$\therefore$ Our moments equation can be written:

$$I_P\omega_2 - I_P\omega_1 = Jd$$

The moment of momentum of the body about the axis through P is therefore $I_P\omega$, where ω is the angular velocity of the body. It is conventional to call the moment of momentum of a body the **angular momentum** of that body. Hence the above equation can be rewritten as:

Change in angular momentum = Moment of the impulse about P.

And so:

---

1 If a rigid body free to move about a smooth axis through P is given an impulse J, and if ω_1 and ω_2 are the angular velocities of the body immediately before and after the impulse is applied, then

$$I_P\omega_2 - I_P\omega_1 = Jd$$

where Jd is the moment of the impulse about the axis through P and I_P is the moment of inertia of the rigid body about the axis through P.

2 Since $I_P\omega_2$ is the angular momentum of the body immediately after the impulse
and $I_P\omega_1$ is the angular momentum of the body immediately before the impulse,
the above equation becomes:

Change in angular momentum   =   Moment of the impulse about the axis through P

Returning to Figure 2.16, we can get two further equations by resolving. These will only be needed if we have to find the impulsive reactions X and Y. In that case:

- If we resolve in the direction of Y, then
  $$Mr\omega_2 - Mr\omega_1 = Y + J\cos\alpha$$
- If we resolve in the direction of X, then
  $$0 = X - J\sin\alpha$$

Example

A rod AB of length $2a$ and mass $5m$ rests on a smooth table. The rod is pivoted about a vertical axis through A. A particle of mass $3m$ moving with speed u on the table at right angles to the line of the rod strikes the rod at a distance $\frac{4}{3}a$ from the pivot, and sticks to the rod after impact. Find the angular velocity w with which the rod begins to turn

Solution

When the particle strikes the rod there will be an impulsive reaction at the pivot. If the components of the reaction are X and Y then

Figure 2.17

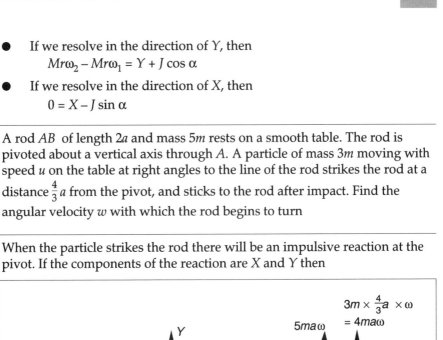

MOMENTUM BEFORE   IMPULSIVE REACTIONS   MOMENTUM AFTER

Since we are not interested in the impulsive reactions X and Y, we take moments about A.

$\therefore$ Total angular momentum = Total angular momentum
about A *after impact*   about A *before impact*.

The total angular momentum about A of the system after impact is

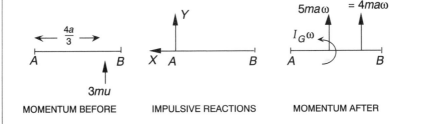

rod   particle

The total angular momentum of the system about A before impact is

$$0 \quad + \quad \frac{4a}{3}\,3mu \quad = \quad 4mau$$

rod   particle

$\therefore$ Conservation of angular momentum gives

$$12ma^2\omega = 4mau \quad \text{i.e. } \omega = \frac{u}{3a}$$

$\therefore$ The angular velocity of the system after impact is $\frac{u}{3a}$

Example	A uniform rod AB of mass m and length $2a$ can rotate freely in a vertical plane about the end A. It rests with B vertically below A when it is struck a blow of impulse P at right angles to AB at the midpoint of AB. Find P if in the subsequent motion AB just reaches the horizontal position.
Solution	First of all the three diagrams:
Figure 2.18	

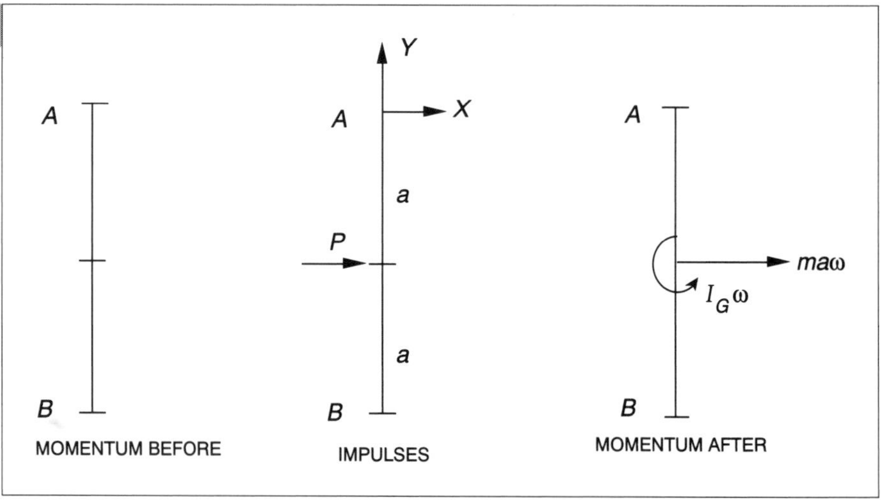

MOMENTUM BEFORE   IMPULSES   MOMENTUM AFTER

Angular momentum about A after $= \left(\frac{4}{3} ma^2\right) \omega$

Angular momentum about A before $= 0$

Moment of the impulses about $A = Pa$

$\therefore \qquad \frac{4}{3} ma^2 \omega - 0 = Pa$

$\therefore \qquad P = \frac{4}{3} ma\omega$ ... ①

For the second stage, use conservation of energy.

Initial KE + PE $= \frac{1}{2} \left(\frac{4}{3} ma^2\right) \omega^2 - mga$
taking the zero level, for PE as the horizontal through A

Final KE + PE $= 0 + 0$ (it *just* reaches this position)

$\therefore \quad \frac{1}{2} \left(\frac{4}{3} ma^2\right) \omega^2 - mga = 0 \quad \therefore \quad 2a\omega^2 = 3g$ ... ②

Eliminating ω between ① and ② we get

$$P = \frac{4}{3} ma \sqrt{\frac{3g}{2a}} \text{ or } 4m \sqrt{\frac{ga}{6}}$$

$\therefore$ The impulse P equals $4m \sqrt{\dfrac{ga}{6}}$.

Example	A uniform disc, of mass m and radius r, is rotating with constant angular speed ω, in a horizontal plane, about a smooth vertical axis through its centre. A particle of mass M is held at rest just above the surface of the disc at a distance $\frac{1}{2}r$ from the centre of the disc. The particle is released and immediately adheres to the disc. Show that the new angular speed of the disc is $\dfrac{2m\omega}{2m + M}$.

Solution	First of all the three diagrams

Figure 2.19

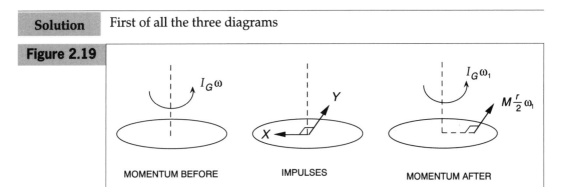

(Let ω_1 be the angular velocity afterwards.)

Since we are not interested in the impulses X and Y, we take moments about the vertical axis through the centre of the disc, i.e. we use conservation of angular momentum about that axis.

$$\therefore \text{ Angular momentum afterwards} = \underbrace{\tfrac{1}{2}mr^2\omega_1}_{\text{disc}} + \underbrace{M\left(\tfrac{r}{2}\right)^2\omega_1}_{\text{particle}} = \frac{r^2\omega_1}{4}(2m + M)$$

And angular momentum before $= \left(\tfrac{1}{2}mr^2\right)\omega$ (disc only)

$$\therefore \overset{\curvearrowleft}{centre)} : \quad \frac{r^2\omega_1}{4}(2m + M) - \tfrac{1}{2}mr^2\omega = 0$$

$$\therefore \omega_1 = \frac{2m\omega}{2m + M} \quad \text{as required.}$$

You should now be able to work through Exercises 25–32 on p. 39.

EXERCISES

1 A uniform circular disc of mass m and radius a can turn freely in a vertical plane about a horizontal axis through a point O on its rim. A particle P of mass m is attached to the point of the rim diametrically opposite to O. The system is disturbed from rest with the particle vertically above O.

Show that the angular velocity of the disc after it has turned through an angle θ is given by

$$11a\dot{\theta}^2 = 12g(1 - \cos\theta)$$

Find the magnitude of the force at O when $\theta = \pi$.

2 Two uniform rods AB and CD, of lengths $2a$ and a respectively, are each of the same mass per unit length. The rods are rigidly joined together at right angles so that C coincides with the mid-point of AB. If the system is pivoted at D so that it can move in a vertical plane, and it starts to move from rest with AB vertical, prove that when this rod is horizontal the angular velocity of the system is $\sqrt{\dfrac{5g}{3a}}$.

3 Find the moment of inertia of a uniform rod AB, of mass m and length $2l$, about one end.

The rod is freely hinged to a fixed point at A, and a particle of mass M is fixed to the end B. If the rod is just displaced from the position of unstable equilibrium in which B is vertically above A, show that the angular velocity w of the rod when it becomes horizontal is given by

$$\omega^2 = \frac{3(m + 2M)}{2(m + 3M)} \times \frac{g}{l}$$

4 A uniform disc, of diameter 2.4 metres, is mounted on a smooth horizontal axle of negligible diameter, the disc being in a vertical plane and the axle at a distance of 0.1 metre from the centre of the disc. If the disc is allowed to move from rest in the unstable position of equilibrium, find its greatest angular velocity in the subsequent motion.

5 Find the moment of inertia of a uniform circular disc, of mass M and radius a about an axis perpendicular to its plane through its centre.

This axle is fixed horizontally and the disc can rotate freely about it in a vertical plane.

A particle of mass m is attached to the disc at a distance $\frac{1}{2}a$ from the centre, and in one revolution the greatest and least angular velocities of the disc are $\sqrt{\dfrac{g}{4a}}$ and $\sqrt{\dfrac{g}{8a}}$, respectively. Show that $\dfrac{m}{M} = \dfrac{2}{63}$.

6 A uniform rectangular plate *ABCD* is freely pivoted at the midpoint of *AD* so that it can rotate in a vertical plane about a horizontal axis there. If *AB* = 2*a* and *BC* = 2*b*, *a* > *b* and the rectangle is held with *AB* horizontal and allowed to fall, find the angular velocity when *AB* is vertical.

7 A uniform circular disc of radius *a* can turn in a vertical plane about a horizontal axis at a point *A* of its rim. At *B*, the point diametrically opposite *A*, a particle of the same mass as the disc is attached to the disc and the disc is held with *AB* horizontal. Find the speed of *B* when *AB* is next vertical.

8 A uniform rod *AB* of length 2*l* is hinged about a horizontal axis perpendicular to the rod at its centre and carries at one end *A* a particle whose mass is equal to that of the rod. The rod is at rest with *A* vertically below *B*, and *A* is given a velocity of just sufficient to bring the rod to the horizontal position. Find this velocity.

9 A uniform circular disc of mass *M* and radius *a* is free to turn about a horizontal axis through its centre perpendicular to its plane. A particle of mass *m* is attached to the edge of the disc. If motion starts from the position in which the radius to the particle makes 60° to the upward vertical, find the angular velocity when *m* is its lowest position.

10 A uniform circular disc of mass *M* and radius *a* can turn freely in its own plane about its centre. A particle of mass *m* is attached to a point on the rim of the disc. Show that if w_1 and w_2 are the angular velocities of the disc when the particle is at its highest and lowest points $a(M + 2m) (w_2{}^2 - w_1{}^2) = 8mg$.

11 A thin uniform rod *AB*, of mass *M* and length 2*L*, is free to rotate in a vertical plane about a smooth horizontal axis through the end *A*. The rod is held with *AB* making an angle of $\frac{\pi}{4}$ with the upward vertical through *A* and is then released. Find, in terms of *M* and *g*, the magnitude and direction of the force exerted on the axis by the rod when *AB* is vertical.

12

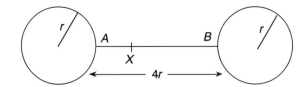

The figure represents a system of weights used in a gym. It consists of two uniform spheres each of mass $10m$ and radius r, joined by a thin uniform rod AB of length $4r$ and mass $3m$. The points A and B lie on the line joining the centres of the spheres. The system is free to rotate about a smooth horizontal axis which is perpendicular to the rod and passes through the point X on the rod where $AX = r$.

(a) Show that the moment of inertia of the system about the axis is $215\,mr^2$,

The system is slightly disturbed from rest with B vertically above X.

(b) Find the angular speed of the system when B is directly below X.

13 Find the moment of inertia of a uniform circular disc of mass M and radius a, about an axis perpendicular to its plane through a given point of its rim.

This axis is fixed horizontally and the disc rotates freely about it in a vertical plane. If the greatest angular velocity of the disc is $\sqrt{\dfrac{3g}{a}}$, find its least angular velocity.

14 A uniform circular disc of radius 1 m is pivoted about a horizontal axis through its centre perpendicular to its plane. A particle of twice the mass of the disc is fixed to a point P on the disc 0.5 m from the axis. The disc is held with P almost vertically above the axis, and then released. find the maximum angular velocity of the disc in the subsequent motion.

15 One end of a uniform rod of length l is smoothly hinged to a fixed point. While it is hanging freely, the rod is given an angular velocity $\sqrt{\dfrac{6g}{l}}$. Show that it describes a complete circle.

16 A uniform circular disc of mass m and radius r is free to rotate about a fixed smooth horizontal axis perpendicular to the plane of the disc and at a distance $\dfrac{1}{2}r$ from the centre of the disc. The disc is held at rest with the centre of the disc vertically above the axis. Given that the disc is slightly disturbed from its position of rest, find the magnitude of the force on the axis when the centre of the disc is in the horizontal plane of the axis.

17 A uniform disc of radius a is pivoted at a point on its circumference and makes small oscillations in a vertical plane. Find the period.

18 Calculate the period of small oscillations of a uniform rod of length $2a$ about a horizontal axis through one end when a mass equal to the mass of the rod is attached at its midpoint.

19 A trap door, 1.2 m square and of uniform thickness, is hanging vertically by its hinges. If the door is set swinging through a small angle, find the periodic time, neglecting the friction of the hinges.

20 A uniform circular disc of radius a has a particle of mass equal to that of the disc fixed to a point of its circumference. The disc can turn freely about a fixed horizontal axis through its centre at right angles to its plane. Assuming that the radius of gyration of the disc about this axis is $\dfrac{a}{\sqrt{2}}$, show that the length of the equivalent simple pendulum for small oscillations of the system about its position of stable equilibrium is $\dfrac{3a}{2}$.

21 A uniform circular disc of mass M and radius r is free to rotate about its axis, which is horizontal. Find the period of small oscillations if a small body of mass $\frac{1}{2}M$ is attached to a point of the circumference.

22 A bicycle wheel may be regarded as a hoop of radius 300 mm and mass 2 kg. At the rim is a valve weighing 30 g, which throws the wheel out of balance. The wheel is placed in a vertical plane and makes oscillations about its axis through a small angle, about the position in which the valve is at the lowest point. Find the period.

23 The figure shows a compound pendulum consisting of a thin uniform rod OC, of length $3L$ and mass M, rigidly attached at C to the centre of a uniform disc, of radius L and mass $5M$. The rod OC is in the same vertical plane as the disc. The pendulum is free to rotate in this vertical plane about a fixed smooth horizontal axis through O perpendicular to the plane of the disc.

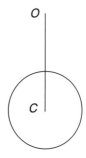

(a) Show that the moment of inertia of the pendulum about the axis through O is $\dfrac{101}{2}ML^2$.

Given that the pendulum performs small oscillations about its position of stable equilibrium,

(b) find, in terms of g and L, the period of oscillations.

24 I wish to design a pendulum for my grandfather clock.

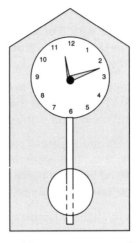

It is to consist of a central bar superimposed on which is a circular disc. It is intended that the mass of the disc will be double the mass of the bar and that the respective distance ratios will be as illustrated below.

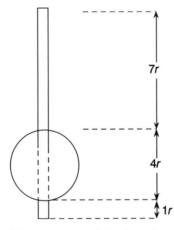

I also want it to 'tick' every second (so that the period of oscillation will be 2 seconds).

The question is, what is the value of r?

By modelling the problem as a uniform solid disc of mass $2m$ and radius $2r$ superimposed on a uniform rod of mass m and length $12r$, show that the moment of inertia of the system about the horizontal axis through the point of suspension (and perpendicular to the plane of the pendulum) is $214\,mr^2$. Hence find the value of r and the corresponding dimensions of the pendulum.

Name one factor in the model that has been neglected but which will affect the result.

25   A uniform rod AB of length $2a$ and mass m is freely pivoted at A and can rotate in a vertical plane. It is held with B vertically above A. Calculate the angular velocity of the rod when AB is horizontal. What will be the impulsive blow on a stop which catches the end B when AB is horizontal and holds it?

26   A uniform rod of length $2a$ and mass m swinging about one end starts from the horizontal position and when vertical, is struck a blow at its middle point which reverses and halves its angular velocity. Show that the impulse of the blow is $m\sqrt{6ga}$.

27   A rod of mass m and length l hangs from one end, and is free to rotate in a vertical plane about that end. How large should be the impulse of a blow given to the rod at its lower end to cause it to make complete revolutions?

28   A uniform circular lamina of mass M and radius a is free to move in its own plane (which is vertical) about the extremity A of a diameter AB. The lamina hangs in equilibrium with B vertically below A, and is struck by a blow applied horizontally at B in the plane of the lamina.

If the lamina first comes to rest when AB has turned through an angle of $60°$, calculate, in terms of M and a, the impulse of the blow.

29   A uniform gate of length l can swing freely about vertical hinges at one end. When the gate is at rest a particle of mass m and moving with velocity v strikes the gate normally at its midpoint. The moment of inertia of the gate about the hinge is $\frac{1}{8}ml^2$ and the coefficient of restitution is $\frac{1}{2}$. Find the velocity of the particle and the angular velocity of the gate immediately after the impact.

30   A uniform rod AB of length $2a$ and mass M rests on a smooth table and is freely pivoted to the table at A. An inelastic particle of mass m rests against the rod at C where $AC = b$. A horizontal blow of impulse P is given to the rod at D, where $AD = x$, the impulse being normal to the rod. Find the instantaneous angular velocity of the rod.

31   A uniform rod of mass m and length $2a$ is free to rotate in a vertical plane about one end A. It falls from a vertical position and when it is horizontal strikes a fixed inelastic stop at a distance B from A. Show that the impulse of the blow is $\frac{2ma}{b}\sqrt{\frac{2}{3}ag}$.

32   What are the units of measurement for:

(a)   moment of inertia and

(b)   angular momentum?

You should now know that when a rigid body is spinning about a fixed smooth axis through *P* then, with the usual notations:

- the moments equation is $I_p\ddot{\theta} = -Mgr\cos\theta$

- the conservation of energy equation is

  $\frac{1}{2}I_p\dot{\theta}^2 - Mgr\sin\theta = $ constant,

  where $\frac{1}{2}I_p\dot{\theta}^2$ is the general formula for the kinetic energy of the body

- the force at the hinge can be found by resolving i.e.

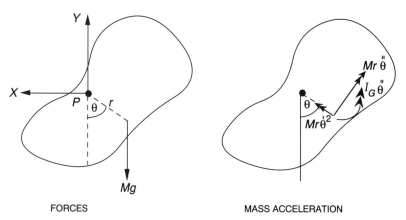

FORCES   MASS ACCELERATION

which gives

$$\uparrow \quad : \quad Y - Mg = Mr\ddot{\theta}\sin\theta + Mr\dot{\theta}^2\cos\theta$$

$$\leftarrow \quad : \quad X = Mr\dot{\theta}^2\sin\theta - Mr\ddot{\theta}\cos\theta$$

- it is called a compound pendulum when the oscillations are small.
  In that case $\sin\theta \approx \theta$ and the consequent equation $\ddot{\theta} = -\omega^2\theta$ gives a period of $\dfrac{2\pi}{\omega}$

- the length of the equivalent simple pendulum is found by quoting

  and using the formula $2\pi\sqrt{\dfrac{l}{g}}$.

- in impulse questions there is nearly always an impulsive reaction at *P* and, consequently, such problems are generally solved by taking moments about *P*. This leads to

$$I_p\omega_2 - I_p\omega_1 = Jd$$

  where ω_1 and ω_2 are the angular velocities of the body immediately before and after the impact and *Jd* is the moment of the impulse *J* about the axis through *P*.

This can be written more simply as:

Angular momentum after – angular momentum before = moment of the impulse about P

● if the impulsive reaction at P is required, then this can be found by resolving, i.e.

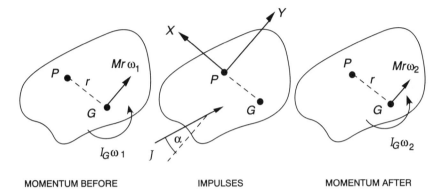

| MOMENTUM BEFORE | IMPULSES | MOMENTUM AFTER |

which gives

$$Mr\omega_2 - Mr\omega_1 = Y + J\cos\alpha$$

and $$0 = X - J\sin\alpha$$

Further motion of particles in one dimension

INTRODUCTION This section is concerned with the application of differential equations to the solution of assorted mechanical problems. We'll be looking again at resisted motion of a particle moving in a straight line and then at damped and forced harmonic motion. Finally, we'll improve further our techniques of mathematical modelling by considering the question of variable mass.

When you've finished this section you should be able to:

- solve questions involving resisted linear motion when the resisting forces are of the form $a + bv$ or $a + bv^2$, where a and b are constants and v is the velocity
- use your knowledge of differential equations to solve questions involving damped and forced harmonic motion
- set up and solve differential equations relating to variable mass.

Knowledge assumed

Before embarking upon this section you need to be able to:

- evaluate the following integrals

$$\int \frac{dx}{a^2 + b^2x^2} \ , \quad \int \frac{dx}{a^2 - b^2x^2} \ , \quad \int \frac{xdx}{a + bx^2} \quad \text{and} \quad \int \frac{x^2dx}{a + bx^3}$$

where a and b are constants

- solve the second order differential equations

$$a\frac{d^2y}{dx^2} + b\frac{dy}{dx} + cy = f(x)$$

where a, b and c are constants and $f(x)$ is a 'simple' function of x.

If you have already covered these topics in Module P3, and you feel happy about them, then you can omit the next few pages and move straight on to page 47. However, if you feel in need of a refresher, or if you haven't met these topics before, then read on.

Relevant integration techniques from Module P3

You need to be able to use the following four standard results.

1 $\displaystyle\int \frac{dx}{a^2 + b^2x^2} = \frac{1}{ab}\tan^{-1}\left(\frac{bx}{a}\right) + c$

2 $\displaystyle\int \frac{dx}{a^2 - b^2x^2} = \frac{1}{2ab}\ln\left(\frac{a + bx}{a - bx}\right) + c$

3 $\displaystyle\int \frac{x\,dx}{a + bx^2} = \frac{1}{2b}\ln(a + bx^2) + c$

4 $\displaystyle\int \frac{x^2\,dx}{a + bx^3} = \frac{1}{3b}\ln(a + bx^3) + c$

[To prove result 1, you need a knowledge of inverse trig functions. Result 2 can be obtained by means of partial fractions and results 3 and 4 are either 'guessable' or obtainable by substitution. Since this section is concerned with *using* integration, I suggest that all four results are committed to memory.]

Example   Evaluate the following integrals:

(a) $\displaystyle\int \frac{dx}{4 + 9x^2}$ (b) $\displaystyle\int_0^{\frac{1}{2}} \frac{5\,dx}{1 + 4x^2}$ (c) $\displaystyle\int \frac{dx}{4 - 9x^2}$ (d) $\displaystyle\int \frac{5x}{6 + 7x^2}\,dx$

(e) $\displaystyle\int \frac{4x^2}{8 + 3x^3}\,dx$ (f) $\displaystyle\int \frac{dv}{p + qv^2}$ (p and q are constants)

Solution   (a)   Use result **1** with $a = 2$ and $b = 3$

$\therefore \displaystyle\int \frac{dx}{4 + 9x^2} = \frac{1}{6}\tan^{-1}\frac{3x}{2} + c$

(b)   Use result **1** with $a = 1$ and $b = 2$

$\therefore \displaystyle\int_0^{\frac{1}{2}} \frac{5\,dx}{1 + 4x^2} = \left[\frac{5}{2}\tan^{-1} 2x\right]_0^{\frac{1}{2}} = \frac{5}{2}\tan^{-1}1 = \frac{5}{2}\cdot\frac{\pi}{4} = \frac{5\pi}{8}$

(Remember always to *use radians* when integrating.)

(c)   Use result **2** with $a = 2$ and $b = 3$

$\therefore \displaystyle\int \frac{dx}{4 - 9x^2} = \frac{1}{12}\ln\left(\frac{2 + 3x}{2 - 3x}\right) + c$

43

(d)   Use result **3**, i.e. a 'guessable' type

$$\therefore \quad \int \frac{5x}{6 + 7x^2}\, dx = \frac{5}{14}\ln(6 + 7x^2) + c$$

(e)   Use result **4**, i.e. a 'guessable' type

$$\therefore \quad \int \frac{4x^2}{8 + 3x^3}\, dx = \frac{4}{9}\ln(8 + 3x^3) + c$$

(f)   Use result **1** with $a = \sqrt{p}$ and $b = \sqrt{q}$

$$\therefore \quad \int \frac{dv}{p + qv^2} = \frac{1}{\sqrt{pq}}\tan^{-1} v \sqrt{\frac{q}{p}} + c$$

Solving second order differential equations

The general solution of the differential equation

$$a\frac{d^2t}{dx^2} + b\frac{dy}{dx} + cy = f(x)$$

can be written $y = C(x) + P(x)$, where **C(x) is the complementary function** and **P(x) is a particular integral**.

The *method for finding the complementary function* C(x) is as follows:

- Solve the (auxiliary) equation $am^2 + bm + c = 0$ to find roots m_1 and m_2.

- If m_1 and m_2 are real and unequal ,then $C(x) = Ae^{m_1 x} + Be^{m_2 x}$

- If m_1 and m_2 are equal then $C(x) = (A + Bx)\, e^{mx}$, where m is the value of m_1 and m_2

- If m_1 and m_2 are complex, then these roots will be of the form $\alpha \pm i\beta$. In that case $C(x) = (A\cos\beta x + B\sin\beta x)e^{\alpha x}$.

The *method for finding the particular integral* P(x) requires sensible substitutions.

- If $f(x) = $ a constant, try $P(x) = C$, another constant
- If $f(x) = px + q$, try $P(x) = Cx + D$
- If $f(x) = pe^{qx}$, try $P(x) = Ce^{qx}$ or $P(x) = Cxe^{qx}$
- If $f(x) = p\sin rx + q\cos rx$, try $P(x) = A\sin rx + B\cos rx$

Example	Find the general solutions of the following differential equations:

1 $\dfrac{d^2y}{dx^2} - 5\dfrac{dy}{dx} + 6y = 7$

3 $\dfrac{d^2y}{dx^2} - 6\dfrac{dy}{dx} + 8y = e^{4x}$

2 $\dfrac{d^2y}{dx^2} - 6\dfrac{dy}{dx} + 9y = e^{4x}$

4 $\dfrac{d^2y}{dx^2} - 4\dfrac{dy}{dx} + 13y = \sin 2x$

Solution	

1 The auxiliary equation $m^2 - 5m + 6 = 0 \Rightarrow m = 2$ or 3

$\therefore$ The complementary function $C(x) = Ae^{2x} + Be^{3x}$

A particular integral is found by trying $y = C \Rightarrow 6C = 7 \Rightarrow C = \dfrac{7}{6}$

$\therefore$ The general solution is given by

$y = Ae^{2x} + Be^{3x} + \dfrac{7}{6}$

2 The auxiliary equation $m^2 - 6m + 9 = 0 \Rightarrow m = 3$ twice

$\therefore$ The complementary function $C(x) = (A + Bx)e^{3x}$

A particular integral is found by trying $y = Ce^{4x}$

$\therefore$ $\dfrac{dy}{dx} = 4Ce^{4x}$ and $\dfrac{d^2y}{dx^2} = 16Ce^{4x}$

$\therefore$ Substituting in the given equation we get

$16Ce^{4x} - 24Ce^{4x} + 9Ce^{4x} = e^{4x} \Rightarrow C = 1$

$\therefore$ The general solution is given by

$y = (A + Bx)e^{3x} + e^{4x}$

3 The auxiliary equation $m^2 - 6m + 8 = 0 \Rightarrow m = 2$ or 4

$\therefore$ The complementary function $C(x) = Ae^{2x} + Be^{4x}$

Since e^{4x} is already part of the complementary function, when it comes to the particular integral we'll need to try $y = Cxe^{4x}$

$\therefore$ $\dfrac{dy}{dx} = (C + 4Cx)e^{4x}$ and $\dfrac{d^2y}{dx^2} = (8C + 16Cx)e^{4x}$

(having differentiated two products)

$\therefore$ Substituting in the given equation we get

$(8C + 16Cx)e^{4x} - 6(C + 4Cx)e^{4x} + 8Cxe^{4x} = e^{4x} \Rightarrow C = \dfrac{1}{2}$

$\therefore$ The general solution is given by

$y = Ae^{2x} + Be^{4x} + \dfrac{1}{2}xe^{4x}$

4 The auxiliary equation

$$m^2 - 4m + 13 = 0 \quad \Rightarrow m = \frac{4 \pm \sqrt{-36}}{2} \quad \Rightarrow m = 2 \pm i3$$

(where the complex number i stands for $\sqrt{-1}$)

∴ The complementary function $C(x) = (A \cos 3x + B \sin 3x) \, e^{2x}$

A particular integral is found by trying $y = C \sin 2x + D \cos 2x$

∴ $\dfrac{dy}{dx} = 2C \cos 2x - 2D \sin 2x$ and $\dfrac{d^2y}{dx^2} = -4C \sin 2x - 4D \cos 2x$

∴ Substituting in the given equation we get

$(-4C \sin 2x - 4D \cos 2x) - 4(2C \cos 2x - 2D \sin 2x)$
$+ 13(C \sin 2x + D \cos 2x) = \sin 2x$

∴ $9C + 8D = 1$ and $-8C + 9D = 0$, ∴ $C = \dfrac{9}{145}$ and $D = \dfrac{8}{145}$

∴ The general solution is given by

$$y = (A \cos 3x + B \sin 3x) \, e^{2x} + \frac{9}{145} \sin 2x + \frac{8}{145} \cos 2x$$

Example

Solve the differential equation $\dfrac{d^2y}{dx^2} - 6\dfrac{dy}{dx} + 5y = x$

given that when $x = 0$, $y = 5.24$ and $\dfrac{dy}{dx} = 17$

Solution

The auxiliary equation $m^2 - 6m + 5 = 0 \Rightarrow m = 1$ or 5

∴ The complementary function $C(x) = Ae^x + Be^{5x}$

A particular integral is found by trying $y = Cx + D$

∴ $\dfrac{dy}{dx} = C$ and $\dfrac{d^2y}{dx^2} = 0$

∴ Substituting in the given equation we get

$0 - 6C + 5(Cx + D) = x \Rightarrow C = \dfrac{1}{5}$ and $D = \dfrac{6}{25}$

∴ The general solution is given by

$$y = Ae^x + Be^{5x} + \frac{1}{5}x + \frac{6}{25}$$

Now we use the given conditions to work out the constants A and B.

∴ $x = 0, y = 5.24 \Rightarrow 5.24 = A + B + \dfrac{6}{25} \Rightarrow A + B = 5$ ... ①

and $x = 0$, $\dfrac{dy}{dx} = 17 \Rightarrow 17 = A + 5B$ ... ②

Solving ① and ② simultaneously we get $A = 2$ and $B = 3$

∴   The required solution is given by

$$y = 2e^x + 3e^{5x} + \frac{1}{5}x + \frac{6}{25}$$

Resisted motion in a straight line

For these problems we'll need the following:

$$\text{Acceleration} = \frac{dv}{dt} = v\frac{dv}{dx} = \frac{d^2x}{dt^2}$$

where v is the velocity and x the displacement at time t.

But how do we know which of these three expressions to use?

- If v is required in terms of t, then take the acceleration as $\dfrac{dv}{dt}$

- If v is required in terms of x, then take the acceleration as $v\dfrac{dv}{dx}$

- If x is required in terms of t, then take the acceleration as $\dfrac{d^2x}{dt^2}$.

Example

A body of mass 2 kg is projected on a smooth horizontal plane in a medium which exerts a resistance proportion velocity of the body. Initially the velocity of the body is 8 m s⁻¹ and the resistance is 20 N.

Find the time taken before the velocity is reduced to 4 m s⁻¹ and the distance travelled in that time.

Solution

First get an exact expression for the resistance.

Let resistance $= kv$ N. But resistance $= 20$ N when $v = 8$ m s⁻¹

∴ $k = 2.5$ so that resistance $= 2.5v$ N

Now use $F = ma$ to get the equation of motion

∴ $-2.5v = 2a$

Since we have to find v in terms of t, take the acceleration a as $\dfrac{dv}{dt}$

∴ $-2.5v = 2\dfrac{dv}{dt}$

Separate the variables to get $\displaystyle\int -1.25\, dt = \int \frac{dv}{v}$

Now integrate to get $-1.25\,t = \ln v + c$

But $v = 8$ when $t = 0$, $\therefore$ $c = -\ln 8$

$\therefore$ We have $-1.25t = \ln v - \ln 8$

$\therefore$ When $v = 4$, $-1.25t = \ln 4 - \ln 8 \Rightarrow t = 0.55$ seconds

$\therefore$ The time taken before the velocity is reduced to 4 m s^{-1} is 0.55 seconds.

Finally, in order to get the distance, we use $v\dfrac{dv}{dx}$ for the acceleration.

$\therefore$ Equation of motion is $-2.5\,v = 2v\,\dfrac{dv}{dx}$ or $-2.5 = 2\dfrac{dv}{dx}$

$\therefore$ Integration gives us $-2.5x = 2v + c$.

But $v = 8$ when $x = 0$, $\therefore$ $c = -16$

$\therefore$ We have $-2.5x = 2v - 16$

$\therefore$ When $v = 4$, $x = 3.2$

$\therefore$ The body covers 3.2 m in that time.

Example

A body of mass 50 kg is travelling horizontally in a medium which exerts a resistance of $40v$ N, where v m s^{-1} is the velocity of the body. There is also a constant propulsion force of 200 N acting on the body. Find the time taken to reach a velocity of 2 m s^{-1} from rest, and also the time taken to accelerate from 2 m s^{-1} to 4 m s^{-1}.

Solution

It is often a good idea to draw separate force and mass acceleration diagrams to avoid making any mistakes, and so:

Figure 3.1

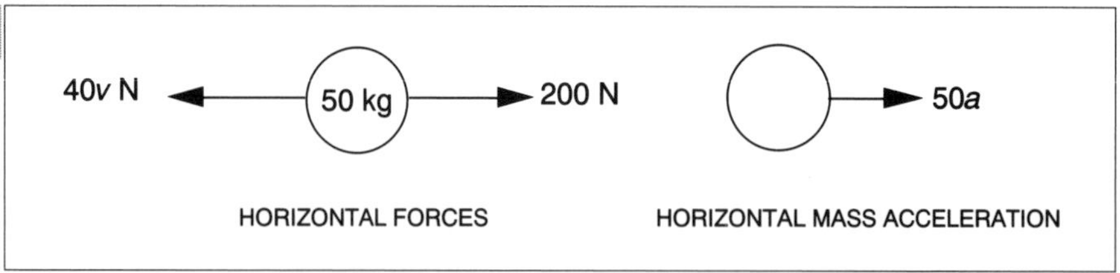

HORIZONTAL FORCES   HORIZONTAL MASS ACCELERATION

Using $F = ma$ to get the equation of motion, gives us

$$200 - 40v = 50a$$

Since we want v in terms of t, we take the acceleration a as $\dfrac{dv}{dt}$

$\therefore$ $200 - 40v = 50\dfrac{dv}{dt}$

Separate the variables to get $\displaystyle\int dt = \int \dfrac{5\,dv}{20 - 4v}$

Now integrate to get $t = -\dfrac{5}{4}\ln(20 - 4v) + c$

But $v = 0$ when $t = 0$, $\therefore$ $c = \dfrac{5}{4}\ln 20$

$\therefore$ We have $t = -\dfrac{5}{4}\ln(20 - 4v) + \dfrac{5}{4}\ln 20$

or $t = \dfrac{5}{4}\ln\left(\dfrac{20}{20 - 4v}\right)$

When $v = 2$, $t = \dfrac{5}{4}\ln\left(\dfrac{20}{12}\right)$ or 0.64

$\therefore$ The time required is 0.64 seconds

Also $v = 4 \Rightarrow t = \dfrac{5}{4}\ln\left(\dfrac{20}{4}\right)$ or 2.01

$\therefore$ Time required is $2.01 - 0.64 = 1.37$ seconds.

Example

A body is projected vertically upwards with velocity U, the air resistance at speed v being kv^2 per unit mass. Show that the body is instantaneously at rest after time

$$\frac{1}{\sqrt{kg}} \tan^{-1}\left(U\sqrt{\frac{k}{g}}\,\right)$$

at a height $\dfrac{1}{2k}\ln\dfrac{g + kU^2}{g}$

above the point of projection. Verify that if k is small these are approximately equal to $\dfrac{U}{g}$ and $\dfrac{U^2}{2g}$ respectively.

Solution

Begin with the two separate diagrams:

Figure 3.2

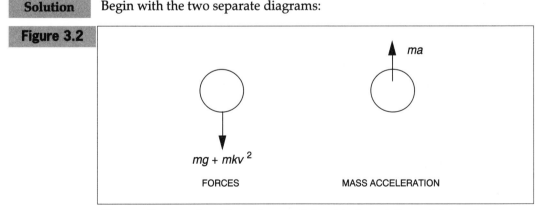

FORCES   MASS ACCELERATION

(In questions such as these, be careful not to forget the weight mg.)

Using $F = ma$ to get the equation of motion, gives us

$$mg + mkv^2 = -ma$$

Since we want v in terms of t, we take the acceleration a as $\dfrac{dv}{dt}$

$\therefore$ $\qquad mg + mkv^2 = -m \dfrac{dv}{dt}$

i.e. $\qquad g + kv^2 = -\dfrac{dv}{dt}$

Separate the variables to get $\displaystyle\int -dt = \int \dfrac{dv}{g + kv^2}$

Now integrate to get $-t = \dfrac{1}{\sqrt{gk}} \tan^{-1}\left(v\sqrt{\dfrac{k}{g}}\right) + c$

But $v = U$ when $t = 0$,

$\therefore$ $\quad c = -\dfrac{1}{\sqrt{gk}} \tan^{-1}\left(U\sqrt{\dfrac{k}{g}}\right)$

$\therefore$ $\quad$ We have $-t = \dfrac{1}{\sqrt{gk}} \tan^{-1}\left(v\sqrt{\dfrac{k}{g}}\right) - \dfrac{1}{\sqrt{gk}} \tan^{-1}\left(U\sqrt{\dfrac{k}{g}}\right)$

$\therefore$ $\quad v = 0 \Rightarrow t = \dfrac{1}{\sqrt{gk}} \tan^{-1}\left(U\sqrt{\dfrac{k}{g}}\right)$, as required.

In the second part, we require v in terms of x and so we take the acceleration a as $v\dfrac{dv}{dx}$.

$\therefore$ $\quad$ The equation of motion becomes

$$mg + mkv^2 = -mv\dfrac{dv}{dx}$$

i.e. $\qquad g + kv^2 = -v\dfrac{dv}{dx}$.

Separate the variables to get $\displaystyle\int dx = \int -\dfrac{v\, dv}{g + kv^2}$

Now integrate to get $\quad x = -\dfrac{1}{2k} \ln(g + kv^2) + c$

But $v = U$ when $x = 0$ $\therefore$ $c = \dfrac{1}{2k} \ln(g + kU^2)$

$\therefore$ $\quad$ We have $x = -\dfrac{1}{2k} \ln(g + kv^2) + \dfrac{1}{2k} \ln(g + kU^2)$

$$v = 0 \quad \Rightarrow x = -\frac{1}{2k} \ln g + \frac{1}{2k} \ln (g + kU^2)$$

$$\Rightarrow x = \frac{1}{2k} \ln \left(\frac{g + kU^2}{g} \right), \text{ as required.}$$

Finally*, for small θ, $\tan^{-1} \theta \approx \theta$ and $\ln (1 + \theta) \approx \theta$,

$$\therefore \quad \frac{1}{\sqrt{kg}} \tan^{-1} \left(U \sqrt{\frac{k}{g}} \right) \approx \frac{1}{\sqrt{kg}} \cdot \left(U \sqrt{\frac{k}{g}} \right) = \frac{U}{g}, \text{ as required}$$

and $\frac{1}{2k} \ln \left(1 + \frac{kU^2}{g} \right) \approx \frac{1}{2k} \cdot \frac{kU^2}{g} = \frac{U^2}{2g}$, as required.

(*If you have already covered Module P3 then you will have met these approximations before. If not, I suggest that you add these approximations to your memory bank!)

Example A body falls under gravity subject also to a resistance force proportional to the speed. Its terminal speed is 100 m s^{-1} and it was initially at rest. Find the acceleration when the speed is 70 m s^{-1}.

Solution Begin with the two separate diagrams.

Figure 3.3

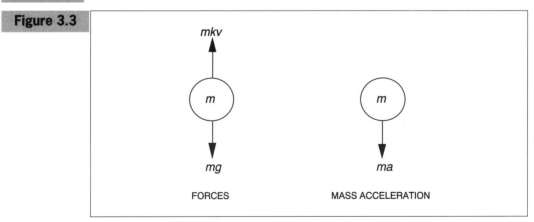

Using $F = ma$ to get the equation of motion, gives us

$$mg - mkv = ma$$

Since we want v in terms of t, we take the acceleration a as $\dfrac{dv}{dt}$

$$\therefore \quad mg - mkv = m \frac{dv}{dt}$$

i.e. $\quad g - kv = \dfrac{dv}{dt}$

Separate and integrate to get $t = \dfrac{-1}{k} \ln (g - kv) + c$

But $v = 0$ when $t = 0$, $\therefore$ $c = \dfrac{1}{k} \ln g$

$\therefore$ $\quad -kt = \ln \left(\dfrac{g - kv}{g} \right)$

$\therefore$ $\quad e^{-kt} = 1 - \dfrac{kv}{g}$

$\therefore$ $\quad v = \dfrac{g}{k} (1 - e^{-kt})$

As $t \rightarrow \infty$, $v \rightarrow \dfrac{g}{k}$ and this is called *the terminal speed*.

But in this question the terminal speed is given as 100 m s^{-1}.

$\therefore$ $\quad \dfrac{g}{k} = 100$, $\therefore$ $k = \dfrac{g}{100}$

$\therefore$ $\quad$ Since acceleration $= g - kv$,

$\qquad v = 70 \Rightarrow$ acceleration $= g - \dfrac{g}{100} \times 70 = 0.3\,g$

$\therefore$ $\quad$ The acceleration required is 0.3 g or 2.94 m s^{-2}.

And so, when tackling problems involving resisted motion in a straight line, you should:

- Draw a diagram for the forces and another diagram showing the mass acceleration
- Use $F = ma$ to set up the equation of motion
- Re-read the question to decide which expression to use for a

  If v is required in terms of t, then use $a = \dfrac{dv}{dt}$

  If v is required in terms of x, then use $a = v\dfrac{dv}{dx}$

  If x is required in terms of t, then use $a = \dfrac{d^2x}{dt^2}$

- Having chosen your expression for a, separate the variables and integrate. (Don't forget the + c.)
- Use the given conditions to work out c and hence answer the question.

You should now be able to work through Exercises 1–11 on pp. 63–65.

Damped harmonic oscillations

The equation of motion of a particle moving in a straight line under the action of a force directed towards a fixed point in the line and proportional to the displacement of the particle from the point is $\frac{d^2x}{dt^2} + \omega^2 x = 0$. We met this in Module M2 and it provides an example of simple harmonic motion. When the particle is also subject to a resistance which is proportional to its velocity, the equation of motion becomes

$$\frac{d^2x}{dt^2} + \omega^2 x + 2\lambda \frac{dx}{dt} = 0,$$

where λ is a constant. This is the equation of motion for damped harmonic oscillations.

Example

Given the equation for damped harmonic oscillations:

$$\frac{d^2x}{dt^2} + \omega^2 x + 2\lambda \frac{dx}{dt} = 0,$$

find x as a function of t in the following cases.

(a) $\lambda = 1.5$, $\omega = \sqrt{2}$ and initially $x = 1$ and $\frac{dx}{dt} = 0$

(b) $\lambda = 1$, $\omega = \sqrt{2}$ and initially $x = 1$ and $\frac{dx}{dt} = 0$

(c) $\lambda = 1$, $\omega = 1$ and initially $x = 2$ and $\frac{dx}{dt} = 0$

Solution

(a)   We have to solve $\frac{d^2x}{dt^2} + \frac{3dx}{dt} + 2x = 0$

The auxiliary equation is $m^2 + 3m + 2 = 0$, which has roots -1 and -2. The general solution is therefore:

$$x = Ae^{-t} + Be^{-2t}$$

But $x = 1$ when $t = 0 \Rightarrow 1 = A + B$ ... ①

Also $\frac{dx}{dt} = -Ae^{-t} - 2Be^{-2t}$

and $\frac{dx}{dt} = 0$ when $t = 0 \Rightarrow 0 = -A - 2B$ ... ②

Solve equations ① and ② simultaneously to get $A = 2$, $B = -1$.

$\therefore$ $x = 2e^{-t} - e^{-2t}$

(b) We have to solve $\dfrac{d^2x}{dt^2} + 2\dfrac{dx}{dt} + 2x = 0$

The auxiliary equation is $m^2 + 2m + 2 = 0$, which has complex roots $-1 \pm i$. The general solution is therefore: $x = e^{-t}(A \cos t + B \sin t)$

But $x = 1$ when $t = 0 \Rightarrow 1 = A \Rightarrow x = e^{-t}(\cos t + B \sin t)$

Also $\dfrac{dx}{dt} = 0$ when $t = 0$

Differentiating x as a product gives us

$$\frac{dx}{dt} = e^{-t}(-\sin t + B \cos t) - e^{-t}(\cos t + B \sin t)$$

and $\dfrac{dx}{dt} = 0,\ t = 0 \Rightarrow 0 = B - 1 \Rightarrow B = 1$

∴ $x = e^{-t}(\cos t + \sin t)$

(c) We have to solve $\dfrac{d^2x}{dt^2} + \dfrac{2dx}{dt} + x = 0$

The auxiliary equation is $m^2 + 2m + 1 = 0$, which has a repeated root of -1. The general solution is therefore: $x = (At + B)\,e^{-t}$

But $x = 2$ when $t = 0 \Rightarrow 2 = B \Rightarrow x = (At + 2)e^{-t}$

Differentiating x as a product we get

$$\frac{dx}{dt} = -(At + 2)\,e^{-t} + Ae^{-t}$$

and $\dfrac{dx}{dt} = 0,\ t = 0 \Rightarrow 0 = -2 + A \Rightarrow A = 2$

∴ $x = (2t + 2)\,e^{-t}$

Example

A simple pendulum whose period of small oscillations *in vacuo* is $\dfrac{\pi}{2}$ seconds is made to perform oscillations under gravity in a fluid which offers resistance to the motion of the bob. The force of resistance is $2mkv$ where m is the mass and v the speed of the bob: k is a constant whose value depends on the fluid being used. Prove that the angular displacement, θ, of the pendulum from the vertical during the small oscillations satisfies the following differential equation,

$$\frac{d^2\theta}{dt^2} + 2k\frac{d\theta}{dt} + 16\theta = 0.$$

If the resistance is such that $k = 3$, show that

$$\theta = Ae^{-3t} \sin \sqrt{7}t$$

gives a possible motion, where A is arbitrary but small. If the fluid is such that the resistance is greater, $k = 5$, show that $\theta = A(e^{-2t} - e^{-8t})$ is a possible motion. By means of rough graphs of θ against the time t, point out the chief characteristics of these two motions.

Solution   Begin by drawing two separate diagrams

Figure 3.4

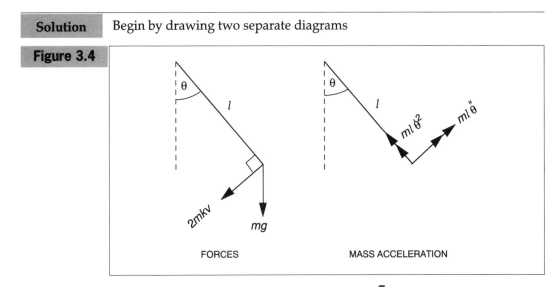

FORCES   MASS ACCELERATION

Since the 'usual' period of small oscillations is $\dfrac{\pi}{2}$ seconds it follows that:

$$\frac{\pi}{2} = 2\pi \sqrt{\frac{l}{g}} \quad \text{i.e. } l = \frac{g}{16} \qquad \dots \text{①}$$

Using $F = ma$ perpendicular to the string gives us

$$2mkv + mg \sin \theta = -ml\ddot{\theta}$$

$$\therefore \quad l\ddot{\theta} + 2kv + g \sin \theta = 0 \qquad \dots \text{②}$$

But $v = l\dot{\theta}$, so equation ② becomes

$$l\ddot{\theta} + 2kl\dot{\theta} + g \sin \theta = 0 \qquad \dots \text{③}$$

Since the oscillations are small, $\sin \theta \approx \theta$, so equation ③ becomes

$$l\ddot{\theta} + 2kl\dot{\theta} + g\theta = 0 \qquad \dots \text{④}$$

Now use the value of l from equation ① to get

$$\ddot{\theta} + 2k\dot{\theta} + 16\theta = 0, \text{ as required}$$

When $k = 3$ the equation becomes $\ddot{\theta} + 6\dot{\theta} + 16\theta = 0$.

The auxiliary equation is $m^2 + 6m + 16 = 0$ which has roots $-3 \pm i\sqrt{7}$.

The general solution is therefore:

$$\theta = e^{-3t}(A \sin \sqrt{7}t + B \cos \sqrt{7}t)$$

But when $t = 0, \theta = 0$ ∴ $B = 0$

∴ $\theta = Ae^{-3t} \sin \sqrt{7}t$, as required.

Now for the rough graph. Since $\sin \sqrt{7}t$ always lies between 1 and –1, θ must always lie between Ae^{-3t} and $-Ae^{-3t}$.

∴   The graph of $\theta = Ae^{-3t} \sin \sqrt{7}t$ must 'bounce' between the graphs of $\theta = Ae^{-3t}$ and $= -Ae^{-3t}$.

∴   We have:

Figure 3.5

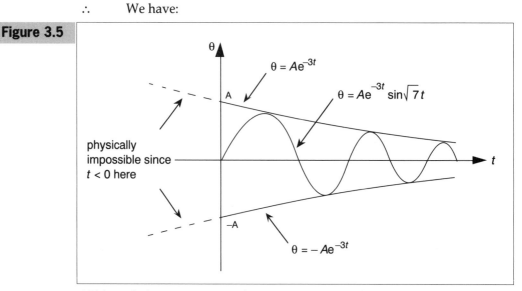

(Although the maximum and minimum values of θ alternate, and the graph of θ against t touches the two boundary exponential curves, these maximum and minimum values do *not* coincide with the 'touching' points.) It follows that the simple pendulum oscillates with decreasing amplitude of oscillation.

When k = 5 the equation becomes $\ddot{\theta} + 10\dot{\theta} + 16\theta = 0$

The auxiliary equation is $m^2 + 10m + 16 = 0$ which has roots -2 and -8

The general solution is therefore:

$$\theta = Ae^{-2t} + Be^{-8t}$$

But when $t = 0, \theta = 0$ ∴ $B = -A$

∴ $\theta = A(e^{-2t} - e^{-8t})$, as required.

Now for the rough graph. The maximum value of θ occurs when $\dot{\theta} = 0$,

i.e. when $-2e^{-2t} + 8e^{-8t} = 0 \Rightarrow e^{6t} = 4 \Rightarrow t = \frac{1}{6}\ln 4$

$\therefore$ We have:

Figure 3.6

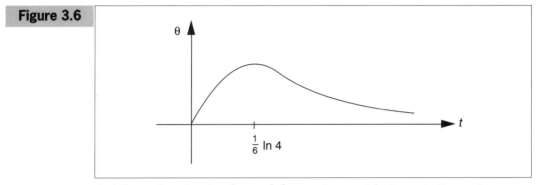

It follows that the simple pendulum swings out *just once* to its maximum value and then slowly it returns asymptotically to its original position.

You should now be able to answer Exercises 12–14 on pp. 65–66.

Forced harmonic oscillations

If we have a damped harmonic oscillation and, at the same time, the particle is also subjected to a force which is a function of time, then the equation of motion becomes:

$$\frac{d^2x}{dt^2} + \omega^2 x + 2\lambda \frac{dx}{dt} = f(t)$$

Example   A particle P of mass m moves along a straight line so that $OP = x$, where O is a fixed point on the line. The forces acting on P are:

(a)   a force mn^2x directed towards O

(b)   a resistance $2mnv$, where v is the speed of P

(c)   a force $F = ma \cos nt$ acting along the direction x increasing.

Write down the differential equation satisfied by x and solve this equation given that at time $t = 0$ the particle is at rest at O.

Find the rate at which the force F is doing work at time t.

The two separate diagrams are shown in Figure 3.7.

Figure 3.7

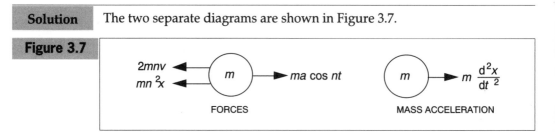

$$\therefore \quad ma\ \cos nt - 2\ mnv - mn^2x = m\frac{d^2x}{dt^2}$$

$$\Rightarrow \quad \frac{d^2x}{dt^2} + 2n\frac{dx}{dt} + n^2x = a\cos nt \quad \left(\text{putting } v = \frac{dx}{dt}\right)$$

The complementary function is found by solving

$$\frac{d^2x}{dt^2} + 2n\frac{dx}{dt} + n^2x = 0$$

The auxiliary equation is $m^2 + 2nm + n^2 = 0$ which has a repeated root of $-n$.

The complementary function is therefore:

$$e^{-nt}(At + B)$$

To find a particular solution, try $x = \alpha \sin nt + \beta \cos nt$

Substituting, we get:

$$(-\alpha n^2 \sin nt - \beta n^2 \cos nt) + 2n(\alpha n \cos nt - \beta n \sin nt) + n^2(\alpha \sin nt + \beta \cos nt)$$

$$= a \cos nt$$

$$\therefore \quad \beta = 0 \text{ and } \alpha = \frac{a}{2n^2}$$

$\therefore$ The general solution is given by:

$$x = e^{-nt}(At + B) + \frac{a}{2n^2}\sin nt$$

But $x = 0$ when $t = 0$ $\therefore B = 0$ $\therefore x = Ate^{-nt} + \frac{a}{2n^2}\sin nt$

Differentiating x as a product we get:

$$\frac{dx}{dt} = -nAte^{-nt} + Ae^{-nt} + \frac{a}{2n}\cos nt$$

But $\frac{dx}{dt} = 0$ when $t = 0$, $\therefore 0 = A + \frac{a}{2n}$ $\therefore A = -\frac{a}{2n}$

$$\therefore \qquad x = \frac{-at}{2n}e^{-nt} + \frac{a}{2n^2}\sin nt$$

Finally, the rate at which F is doing work

$$= F\frac{dx}{dt}$$

$$= ma\,\cos nt\left(\frac{at}{2}e^{-nt} - \frac{a}{2n}e^{-nt} + \frac{a}{2n}\cos nt\right)$$

i.e.   at the rate $\dfrac{ma^2}{2n}\cos nt\left(nte^{-nt} - e^{-nt} + \cos nt\right)$

Example

A light spring AB of natural length a and modulus of elasticity $3amn^2$, initially lies straight and at its natural length on a horizontal table, and a particle of mass m is attached to it at B. Starting at time $t = 0$, the end A is moved in the direction BA with constant speed V. The motion of the particle is resisted by a force equal to $4mn$ times the speed of the particle. If x is the extension of the spring at time t, prove that

$$\frac{d^2x}{dt} + 4n\frac{dx}{dt} + 3n^2x = 4nV$$

Find x in terms of t, and deduce the value of the force applied at A at time t.

Solution

Begin with the usual two diagrams.

Figure 3.8

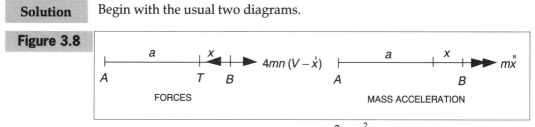

If the extension is x, then the tension $T = \dfrac{3amn^2x}{a}$, i.e. $T = 3mn^2x$.

Now use $F = ma$ to get

$$4mn(V - \overset{\text{'}}{x}) - 3mn^2x = m\overset{\text{''}}{x}$$

$\therefore$ $4nV = \overset{\text{''}}{x} + 4n\overset{\text{'}}{x} + 3n^2x$, as required.

The complementary function is found by solving

$$\frac{d^2x}{dt^2} + 4n\frac{dx}{dt} + 3n^2x = 0$$

The auxiliary equation is $m^2 + 4nm + 3n^2 = 0$ which has roots $-n$ and $-3n$.
The complementary function is therefore:

$$Ae^{-nt} + Be^{-3nt}$$

A particular solution is given by the constant $\dfrac{4nV}{3n^2}$ i.e. $\dfrac{4V}{3n}$

$\therefore$ The general solution is given by

$$x = Ae^{-nt} + Be^{-3nt} + \frac{4V}{3n}$$

But when $t = 0$, $x = 0$ $\therefore$ $0 = A + B + \dfrac{4V}{3n}$ ... ①

Differentiation gives $\overset{\text{.}}{x} = -nAe^{-nt} - 3nBe^{-3nt}$

But $\overset{\text{.}}{x} = V$ when $t = 0$ $\therefore$ $V = -nA - 3nB$ ... ②

Solving equations ① and ② simultaneously gives $A = \dfrac{-3V}{2n}$ and $B = \dfrac{V}{6n}$.

$\therefore$ $x = \dfrac{-3V}{2n}e^{-nt} + \dfrac{V}{6n}e^{-3nt} + \dfrac{4V}{3n}$, which gives us x in terms of t

The force applied at A at time t must be equal and opposite to the tension at A, i.e. $3mn^2x$

$\therefore$ The force applied at A is $3mn^2\left(\dfrac{-3V}{2n}e^{-nt} + \dfrac{V}{6n}e^{-3nt} + \dfrac{4V}{3n}\right)$

which simplifies to give

$$\frac{Vmn}{2}(8 - 9e^{-nt} + e^{-3nt})$$

You should now be able to answer Exercises 15–17 on pp. 67–68.

Motion of a particle with variable mass

In all of our preceding work we have assumed that the mass of the object being considered remains constant. However, this is a poor mathematical model in cases such as the motion of a car or a rocket. In both cases fuel is consumed (and so the total mass goes down) and, in the case of the rocket, it is possible that there could be some underlying increase in mass, as the rocket may well pick up particles of matter, as it flies through space.

When tackling problems such as these, we have to return to the basic momentum equations

   $Ft = mv - mu$

where F is the total external force on the whole system. Moreover we'll be considering small quantities in small intervals of time, so that any term of order two in these quantities will be taken as zero.

Such considerations will inevitably lead to a separable differential equation and, in your examination, you'll almost certainly be given the equation, which you'll be expected to verify. Always remember that , even if you can't quite verify the equation, you can still go on to solve it. That process is known as 'examination technique'!

Example

A body falls from rest. At a subsequent time t its mass is m and its speed v. As it falls, the body picks up small particles of stationary material. Prove that:

$$m\frac{dv}{dt} + v\frac{dm}{dt} = mg$$

If $v = 2tg$, find a general solution of the above equation, giving m as a function of t.

Solution

A couple of momentum diagrams to begin with:

Figure 3.9

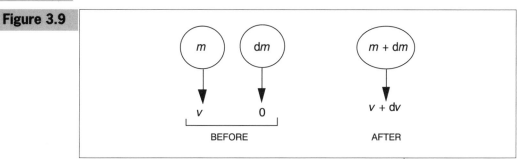

The external force acting on the whole system is $(m + dm)\, g$

$\therefore$ $(m + dm)\,(v + dv) - mv = (m + dm)\, g \times dt$

When we now multiply out the brackets we can ignore $dmdv$ and $dmdt$ since they are much smaller than the other terms.

$\therefore$ We get $mdv + vdm = mgdt$

Now divide by dt to get:

$$m\frac{dv}{dt} + v\frac{dm}{dt} = mg\ ,\ \text{as required}$$

If $v = 2tg$ then $\dfrac{dv}{dt} = 2g$

Substitute in the original equation to get:

$$m \times 2g + 2tg\,\frac{dm}{dt} = mg$$

$\therefore$ $2t\dfrac{dm}{dt} = -m \Rightarrow 2\dfrac{dm}{m} = -\dfrac{dt}{t} \Rightarrow 2\ln m = -\ln t + c$

$\Rightarrow \ln m^2 t = c \Rightarrow m^2 t = e^c \Rightarrow m = \dfrac{A}{\sqrt{t}}$, where A is a constant.

$\therefore$ The general solution is given by $m = \dfrac{A}{\sqrt{t}}$.

Example A body falls under constant gravity picking up matter as it falls, so that at time t its mass is m and speed v. If the matter it picks up is moving downwards with speed u, prove that:

$$m\frac{dv}{dt} + v\frac{dm}{dt} - u\frac{dm}{dt} = mg$$

Solution Let's start with a couple of momentum diagrams, as shown in Figure 3.10.

Figure 3.10

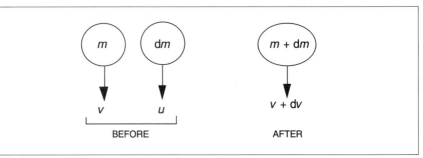

The external force acting on the whole system is $(m + dm)\, g$.

$\therefore$ $(m + dm)\,(v + dv) - mv - dm \times u = (m + dm)\, g \times dt$

Now multiply out the brackets and, remembering that $dm\,dv$ and $dm\,dt$ are much smaller than the other terms, we get

$$mdv + vdm - udm = mgdt$$

Finally divide by dt to get:

$$m\frac{dv}{dt} + v\frac{dm}{dt} - u\frac{dm}{dt} = mg,\ \text{as required}$$

Example A rocket continuously ejects matter backwards with velocity u relative to itself. Show that if gravity is neglected the velocity v and total mass m of the rocket are related by the equation

$$m\frac{dv}{dt} + u\frac{dm}{dt} = 0$$

Deduce that v and m are related by the formula

$$v = m \ln (A\, m^{-1})$$

where A is a constant.

Solution	Again, let's start with a couple of momentum diagrams.

Figure 3.11

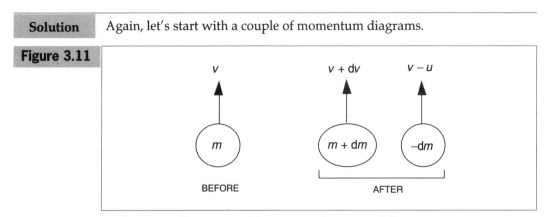

In this example we are told to ignore the external force.

$$\therefore \qquad (m + dm)(v + dv) - dm(v - u) - mv = 0$$

$$\Rightarrow \qquad mdv + u\,dm = 0 \quad \text{(ignoring small terms of order two)}$$

$$\Rightarrow \qquad m\frac{dv}{dt} + u\frac{dm}{dt} = 0, \text{ as required.}$$

$$\Rightarrow \qquad dv = -u\frac{dm}{m} \Rightarrow v = -u \ln m + c$$

$$\Rightarrow \quad v = -u \ln m + u \ln A \quad (\text{letting } c = u \ln A)$$

$$\Rightarrow \quad v = u \ln (Am^{-1}), \text{ as required.}$$

You should now be able to answer Exercises 18–22 on pp. 68–69
Remember: even if you can't get the equation, at least solve it!

EXERCISES

1 A particle of mass m falls from rest; the resistance of the air when the speed is v is kv^2 where k is a constant. Show that after time t the velocity is given by:

$$t = \frac{V}{2g} \ln\left(\frac{V + v}{V + v}\right) \text{ where } V^2 = \frac{mg}{k}.$$

If s is the distance fallen in time t prove

$$s = \frac{V^2}{2g} \ln\left(\frac{V^2}{V^2 - v^2}\right)$$

2 A particle is projected vertically upwards with speed u. The air resistance is $\dfrac{v^2}{k^2}$ times the weight, where k is constant and v is the velocity at any time t. Prove that the particle reaches a height $\dfrac{k^2}{2g} \ln \left(\dfrac{k^2 + u^2}{k^2} \right)$ above the point of projection.

3 A particle moves from rest along a straight line under a force $(A - \dfrac{v}{10})$ N per kg, where v is the velocity in m/s and A is constant. If the velocity at the end of 10 sec is 3 m/s, show that the displacement then is about 17.5 m.

4 A particle of unit mass falls from rest in a medium in which the resistance is kv, where v is the velocity at any time t. Find v in terms of t and prove that the velocity can never exceed $\dfrac{g}{k}$.

5 A particle P, of mass m, is projected vertically upwards from ground level with speed U. The motion takes place in a medium in which the resistance is of magnitude $\dfrac{mgv^2}{k^2}$, where v is the speed of P and k is a positive constant.

Show that P reaches its maximum height above the ground after a time T given by

$$T = \frac{k}{g} \tan^{-1} \left(\frac{U}{k} \right).$$

6 At time $t = 0$ a particle of mass m falls from rest at the point A which is at a height h above a horizontal plane. The particle is subject to a resistance of magnitude mkv^2, where v is the speed of the particle of time t and k is a positive constant. The particle strikes the plane with speed V. Show that:

$$kV^2 = g(1 - e^{-2kh}) .$$

7 A particle of mass m is projected vertically upwards with speed V. The air resistance is kmv^2 when v is the speed. If the particle returns to the point of projection with speed V_1 prove

$$\frac{1}{V_1^2} = \frac{1}{V^2} + \frac{k}{g}$$

8 A car of mass 1000 kg is driven by an engine which generates a constant power of 12 kW. The only resistance to the car's motion is air resistance of magnitude $10v^2$ N where v m s^{-1} is the speed of the car. Find the distance travelled as the car's speed increases from 5 m s^{-1} to 10 m s^{-1}.

9 A particle of mass m is projected vertically upwards, with an initial speed of u, in a medium which exerts a resistance of magnitude mkv, where k is a positive constant and v is the speed of the particle after time t.

Find, in terms of k, g and u, the time taken for the particle to reach its greatest height.

10 A particle P of mass m falls vertically into a container of liquid, entering the liquid with speed U. The particle continues to fall vertically, and when it has fallen a distance x through the liquid, its speed is v. The motion of P through the liquid is resisted by a force of magnitude mkv^2, where k is a constant. Show that:

$$x = \frac{1}{2k} \ln \left(\frac{g - kU^2}{g - kv^2} \right)$$

11 A particle of mass m is released from rest at a point, height h above horizontal ground. The particle moves in a medium which exerts a resistance of magnitude mkv^2, where v is the speed of the particle and k is a positive constant. The coefficient of restitution between the particle and the ground is $\dfrac{1}{\sqrt{2}}$.

Show that, after one bounce on the ground the particle reaches a maximum height H, where H is given by

$$H = \frac{1}{2k} \ln \left(\frac{3 - e^{-2kh}}{2} \right).$$

12 A particle moves in a straight line so that its distance x from a fixed point in the line satisfies the differential equation

$$\frac{d^2x}{dt^2} + 4\frac{dx}{dt} + 4x = 0$$

The particle starts from rest at time $t = 0$ when $x = a$ Prove that its greatest speed in the ensuing motion is $2a\,e^{-1}$.

13

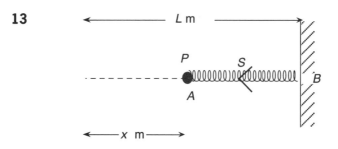

The figure represents a model of a shock absorber. A particle P, of mass m kg, is attached to one end A of a light horizontal spring AB, of natural length L metres. The end B of the spring is fixed. The spring exerts a resistance S, of $0.6m$ newtons for every 0.1 m of compression, and the whole system is immersed in a medium which exerts a resistance on the particle of magnitude $5mv$ newtons, where v m s^{-1} is the speed of P at time t seconds. The compression of the spring at time t seconds is x metres. The motion of the particle takes place in a fixed horizontal line through B. There are no other horizontal forces acting on the particle.

(a) Show that:

$$\frac{d^2x}{dt^2} + 5\frac{dx}{dt} + 6x = 0$$

Given that $x = 2$ and $\dfrac{dx}{dt} = -4$ when $t = 0$,

(b) find x in terms of t

(c) Sketch the graph of x against t.

14 A particle P of mass m is attached to one end of a light elastic string of natural length $2L$ and modulus of elasticity $3\,mg$. The other end of the string is attached to a fixed point O and P hangs freely in equilibrium. Particle P is pulled down a distance L below the equilibrium position and then released from rest. The subsequent motion takes place in a medium in which the resistance is of magnitude $2\,mv\,\sqrt{\left(\dfrac{g}{L}\right)}$,

where v is the speed of P.

Given that at time t the displacement of P from its equilibrium position is x.

(a) Show that provided the string is taut

$$\frac{d^2x}{dt^2} + 2\sqrt{\left(\frac{g}{L}\right)}\frac{dx}{dt} + \frac{3}{2}\left(\frac{g}{L}\right)x = 0 \qquad \ldots ①$$

(b) Show that ① represents damped harmonic motion.

Given that a general solution of ① is of the form

$$x = Ce^{-at} \cos(bt + \varepsilon),$$

where C and ε are arbitrary constants,

(c)   find the value of a and the value of b

(d)   Show that the string does not go slack.

15   A light spring AB, of natural length 1 m, lies at rest on a smooth horizontal table. A particle of mass 0.5 kg is attached at B. The modulus of elasticity of the spring is 2 N. The end A of the spring starts to oscillate in the direction AB in such a way that its displacement after t seconds is $(2 \sin t)$ metres. The extension in the spring at time t seconds is y metres. Show that:

$$\frac{d^2y}{dt^2} + 4y = 2 \sin t$$

Given that $y = 0$ and $\dfrac{dy}{dt} = -2$ at $t = 0$,

(a)   show that $y = \dfrac{2}{3}(\sin t - 2 \sin 2t)$.

(b)   Find the value of t when the spring first returns to its natural length.

16

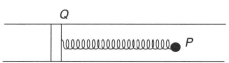

A particle P of mass 2 kg is free to slide horizontally inside a smooth cylindrical tube. P is attached to one end of a light elastic spring of natural length 0.2 m and modulus of elasticity 3.6 N. The system is initially at rest. The other end Q of the spring is then forced to oscillate with simple harmonic motion so that at time t seconds its displacement from its initial position is $(\sin 2t)$ metres. The displacement of P from its initial position at time t seconds is x metres, measured in the same direction as the displacement of Q.

(a)   Show that $\dfrac{d^2x}{dt^2} + 9x = 9 \sin 2t$.

(b)   Hence find the first time, after the motion starts, at which P is instantaneously at rest.

17 At time t seconds, a particle P, of mass 1 kg, has a displacement x metres from a fixed point O. It is moving in a straight line and performs forced harmonic motion so that:

$$\frac{d^2x}{dt^2} + 4x = 6 \cos 2t.$$

(a)   Solve this differential equation.

(b)   Describe briefly the motion of the particle.

18 A spherical raindrop of initial radius a falls from rest under gravity. Its radius increases with time at a constant rate λ owing to condensation from a surrounding cloud which is at rest. At time t the radius of the raindrop is r and its downward velocity if v. Show that:

(a) $r = a + \lambda t$

(b) $\dfrac{d}{dt}\left((a + \lambda t)^3\, v \right) = (a + \lambda t)^3\, g$

Hence find the velocity v as a function of time.

19 A rocket of initial total mass M propels itself by ejecting mass at a constant rate λ per unit time with speed u relative to the rocket. If the rocket is at rest, directed vertically upwards, and then leaves the ground, so that at time t its velocity is v, prove that:

(a)   its mass at time t is $M - \lambda t$

(b) $\dfrac{dv}{dt} = \dfrac{\lambda u}{M - \lambda t} - g$

Deduce that the rocket can only leave the ground provided $\lambda u > Mg$.

Deduce further that $v = u \ln\left(1 - \dfrac{\lambda t}{M} \right) - gt$.

Show also that when the mass of the rocket has been reduced to half the initial value, its height above ground level will be:

$$\frac{uM}{2\lambda} \left\{ 1 - \ln 2 - \frac{Mg}{4\lambda u} \right\}$$

20 At time t, the mass of a rocket is $M(1 - kt)$, where M and k are constants. At time t, the rocket is moving with speed v vertically upwards near the earth's surface against constant gravity. Burnt fuel is expelled vertically downwards at speed u relative to the rocket. Show that:

$$(1 - kt)\,\frac{dv}{dt} = ku - g\,(1 - kt)$$

Given that $v = 0$ when $t = 0$, find v in terms of g, u, k and t.

21 A spherical hailstone, falling under gravity in still air, increases its radius r by condensation according to the law $\dfrac{dr}{dt} = \lambda r$, where λ is constant. If air resistance is neglected, prove that the hailstone approaches a limiting velocity $\dfrac{g}{3\lambda}$.

22 A rocket driven car, of total initial mass M, loses mass at a constant rate m per unit time at constant ejection speed V relative to the car. If the total resistance to motion is kv when the velocity is v, show that the acceleration of the car along a straight horizontal road is:

$$\frac{mV - kv}{M - mt}$$

at time t from the start, and hence that the speed from rest is then

$$\frac{mV}{k}\left[1 - \left(\frac{1 - mt}{M}\right)^{k/m}\right]$$

SUMMARY

You should now be able to:

- use the expressions $\dfrac{dv}{dt}$ or $v\dfrac{dv}{dx}$ for acceleration, in order to set up an equation of motion.

- solve the following equations ($a, b > 0$)

(a) $\dfrac{dv}{dt} = a + bv$. $\left(\text{Ans: } \dfrac{1}{b} \ln (a + bv) = t + c\right)$

(b) $\dfrac{dv}{dt} = a + bv^2$. $\left(\text{Ans: } \dfrac{1}{\sqrt{ab}} \tan^{-1} v \sqrt{\dfrac{b}{a}} + c\right)$

(c) $\dfrac{dv}{dt} = a - bv^2$. $\left(\text{Ans: } \dfrac{1}{2\sqrt{ab}} \ln \left(\dfrac{\sqrt{a} + v\sqrt{b}}{\sqrt{a} - v\sqrt{b}}\right) = t + c\right)$

(d) $v\dfrac{dv}{dx} = a + bv$. $\left(\text{Ans: } \dfrac{v}{b} - \dfrac{a}{b^2} \ln (a + bv) = x + c \quad \text{if } b \neq 0\right)$

(e) $v\dfrac{dv}{dx} = a + bv^2$. $\left(\text{Ans: } \dfrac{1}{2b} \ln (a + bv^2) = x + c\right)$

- recognise the equation for damped harmonic motion, i.e.

$$\frac{d^2x}{dt^2} + \omega^2 x + 2\lambda \frac{dx}{dt} = 0$$

- solve the equation for damped harmonic motion

- recognise the equation for forced harmonic motion, i.e.

$$\frac{d^2x}{dt^2} + \omega^2 x + 2\lambda \frac{dx}{dt} = f(t)$$

- solve the equation for forced harmonic motion

- use the equation $mv - mu = Ft$, to set up a differential equation for variable mass

- integrate this equation by separating the variables

- recall that *terminal velocity* means the limiting velocity as $t \to \infty$,
  e.g. if $v = a(b - e^{-t})$, then the terminal velocity is *ab*.

Elastic collisions in two dimensions

If you drop a tennis ball onto a flat elastic surface then, after impact, the ball will bounce straight up again. But if the surface is inclined, then how does the ball bounce this time?

Then again, suppose that you and a friend are potting some balls on a snooker table. Just for fun you each place a ball on the table and then hit them in such a way that the balls eventually collide.

What paths do the balls follow after the collision?

It is questions such as these that we will be looking at in this section.

When you've finished this section you should be able to solve problems involving:

● the collision of a smooth sphere with a fixed surface

● oblique impact between two smooth elastic spheres.

Important formulae from Module M2

You saw in Module M2 that, in the case of a direct impact between two smooth elastic spheres, we had the following situation:

Figure 4.1

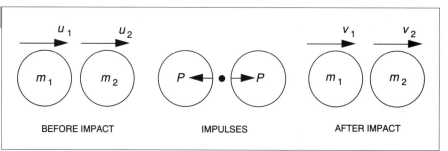

BEFORE IMPACT   IMPULSES   AFTER IMPACT

The useful formulae are:

(a)   If the impulse P is required, then either of the impulse equations

$m_2v_2 - m_2u_2 = P$ and $m_1v_1 - m_1u_1 = -P$ can be used. Otherwise, the following two equations will be sufficient

(b)   The conservation of linear momentum

$m_1u_1 + m_2u_2 = m_1v_1 + m_2v_2$

(c)   Newton's Experimental Law

$v_2 - v_1 = -e(u_2 - u_1)$

Remember that $0 \leq e \leq 1$. When $e = 0$, the surfaces are inelastic (i.e. there is no bouncing) and when $e = 1$, the surfaces are perfectly elastic (but, in the real world, this is probably unachievable).

As a special case of (c), if a smooth sphere hits a flat surface with velocity v, then it will rebound with velocity ev.

Figure 4.2

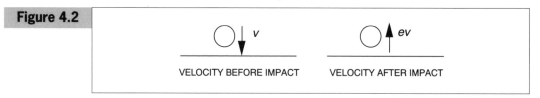

VELOCITY BEFORE IMPACT   VELOCITY AFTER IMPACT

The impact of a smooth sphere with an inclined surface

Suppose that we have the following situation:

Figure 4.3

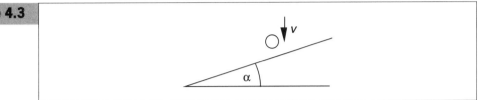

(A smooth sphere is travelling vertically downwards with velocity v when it hits a plane inclined at angle α.)

First we resolve the velocity into two components – one perpendicular to the plane and the other parallel to the plane. This gives us:

Figure 4.4

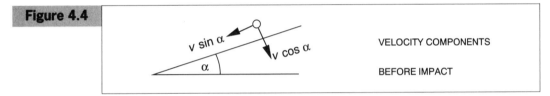

VELOCITY COMPONENTS

BEFORE IMPACT

After impact:

● the velocity component down the plane is unchanged

● the velocity component perpendicular to the plane is reversed and multiplied by e.

This gives us:

Figure 4.5

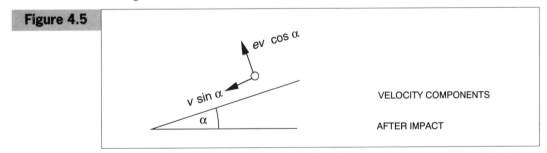

VELOCITY COMPONENTS

AFTER IMPACT

Similarly, if a smooth sphere hits a fixed horizontal plane at an angle, then we have:

Figure 4.6

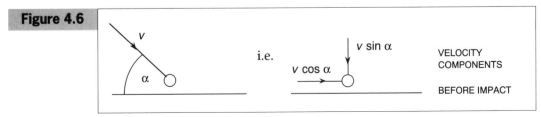

i.e.

VELOCITY COMPONENTS

BEFORE IMPACT

(The velocity at impact is v, whose line of action makes an angle α with the fixed horizontal plane.)

After impact:

● the velocity component parallel to the plane is unchanged

● the velocity component perpendicular to the plane is reversed and multiplied by e.

This gives us:

Figure 4.7

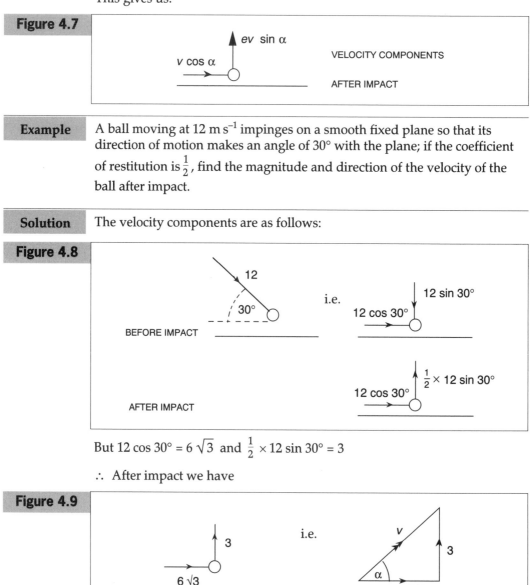

Example   A ball moving at 12 m s^{-1} impinges on a smooth fixed plane so that its direction of motion makes an angle of 30° with the plane; if the coefficient of restitution is $\frac{1}{2}$, find the magnitude and direction of the velocity of the ball after impact.

Solution   The velocity components are as follows:

Figure 4.8

But $12 \cos 30° = 6\sqrt{3}$ and $\frac{1}{2} \times 12 \sin 30° = 3$

∴ After impact we have

Figure 4.9

∴   Magnitude of resultant velocity v is given by:

$$v^2 = (6\sqrt{3})^2 + 3^2 \Rightarrow v^2 = 117 \Rightarrow v = 3\sqrt{13}$$

and α is given by $\tan\alpha = \dfrac{3}{6\sqrt{3}} \Rightarrow \alpha = \tan^{-1}\left(\dfrac{1}{2\sqrt{3}}\right)$

∴   The magnitude and direction of the velocity after impact is $3\sqrt{13}$ m s^{-1} and $\tan^{-1}\left(\dfrac{1}{2\sqrt{3}}\right)$ respectively.

Example   A ball falls from a height of 10 m upon an inclined plane, the coefficient of restitution being $\dfrac{1}{5}$. Find the magnitude and direction of the velocity of the ball after impact, when the inclination of the plane is 60°.

Solution   The ball hits the plane with velocity v where $v^2 = 0^2 + 2 \times 10 \times g$

i.e. $v = \sqrt{20g}$ (using the constant acceleration formula $v^2 = u^2 + 2as$)

Figure 4.10

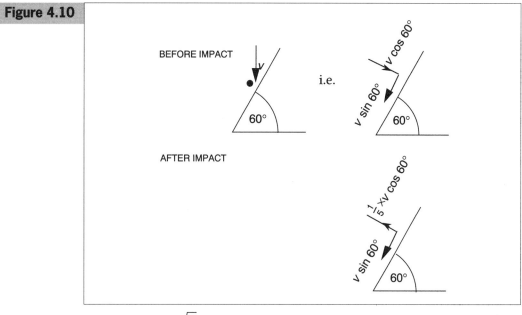

But $v \sin 60° = \dfrac{v\sqrt{3}}{2}$ and $\dfrac{1}{5} \times v \cos 60° = \dfrac{v}{10}$.

THIS BOOK IS THE PROPERTY
OF CORNWALL COLLEGE

∴ The velocity of the ball after impact is given by:

Figure 4.11

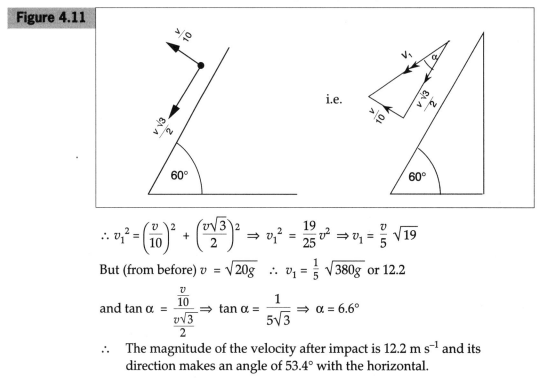

i.e.

$$\therefore v_1^2 = \left(\frac{v}{10}\right)^2 + \left(\frac{v\sqrt{3}}{2}\right)^2 \Rightarrow v_1^2 = \frac{19}{25}v^2 \Rightarrow v_1 = \frac{v}{5}\sqrt{19}$$

But (from before) $v = \sqrt{20g}$ ∴ $v_1 = \frac{1}{5}\sqrt{380g}$ or 12.2

and $\tan \alpha = \dfrac{\dfrac{v}{10}}{\dfrac{v\sqrt{3}}{2}} \Rightarrow \tan \alpha = \dfrac{1}{5\sqrt{3}} \Rightarrow \alpha = 6.6°$

∴   The magnitude of the velocity after impact is 12.2 m s^{-1} and its
direction makes an angle of 53.4° with the horizontal.

You should now be able to answer Exercises 1–6 on pp. 84–85. Remember
to make your methods clear by using diagrams throughout.

Oblique impact of two smooth elastic spheres

Suppose that two smooth elastic spheres collide obliquely. A bird's eye
view of the situation would be:

Figure 4.12

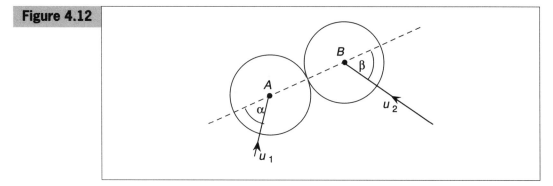

The centres of the spheres are A and B and the line joining AB is called *the line of centres*. If we now resolve the components of velocity along and perpendicular to the line of centres, we get (again, a bird's eye view):

Figure 4.13

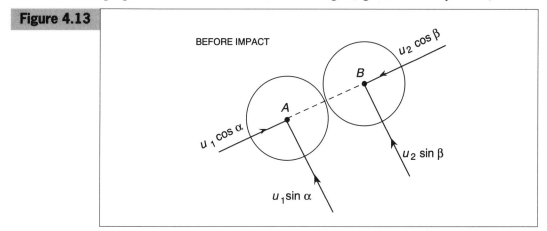

Since the spheres are smooth, there is no force perpendicular to the line of centres. Hence *after impact the velocity components perpendicular to the line of centres will remain unchanged.* Only the velocity components along the line of centres will change. And so:

Figure 4.14

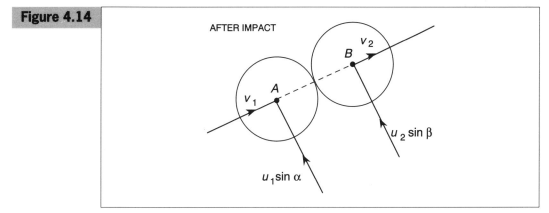

The velocity components v_1 and v_2 can be found from:

(a) the conservation of linear momentum equation:

$$m_1 u_1 \cos \alpha - m_2 u_2 \cos \beta = m_1 v_1 + m_2 v_2$$

(where m_1, m_2 are the masses of the spheres with centres at A and B respectively)

(b) Newton's Experimental Law:

$$v_2 - v_1 = -e\,(-u_2 \cos \beta - u_1 \cos \alpha)$$

It is then a matter of solving simultaneous equations.

Example   A sphere of mass 2 kg moving at 10 m s^{-1}, impinges obliquely on a sphere of mass 4 kg which is at rest, the direction of motion of the first sphere making an angle of 60° with the line of centres at the moment of impact. Find the velocities of the spheres after impact, the coefficient of restitution being $\frac{1}{2}$.

Solution   We are given the situation shown in Figure 4.15.

Figure 4.15

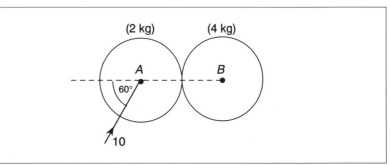

This resolves to give:

Figure 4.16

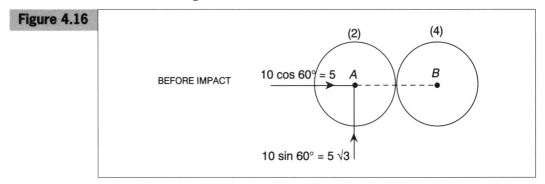

Remembering that the component $5\sqrt{3}$ will remain unchanged during impact, we also have:

Figure 4.17

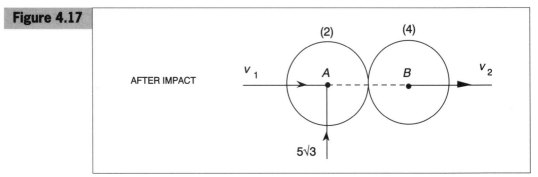

∴ Conservation of linear momentum along AB gives:

$$2 \times 5 + 4 \times 0 = 2v_1 + 4v_2 \implies v_1 + 2v_2 = 5 \qquad \dots ①$$

Newton's law along AB gives:

$$v_2 - v_1 = -\frac{1}{2}(0 - 5) \implies v_2 - v_1 = 2.5 \qquad \dots ②$$

Solve equations ① and ② simultaneously to give:

$$v_2 = 2.5 \text{ and } v_1 = 0$$

∴ After impact the 2 kg sphere is moving at $5\sqrt{3}$ m s^{-1} perpendicular to the line of centres and the 4 kg sphere is moving at 2.5 m s^{-1} along the line of centres.

As indicated in this solution, try and use clear diagrams as much as possible. They help to clarify your thoughts and are also a great help to any examiner who is trying to understand what you are doing. Moreover, always make sure that the answer to the question is clearly stated at the end.

Example

A sphere of mass 2 kg moving with velocity 8 m s^{-1} impinges on a sphere of mass 4 kg, moving with velocity 2 m s^{-1}; if their velocities before impact be in like parallel directions and inclined at an angle of 30° to the line of centres at the moment of impact, find the velocities after impact, the coefficient of restitution being $\frac{1}{3}$.

Solution

We are given:

Figure 4.18

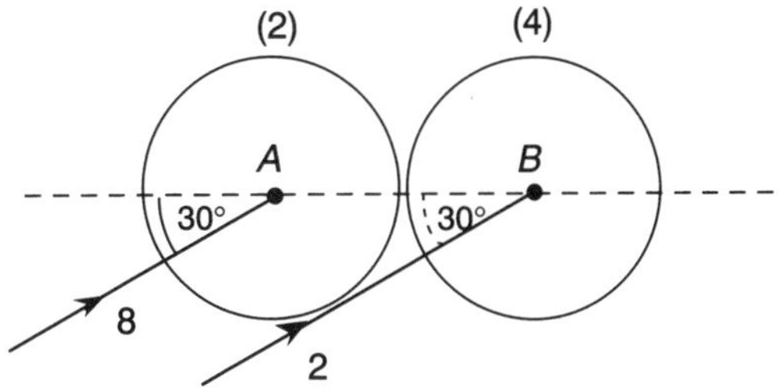

which leads to the system in Figure 4.19:

Figure 4.19

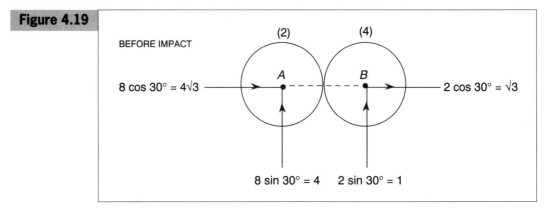

BEFORE IMPACT

Remembering that the components of velocity perpendicular to the line of centres remain unchanged during impact, we also have:

Figure 4.20

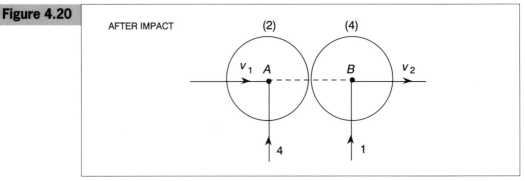

AFTER IMPACT

Conservation of linear momentum along AB gives

$$2 \times 4\sqrt{3} + 4 \times \sqrt{3} = 2v_1 + 4v_2 \implies v_1 + 2v_2 = 6\sqrt{3} \qquad \ldots \text{①}$$

Newton's law along AB gives

$$v_2 - v_1 = -\tfrac{1}{3}(\sqrt{3} - 4\sqrt{3}) \implies v_2 - v_1 = \sqrt{3} \qquad \ldots \text{②}$$

Solve equations ① and ② simultaneously to give:

$$v_2 = \frac{7\sqrt{3}}{3} \quad \text{and} \quad v_1 = \frac{4\sqrt{3}}{3}$$

∴   The magnitude of the velocity of the 2 kg sphere after impact is obtained from Figure 4.21:

Figure 4.21

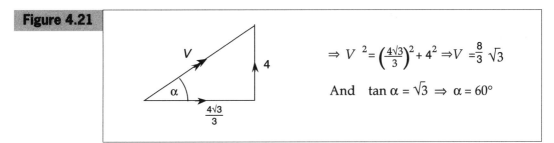

$$\Rightarrow V^2 = \left(\tfrac{4\sqrt{3}}{3}\right)^2 + 4^2 \Rightarrow V = \tfrac{8}{3}\sqrt{3}$$

And $\tan\alpha = \sqrt{3} \Rightarrow \alpha = 60°$

∴   This sphere moves off at $\tfrac{8}{3}\sqrt{3}$ m s⁻¹ at an angle of 60° with the line of centres.

For the 4 kg sphere we have:

Figure 4.22

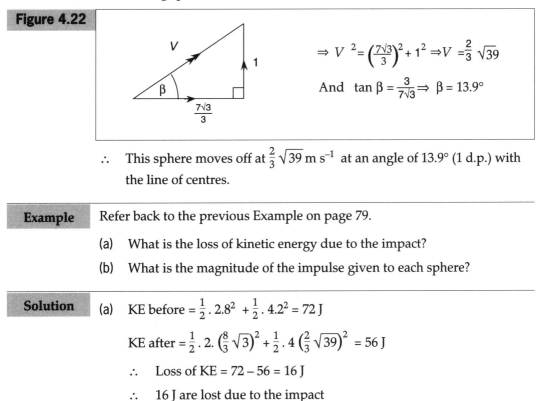

$$\Rightarrow V^2 = \left(\tfrac{7\sqrt{3}}{3}\right)^2 + 1^2 \Rightarrow V = \tfrac{2}{3}\sqrt{39}$$

And $\tan\beta = \tfrac{3}{7\sqrt{3}} \Rightarrow \beta = 13.9°$

∴   This sphere moves off at $\tfrac{2}{3}\sqrt{39}$ m s⁻¹ at an angle of 13.9° (1 d.p.) with the line of centres.

Example

Refer back to the previous Example on page 79.

(a)   What is the loss of kinetic energy due to the impact?

(b)   What is the magnitude of the impulse given to each sphere?

Solution

(a)   KE before $= \tfrac{1}{2} \cdot 2.8^2 + \tfrac{1}{2} \cdot 4.2^2 = 72$ J

KE after $= \tfrac{1}{2} \cdot 2 \cdot \left(\tfrac{8}{3}\sqrt{3}\right)^2 + \tfrac{1}{2} \cdot 4 \left(\tfrac{2}{3}\sqrt{39}\right)^2 = 56$ J

∴   Loss of KE = 72 – 56 = 16 J

∴   16 J are lost due to the impact

(b)   For the 2 kg sphere we have:

Figure 4.23

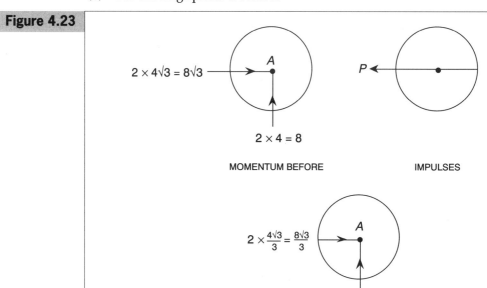

$\therefore$ *Along the line of centres* we use the formula:

Momentum after – Momentum before = Impulse

$\therefore$ $\dfrac{8\sqrt{3}}{3} - 8\sqrt{3} = -P \Rightarrow P = \dfrac{16\sqrt{3}}{3}$

$\therefore$ An impulse of $\dfrac{16\sqrt{3}}{3}$ N s is given to each sphere.

Example

At time $t = 0$ two particles A and B leave the point $\mathbf{i} + 2\mathbf{j}$, the velocity vector of A being $\mathbf{i} + 4\mathbf{j} + \mathbf{k}$ and the velocity of B relative to A being of magnitude $\sqrt{90}$. A third particle C leaves the point $4\mathbf{i} + 3\mathbf{k}$ at time $t = 0$ with velocity vector $2\mathbf{i} - \mathbf{j} + 3\mathbf{k}$.

If the particles travel with constant velocity and if B collides with C, find the initial velocity vector of B.

Find also the value of t at the instant when the collision takes place.

If the particles B and C coalesce on collision and then move in a direction perpendicular to the velocity of A, find the ratio of the masses of the particles B and C.

Solution   At time t the position vector of C is given by

$$\begin{pmatrix} 4 \\ 0 \\ 3 \end{pmatrix} + t \begin{pmatrix} 2 \\ -1 \\ 3 \end{pmatrix}$$

If the initial velocity vector of B is $\mathbf{v}$, then the position vector of B at time t is given by

$$\begin{pmatrix} 1 \\ 2 \\ 0 \end{pmatrix} + t\mathbf{v}$$

Since they collide at time t it follows that

$$\begin{pmatrix} 1 \\ 2 \\ 0 \end{pmatrix} + t\mathbf{v} = \begin{pmatrix} 4 \\ 0 \\ 3 \end{pmatrix} + t \begin{pmatrix} 2 \\ -1 \\ 3 \end{pmatrix}$$

$$\therefore \quad \mathbf{v} = \begin{pmatrix} 2 \\ -1 \\ 3 \end{pmatrix} + \frac{1}{t} \begin{pmatrix} 3 \\ -2 \\ 3 \end{pmatrix} \qquad \dots \text{①}$$

But the velocity of B relative to A has magnitude $\sqrt{90}$

$$\therefore \quad \left| \mathbf{v} - \begin{pmatrix} 1 \\ 4 \\ 1 \end{pmatrix} \right| = \sqrt{90} \qquad \dots \text{②}$$

$\therefore$ Equations ① and ② give us

$$\left| \begin{pmatrix} 1 \\ -5 \\ 2 \end{pmatrix} + \frac{1}{t} \begin{pmatrix} 3 \\ -2 \\ 3 \end{pmatrix} \right| = \sqrt{90}$$

i.e. $$\left(1 + \frac{3}{t} \right)^2 + \left(5 + \frac{2}{t} \right)^2 + \left(2 + \frac{3}{t} \right)^2 = 90$$

$$\therefore \quad t = 1 \text{ and } \mathbf{v} = \begin{pmatrix} 5 \\ -3 \\ 6 \end{pmatrix}$$

$\therefore$ The initial velocity of B is $\begin{pmatrix} 5 \\ -3 \\ 6 \end{pmatrix}$ and the collision takes place after 1 second.

Now for the collision itself.

Figure 4.24

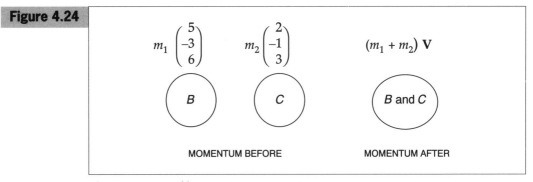

Conservation of linear momentum gives:

$$m_1 \begin{pmatrix} 5 \\ -3 \\ 6 \end{pmatrix} + m_2 \begin{pmatrix} 2 \\ -1 \\ 3 \end{pmatrix} = (m_1 + m_2)\,\mathbf{V} \qquad \ldots ③$$

But $\mathbf{V}$ is perpendicular to $\begin{pmatrix} 1 \\ 4 \\ 1 \end{pmatrix}$ i.e. $\mathbf{V} \cdot \begin{pmatrix} 1 \\ 4 \\ 1 \end{pmatrix} = 0$.

∴ Taking the scalar product of each term in equation ③ with the vector $\begin{pmatrix} 1 \\ 4 \\ 1 \end{pmatrix}$

we get

$$m_1 \begin{pmatrix} 5 \\ -3 \\ 6 \end{pmatrix} \cdot \begin{pmatrix} 1 \\ 4 \\ 1 \end{pmatrix} + m_2 \begin{pmatrix} 2 \\ -1 \\ 3 \end{pmatrix} \cdot \begin{pmatrix} 1 \\ 4 \\ 1 \end{pmatrix} = 0$$

∴ $-m_1 + m_2 = 0$, i.e. $m_1 = m_2$

∴ The masses of B and C must be equal.

You should now be able to answer Exercises 7–16 on pp. 85–87. Remember to make your methods clear by using neat diagrams throughout.

EXERCISES

1 A ball, moving with a velocity of 20 m s^{-1}, impinges on a smooth fixed plane in a direction making an angle of 30° with the plane; if the coefficient of restitution is $\frac{3}{5}$, find the velocity of the ball after the impact.

2 A billiard ball of mass 210 g strikes a smooth cushion when moving at 2.4 m s^{-1} in a direction inclined at 30° to the cushion. If the coefficient of restitution is $\frac{7}{8}$, find the loss of kinetic energy due to the impact.

3 A particle moving on a smooth horizontal floor encounters a smooth plane inclined at 45° to the floor, and the coefficient of restitution between particle and plane is $\frac{1}{2}$. Prove that after rebounding the particle strikes the plane at right angles.

4 A smooth inclined plane whose angle with the horizontal is $\tan^{-1}\left(\frac{1}{3}\right)$ rests on a horizontal floor. A particle dropped from a height of 2.5 m strikes the plane very near its lower edge. The coefficient of restitution is $\frac{2}{3}$. Find the angle with the horizontal at which the particle rebounds, and the distance from the foot of the plane to the point where it first reaches the floor.

5 A staircase has steps 36 cm wide, the rise at each step being 18 cm. A ball, whose coefficient of restitution with each step is $\frac{2}{3}$, bounces down the staircase, striking each step in turn at the same distance from its edge. Find the horizontal and vertical velocities of the ball just before the first impact.

6 A particle strikes a smooth horizontal floor with a speed of 7 m/s, its direction of motion being at 30° to the horizontal. The coefficient of restitution is 0.8. Find the total time during which bouncing continues, and the distance on the floor between the first point of impact and the point where bouncing stops.

7 A sphere of mass 8 kg moving at 6 m s^{-1}, impinges obliquely on a sphere of mass 4 kg which is at rest, the direction of motion making an angle of 30° with the line of centres. Find the velocities of the spheres after impact, the coefficient of restitution being $\frac{3}{4}$.

8 A sphere of mass m impinges obliquely on a sphere of mass M, which is at rest. Show that, if $m = eM$, the directions of motion after impact are at right angles.

9 A boy of mass 37 kg standing on roller skates catches a ball of mass 0.5 kg which is coming to him at 9 m s^{-1} at 60° to the horizontal. With what speed does he move backwards after catching the ball?

10 Two 'dodgem' boats, one of mass 250 kg moving at 3.2 m s^{-1} and the other of mass 300 kg moving at 1 m s^{-1}, are approaching a collision along paths making 120° with each other. The heavier one is brought to rest by the impact. Through what angle is the other deflected, and what is its speed after the collision?

11 Two equal smooth spheres of radius a are moving with equal speeds u in opposite directions along parallel lines whose distance apart is a. The coefficient of restitution between them is $\frac{1}{3}$. Find their velocities after impact.

12 A smooth uniform sphere S, of mass m, is moving with speed u on a horizontal plane when it collides with another smooth uniform sphere, of mass $3m$ and having the same radius as S, which is at rest on the horizontal plane. The direction of motion of S before impact makes an angle θ, $0 < \theta < \frac{\pi}{2}$, with the line of centres of the two spheres.

The coefficient of restitution between the spheres is e. After the impact the spheres are moving in directions which are perpendicular to one another. Find the value of e.

13 A smooth uniform sphere A of mass m moving with speed u on a horizontal table collides with another smooth uniform sphere B of mass $4m$ which is at rest. A and B are of the same size and the direction of motion of A before the impact makes an angle of $\frac{1}{6}\pi$ with the line of centres of the spheres.

Given that the direction of motion of A is turned through a right angle by the impact, find the coefficient of restitution between the spheres.

14

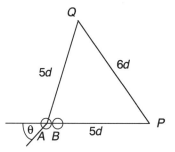

A small smooth sphere A moving with speed u on a horizontal table collides with another identical sphere B which is at rest on the table. The direction of motion of A before impact makes an angle θ, where $\tan \theta = \frac{3}{2}$, with the line of centres of A and B. The coefficient of restitution between the two spheres is $\frac{1}{8}$. Two points P and Q on the table are each at a distance $5d$ from the position of the centre of A at the moment of impact and the distance PQ is $6d$ as shown in the above figure.

After the impact B move towards P.

(a) Find the velocity of A after impact

(b) Show that A moves towards Q.

15 A small smooth sphere T is at rest on a smooth horizontal table. An identical sphere S moving on the table with speed U collides with T. The directions of motion of S before and after impact make angles of $30°$ and $\beta°$ $(0 < \beta < 90)$ respectively with L, the line of centres at the moment of impact. The coefficient of restitution between S and T is e

(a) Show that V, the speed of T immediately after impact, is given by

$$V = \frac{U\sqrt{3}}{4}\left(1 + e\right)$$

(b) Find the components of the velocity of S, parallel and perpendicular to L, immediately after impact.

Given that $e = \frac{2}{3}$,

(c) find, to 1 decimal place, the value of β.

16 A red ball is stationary on a rectangular billiard table $OABC$. It is then struck by a white ball of equal mass and equal radius with velocity.

$u(-2\mathbf{i} + 11\mathbf{j})$

where $\mathbf{i}$ and $\mathbf{j}$ are unit vectors along OA and OC respectively. After impact the red and white balls have velocities parallel to the vectors $-3\mathbf{i} + 4\mathbf{j}$, $2\mathbf{i} + 4\mathbf{j}$ respectively. Prove that the coefficient of restitution between the two balls is $\frac{1}{2}$.

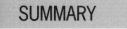

SUMMARY

You should now be able to recall the two following before–after situations.

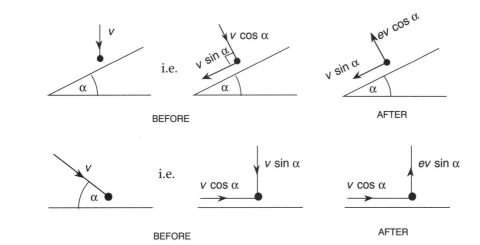

You should also know that in an oblique impact of smooth elastic spheres:

● the velocity components of the spheres perpendicular to the line of centres remain unchanged during impact

● the velocity components of the spheres along the line of centres can be found by using

    (a)   conservation of linear momentum along the line of centres

    (b)   Newton's Experimental Law along the line of centres.

Applications of vectors in mechanics

INTRODUCTION In this section we shall see how valuable are the concepts of scalar product, vector product and the vector equation of a line in the solution of mechanics problems.

When you've finished this section you should be able to:

● tackle questions involving relative motion

● solve first and second order vector differential equations

● use a scalar product to work out the work done by a constant force

● use a vector product to work out the moment of a force about a given point

● use vectors in the reduction of force systems to resultant forces and couples.

Recalling the relevant vector techniques

The following Examples cover the vector techniques that will be assumed in this section. These techniques are covered fully in Modules P3 and P4.

Example A force of 26 N acts in the direction $3\mathbf{i} + 4\mathbf{j} - 12\mathbf{k}$. Express this force as a vector.

Solution The magnitude of $3\mathbf{i} + 4\mathbf{j} - 12\mathbf{k}$ is $\sqrt{3^2 + 4^2 + (-12)^2}$ i.e. 13. But the required force of 26 N has double this magnitude.

∴ Force = $2(3\mathbf{i} + 4\mathbf{j} - 12\mathbf{k})$ or $6\mathbf{i} + 8\mathbf{j} - 24\mathbf{k}$

∴ The required force is $(6\mathbf{i} + 8\mathbf{j} - 24\mathbf{k})$ N

Example The position vector of point P is $\mathbf{r}$. Write down expressions for (a) the velocity vector and (b) the acceleration vector of P.

Solution (a) Velocity vector of $P = \dot{\mathbf{r}} = \mathbf{v}$

(b) Acceleration vector of $P = \ddot{\mathbf{r}} = \dfrac{d\mathbf{v}}{dt}$

Example	A rigid body is acted on by the forces F_1, F_2 such that:

(a) $F_1 = (3i + j + 4k)$ N, acting through the point with position vector $i + 2j + 3k$

(b) $F_2 = (2i + j - k)$ N, acting through the point with position vector $j + 9k$.

The lines of action of F_1 and F_2 meet at a point P. Find:

(a)   a vector equation for the line of action of F_1

(b)   a vector equation for the line of action of F_2

(c)   the angle between these lines of action

(d)   the position vector of P.

Solution	(a) A vector equation for the line of action of F_1 is given by $r = c + \lambda d$, where d gives the direction vector for the line, c is a position vector of a point on the line, and λ is an arbitrary constant.

In this case d is given by the force F_1 and so:

$$d = \begin{pmatrix} 3 \\ 1 \\ 4 \end{pmatrix}. \text{ Also } c = \begin{pmatrix} 1 \\ 2 \\ 3 \end{pmatrix}$$

$\therefore$ A vector equation for the line of action of F_1 is

$$r = \begin{pmatrix} 1 \\ 2 \\ 3 \end{pmatrix} + \lambda \begin{pmatrix} 3 \\ 1 \\ 4 \end{pmatrix}$$

(b)   Following the procedure in (a), the required vector equation is

$$r = \begin{pmatrix} 0 \\ 1 \\ 9 \end{pmatrix} + \mu \begin{pmatrix} 2 \\ 1 \\ -1 \end{pmatrix}$$

(c)   The angle between these two lines is found by means of the scalar product of $d_1 = \begin{pmatrix} 3 \\ 1 \\ 4 \end{pmatrix}$ and $d_2 = \begin{pmatrix} 2 \\ 1 \\ -1 \end{pmatrix}$. Using the definition

$d_1 \cdot d_2 = |d_1| \, |d_2| \cos\theta$ we have

$$|d_1| = \sqrt{3^2 + 1^2 + 4^2} = \sqrt{26}$$
$$|d_2| = \sqrt{2^2 + 1^2 + (-1)^2} = \sqrt{6}$$

$$d_1 \cdot d_2 = \begin{pmatrix} 3 \\ 1 \\ 4 \end{pmatrix} \cdot \begin{pmatrix} 2 \\ 1 \\ -1 \end{pmatrix} = 3 \times 2 + 1 \times 1 + 4 \times (-1) = 3$$

and so $3 = \sqrt{26} \times \sqrt{6} \cos\theta \Rightarrow \theta = 76°$ (2 s.f.)

$\therefore$ The angle between the two lines is $76°$

(d) The position vector of P is found by solving

$$\begin{pmatrix} 1 \\ 2 \\ 3 \end{pmatrix} + \lambda \begin{pmatrix} 3 \\ 1 \\ 4 \end{pmatrix} = \begin{pmatrix} 0 \\ 1 \\ 9 \end{pmatrix} + \mu \begin{pmatrix} 2 \\ 1 \\ -1 \end{pmatrix}$$

$\Rightarrow 1 + 3\lambda = 2\mu$, $2 + \lambda = 1 + \mu$ and $3 + 4\lambda = 9 - \mu$

This gives $\lambda = 1$ and $\mu = 2$

$$\therefore \overrightarrow{OP} = \begin{pmatrix} 1 \\ 2 \\ 3 \end{pmatrix} + (1) \begin{pmatrix} 3 \\ 1 \\ 4 \end{pmatrix} = \begin{pmatrix} 4 \\ 3 \\ 7 \end{pmatrix}$$

Example If $a = 2i + 4j + 7k$ and $b = 3i + 5i + 6k$, find the vector product $a \times b$

Solution $a \times b = (4 \times 6 - 7 \times 5)\, i + (7 \times 3 - 2 \times 6)\, j + (2 \times 5 - 4 \times 3)\, k$

$\Rightarrow a \times b = -11i + 9j - 2k$

$\Bigl($An alternative method for working out $a \times b$ is to use a determinant. Thus

$$a \times b = \begin{vmatrix} i & j & k \\ 2 & 4 & 7 \\ 3 & 5 & 6 \end{vmatrix}$$

$\Rightarrow \quad a \times b = -11i + 9j - 2k$, as before.$\Bigr)$

Relative motion (a second visit)

We first met the idea of relative velocity in Module M1. There we had:

> Velocity of A relative to B = Velocity of A – Velocity of B

All we need to do now is to tackle some slightly more complicated examples of this. An easy one first.

Example Particle A is moving with velocity vector $(2i + 3j)$ m s^{-1}. Particle B is moving with velocity vector $(7i + 2j)$ m s^{-1}. What is the velocity vector of A relative to B?

Solution Velocity vector of A relative to B

$= $ Velocity vector of A – velocity vector of B

$= (2i + 3j) - (7i + 2j) = -5i + j$

$\therefore$ The velocity vector of A relative to B is $(-5i + j)$ m s^{-1}

Example	A man who can row at 2.5 m s^{-1} in still water wishes to cross to the nearest point on the opposite bank of a river 400 m wide. If the stream is running at 1.5 m s^{-1}, how many minutes does it take him to cross?

Solution	In order to go straight across the river, the man must row into the current. This gives us the vector triangle shown in Figure 1.1.

Figure 5.1

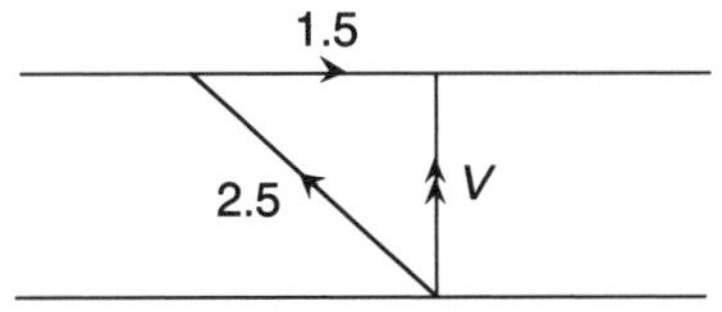

∴ $V^2 = 2.5^2 - 1.5^2 \Rightarrow V = 2$

∴   The man crosses the river directly at 2 m s^{-1}

But the width of the river is 400 m.

∴   It takes him 200 seconds, i.e. $3\frac{1}{3}$ minutes.

∴   The man takes $3\frac{1}{3}$ minutes to cross.

Example	At time t seconds, the position vectors of particles A and B are (in m) $(2t + 2)\mathbf{i} + 5t\mathbf{j}$ and $(t + 3)\mathbf{i} + (3t + 3)\mathbf{j}$ respectively. What is the position vector of A relative to B? Find the time when A and B are nearest to each other.

Solution	Position vector of A relative to B = Velocity vector of A – Velocity vector of B $= [(2t + 2)\mathbf{i} + 5t\mathbf{j}] - [(t + 3)\mathbf{i} + (3t + 3)\mathbf{j}]$ $= (t - 1)\mathbf{i} + (2t - 3)\mathbf{j}$ The magnitude of the relative position vector is least when $(t - 1)^2 + (2t - 3)^2$ is least Simplifying the brackets we get $5t^2 - 14t + 10$. Now differentiate and put equal to zero. ∴ $10t - 14 = 0 \Rightarrow t = 1.4$ ∴ A and B are nearest to each other after 1.4 seconds.

Example

A man bicycling at a constant speed u finds that when his velocity is $u\mathbf{j}$ the velocity of the wind appears to be

$$\tfrac{1}{2} v_1 (\mathbf{i} - \sqrt{3}\mathbf{j}),$$

where $\mathbf{i}$ and $\mathbf{j}$ are unit vectors in the east and north directions respectively: but when his velocity is $\tfrac{1}{2}u (-\sqrt{3}\mathbf{i} + \mathbf{j})$ the velocity of the wind appears to be $v_2\mathbf{i}$. Prove that the true velocity of the wind is

$$\tfrac{1}{6} \sqrt{3}u(\mathbf{i} + \sqrt{3}\mathbf{j}),$$

and find v_1 and v_2 in terms of u.

Solution

Let the true velocity of the wind be $\mathbf{w}$.

$\therefore$ The first part of the question gives us

$$\mathbf{w} - u\mathbf{j} = \tfrac{1}{2}v_1 (\mathbf{i} - \sqrt{3}\,\mathbf{j}) \qquad \qquad \dots \; ①$$

and the second part of the question gives us

$$\mathbf{w} - \tfrac{1}{2}u (-\sqrt{3}\mathbf{i} + \mathbf{j}) = v_2\mathbf{i} \qquad \qquad \dots \; ②$$

Equating the value of $\mathbf{w}$ from the equations gives us

$$\tfrac{1}{2}v_1 \mathbf{i} + \left(u - \tfrac{1}{2}\sqrt{3}\,v_1\right)\mathbf{j} = \left(v_2 - \frac{\sqrt{3}}{2}u\right)\mathbf{i} + \tfrac{1}{2}u\mathbf{j}$$

$$\therefore \quad \tfrac{1}{2}v_1 = v_2 - \frac{\sqrt{3}}{2}u \text{ and } u - \tfrac{1}{2}\sqrt{3}v_1 = \tfrac{1}{2}u$$

These solve simultaneously to give

$$v_1 = \frac{u\sqrt{3}}{3}, \quad v_2 = \frac{u2\sqrt{3}}{3} \text{ and hence } \mathbf{w} = \frac{u\sqrt{3}}{6} (\mathbf{i} + \sqrt{3}\,\mathbf{j})$$

Example

Show that the equation $\mathbf{r} = 4 (\mathbf{i} \cos t + \mathbf{j} \sin t)$, where t is a parameter, represents a circle. Find the position vectors of the points on this circle which are nearest to and furthest from the point P with position vector $\mathbf{u} = 3\mathbf{i} + 4\mathbf{j} + 5\mathbf{k}$.

Solution

Since $| \mathbf{r} | = \sqrt{(4 \cos t)^2 + (4 \sin t)^2} = \sqrt{16 (\cos^2 t + \sin^2 t)} = \sqrt{16} = 4$, the given equation must represent a circle of radius 4, centre the origin.

For the second part, the position vector of any point on the circle relative to P is given by

$$(4 \cos t - 3)\,\mathbf{i} + (4 \sin t - 4)\,\mathbf{j} - 5\mathbf{k}$$

This will have magnitude

$$\sqrt{(4 \cos t - 3)^2 + (4 \sin t - 4)^2 + (-5)^2} \text{ i.e. } \sqrt{66 - 24 \cos t - 32 \sin t}$$

In order to find the maximum and minimum values of this expression, it is sufficient to find the maximum and minimum values of $66 - 24 \cos t - 32 \sin t$.

Differentiating with respect to t and putting the result equal to zero gives

$$24 \sin t - 32 \cos t = 0 \Rightarrow \tan t = \tfrac{4}{3} \Rightarrow t = 53.1° \text{ or } 233.1° \text{ (1 d.p.)}$$

But $t = 53.1° \Rightarrow \mathbf{r} = 2.4\mathbf{i} + 3.2\mathbf{j}$ and $t = 233.1° \Rightarrow \mathbf{r} = -2.4\mathbf{i} - 3.2\mathbf{j}$.

∴ The position vectors of the points on the circle which are nearest to and furthest from the point P are
$$\pm (2.4\mathbf{i} + 3.2\mathbf{j})$$

You should now be able to answer Exercises 1–5 on pp. 102–103.

Solving the vector equation $\frac{d\mathbf{v}}{dt} = k\mathbf{v}$

This equation occurs when the acceleration is proportional to the velocity.

The equation 'seems' to be separable and so we might think of beginning as follows:

$$\frac{d\mathbf{v}}{dt} = k\mathbf{v} \Rightarrow \frac{d\mathbf{v}}{\mathbf{v}} = dt$$

Unfortunately *you cannot divide vectors* and so $\dfrac{d\mathbf{v}}{\mathbf{v}}$ is meaningless.

And yet, as we shall see… But be patient!

So let's solve it by going back to basics. By putting $\mathbf{v} = \alpha\mathbf{i} + \beta\mathbf{j}$, the equation $\dfrac{d\mathbf{v}}{dt} = k\mathbf{v}$ gives us

$$\frac{d\alpha}{dt}\mathbf{i} + \frac{d\beta}{dt}\mathbf{j} = k\left(\alpha\mathbf{i} + \beta\mathbf{j}\right)$$

$$\Rightarrow \quad \frac{d\alpha}{dt} = k\alpha \quad \text{and} \quad \frac{d\beta}{dt} = k\beta$$

Now these differential equations *can* be separated because they only involve scalar quantities.

∴ $\dfrac{d\alpha}{dt} = k\alpha \Rightarrow \dfrac{d\alpha}{\alpha} = k\,dt \Rightarrow \ln|\alpha| = kt + c \Rightarrow \alpha = Ae^{kt}$

Similarly $\dfrac{d\beta}{dt} = k\beta \Rightarrow \beta = Be^{kt}$

∴   Vector $\mathbf{v}$ is given by $Ae^{kt}\mathbf{i} + Be^{kt}\mathbf{j}$

∴ $\mathbf{v} = (A\mathbf{i} + B\mathbf{j})\, e^{kt} \Rightarrow \mathbf{v} = \mathbf{c}\, e^{kt}$

And so we have:

$$\frac{d\mathbf{v}}{dt} = k\mathbf{v} \Rightarrow \mathbf{v} = \mathbf{c}\, e^{kt},$$

where **c** is a constant vector.

In a sense, then, the equation $\frac{d\mathbf{v}}{dt} = k\mathbf{v}$ can be regarded as being separable but the constant of integration must be a vector.

In your examination you will not be expected to justify the result

$$\frac{d\mathbf{v}}{dt} = k\mathbf{v} \Rightarrow \mathbf{v} = \mathbf{c}e^{kt}$$

but you will be expected to know it and to be able to use it.

Example

The velocity **v** m s^{-1} at time t seconds of a particle moving in a plane satisfies

$$\frac{d\mathbf{v}}{dt} = 4\mathbf{v}, \text{ where } \mathbf{v} = 3\mathbf{i} + \mathbf{j} \text{ when } t = 0.$$

Given that the particle passes through the point with position vector $(\mathbf{i} - \mathbf{j})$ m when $t = 0$, find:

(a) the position vector of the particle at time t seconds

(b) the time t when the magnitude of the acceleration equals 320 m s^{-2}

Solution

$$\frac{d\mathbf{v}}{dt} = 4\mathbf{v} \Rightarrow \mathbf{v} = \mathbf{c}\, e^{4t} \text{ (just quote the result)}$$

But $\mathbf{v} = 3\mathbf{i} + \mathbf{j}$ when $t = 0 \Rightarrow \mathbf{c} = 3\mathbf{i} + \mathbf{j}$

∴ $\mathbf{v} = (3\mathbf{i} + \mathbf{j})\, e^{4t}$

(a) Since $\dot{\mathbf{r}} = \mathbf{v}$, we can write our equation as $\dot{\mathbf{r}} = (3\mathbf{i} + \mathbf{j})\, e^{4t}$

Integrating to get the position vector **r**,

$\mathbf{r} = (3\mathbf{i} + \mathbf{j})\, \dfrac{e^{4t}}{4} + \mathbf{d}$, where **d** is a constant vector.

But $\mathbf{r} = \mathbf{i} - \mathbf{j}$ when $t = 0$

∴ $\mathbf{i} - \mathbf{j} = (3\mathbf{i} + \mathbf{j})\dfrac{1}{4} + \mathbf{d} \Rightarrow \mathbf{d} = \dfrac{1}{4}(\mathbf{i} - 5\mathbf{j})$

∴ $\mathbf{r} = (3\mathbf{i} + \mathbf{j})\dfrac{e^{4t}}{4} + \dfrac{1}{4}(\mathbf{i} - 5\mathbf{j})$, the required position vector.

(b) Now we differentiate $\dot{\mathbf{r}}$ to get the acceleration vector $\ddot{\mathbf{r}}$

$\dot{\mathbf{r}} = (3\mathbf{i} + 4\mathbf{j})\, e^{4t} \Rightarrow \ddot{\mathbf{r}} = (3\mathbf{i} + 4\mathbf{j})\, 4e^{4t}$

The magnitude of the acceleration $\ddot{\mathbf{r}}$ is given by

$$4e^{4t} \sqrt{3^2 + 4^2} = 20\, e^{4t}$$

$$\therefore\ 20e^{4t} = 320 \Rightarrow e^{4t} = 16 \Rightarrow t = \frac{1}{4}\ln 16 \text{ or } \ln 2.$$

$\therefore$ The acceleration is 320 m s^{-2} after $\ln 2$ seconds.

You should now be able to answer Exercises 6–8 on p. 103.

Solving the vector equation $\dfrac{d^2\mathbf{r}}{dt^2} + 2k\,\dfrac{d\mathbf{r}}{dt} + (k^2 + n^2)\,\mathbf{r} = 0$

This is a vector equation for damped harmonic oscillations.

If the equation had been of the scalar form

$$\frac{d^2x}{dt^2} + 2k\,\frac{dx}{dt} + (k^2 + n^2)\,x = 0$$

then we would have proceeded as follows:

Auxiliary equation is $m^2 + 2km + k^2 + n^2 = 0$

$\therefore\ (m + k)^2 + n^2 = 0$

$\therefore\ m = -k \pm ni$

The complementary function is therefore:

$$x = e^{-kt}\,(A \cos nt + B \sin nt)$$

And so, if we put $\mathbf{r} = x\mathbf{i} + y\mathbf{j}$ and follow the above procedure, we'll finish up with:

$$\mathbf{r} = e^{-kt}\,(A \cos nt + B \sin nt)\,\mathbf{i} + e^{-kt}\,(C \cos nt + D \sin nt)\,\mathbf{j}$$

$\Rightarrow \qquad \mathbf{r} = (A\mathbf{i} + C\mathbf{j})\,e^{-kt} \cos nt + (B\mathbf{i} + D\mathbf{j})\,e^{-kt} \sin nt$

$\Rightarrow \qquad \mathbf{r} = e^{-kt}\,(\mathbf{c} \cos nt + \mathbf{d} \sin nt)$

And so we have:

$$\frac{d^2\mathbf{r}}{dt^2} + 2k\,\frac{d\mathbf{r}}{dt} + (k^2 + n^2)\,\mathbf{r} = 0$$

$$\Rightarrow \mathbf{r} = e^{-kt}\,(\mathbf{c} \cos nt + \mathbf{d} \sin nt),$$

where $\mathbf{c}$ and $\mathbf{d}$ are constant vectors.

In your examination you'll not be expected to justify this result but you will be expected to know it and to be able to use it.

| **Example** | The position vector **r** metres, relative to a fixed origin O, of particle P at time t seconds satisfies the vector differential equation |

$$\frac{d^2\mathbf{r}}{dt^2} - 2\frac{d\mathbf{r}}{dt} + 10\mathbf{r} = 0$$

Given that when $t = 0$, $\mathbf{r} = 2\mathbf{i}$ and $\dfrac{d\mathbf{r}}{dt} = 5\mathbf{i} + 3\mathbf{j}$, find **r** in terms of t

| **Solution** | The auxiliary equation in scalars is $m^2 - 2m + 10 = 0$ |

$\Rightarrow (m - 1)^2 + 9 = 0 \Rightarrow m = 1 \pm 3i$

$\therefore$ The vector $\mathbf{r} = e^t (\mathbf{c} \cos 3t + \mathbf{d} \sin 3t)$ (just quote the result)

But $\mathbf{r} = 2\mathbf{i}$ when $t = 0 \Rightarrow 2\mathbf{i} = \mathbf{c}$ ... ①

Also $\dfrac{d\mathbf{r}}{dt} = e^t (-3\mathbf{c} \sin 3t + 3\mathbf{d} \cos 3t) + e^t (\mathbf{c} \cos 3t + \mathbf{d} \sin 3t)$

(differentiating as a product)

But $\dfrac{d\mathbf{r}}{dt} = 5\mathbf{i} + 3\mathbf{j}$ when $t = 0 \Rightarrow 5\mathbf{i} + 3\mathbf{j} = 3\mathbf{d} + \mathbf{c}$ ... ②

Solving equations ① and ② gives:

$\quad\quad \mathbf{c} = 2\mathbf{i}$ and $\mathbf{d} = \mathbf{i} + \mathbf{j}$

$\therefore \ \mathbf{r} = e^t \left[2\mathbf{i} \cos 3t + (\mathbf{i} + \mathbf{j}) \sin 3t \right]$.

You should now be able to answer Exercises 9–11 on p. 104.

Work done is F . d

Consider the following situation: AB is a smooth horizontal rod. On this rod there is a smooth, small, ring of mass m. The ring is being dragged along the rod by a force **F**, inclined at θ to AB. The forces acting on the ring are:

| **Figure 5.2** | 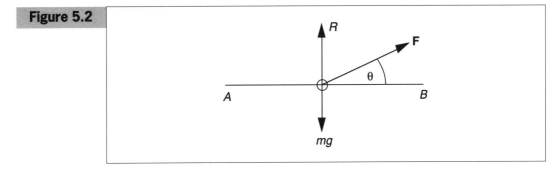 |

The component of the force **F** along the rod is $F \cos \theta$ and so the work done by the force **F**, in dragging this ring from A to B, is $F \cos \theta \times AB$.

But **F** . $\overrightarrow{AB}$ is also $F \cos \theta \times AB$. Hence:

> Work done = **F . d**
>
> where **F** is the force and **d** is the displacement

In your examination you'll not be expected to justify the result but you will be expected to know it and to be able to use it.

Example

Find the work done by a force **F** = **i** + 2**j** + 3**k** (measured in newtons) required to move a particle along a smooth horizontal groove given by

$$\mathbf{r} = (3\mathbf{i} - \mathbf{j} + \mathbf{k}) + \lambda(\mathbf{i} + 4\mathbf{j} + 5\mathbf{k})$$

(measured in metres) from the point $\lambda = 1$ to the point $\lambda = 2$.

Solution

$$\lambda = 1 \implies \mathbf{r} = 4\mathbf{i} + 3\mathbf{j} + 6\mathbf{k}$$
$$\lambda = 2 \implies \mathbf{r} = 5\mathbf{i} + 7\mathbf{j} + 11\mathbf{k}$$

$\therefore$ displacement $\mathbf{d} = (5\mathbf{i} + 7\mathbf{j} + 11\mathbf{k}) - (4\mathbf{i} + 3\mathbf{j} + 6\mathbf{k})$

$$= \mathbf{i} + 4\mathbf{j} + 5\mathbf{k}$$

$\therefore$ $\mathbf{F} . \mathbf{d} = \begin{pmatrix} 1 \\ 2 \\ 3 \end{pmatrix} . \begin{pmatrix} 1 \\ 4 \\ 5 \end{pmatrix} = 1 \times 1 + 2 \times 4 + 3 \times 5 = 24$

$\therefore$ The work done is 24 J.

You should now be able to answer Exercises 12–14 on p. 104.

The moment of a force using vector product

Suppose a force **F** has a line of action which passes through a fixed point P. If O is a fixed point not on this line of action, let's see if we can work out the moment of **F** about O.

Figure 5.3

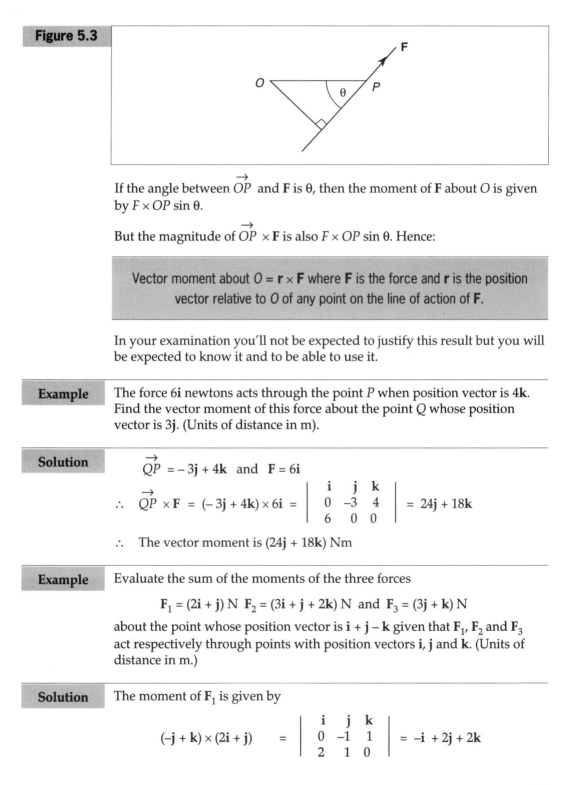

If the angle between $\overrightarrow{OP}$ and **F** is θ, then the moment of **F** about O is given by $F \times OP \sin θ$.

But the magnitude of $\overrightarrow{OP} \times \mathbf{F}$ is also $F \times OP \sin θ$. Hence:

> Vector moment about $O = \mathbf{r} \times \mathbf{F}$ where **F** is the force and **r** is the position vector relative to O of any point on the line of action of **F**.

In your examination you'll not be expected to justify this result but you will be expected to know it and to be able to use it.

Example

The force 6**i** newtons acts through the point P when position vector is 4**k**. Find the vector moment of this force about the point Q whose position vector is 3**j**. (Units of distance in m).

Solution

$$\overrightarrow{QP} = -3\mathbf{j} + 4\mathbf{k} \quad \text{and} \quad \mathbf{F} = 6\mathbf{i}$$

$$\therefore \quad \overrightarrow{QP} \times \mathbf{F} = (-3\mathbf{j} + 4\mathbf{k}) \times 6\mathbf{i} = \begin{vmatrix} \mathbf{i} & \mathbf{j} & \mathbf{k} \\ 0 & -3 & 4 \\ 6 & 0 & 0 \end{vmatrix} = 24\mathbf{j} + 18\mathbf{k}$$

∴   The vector moment is (24**j** + 18**k**) Nm

Example

Evaluate the sum of the moments of the three forces

$$\mathbf{F}_1 = (2\mathbf{i} + \mathbf{j}) \text{ N} \quad \mathbf{F}_2 = (3\mathbf{i} + \mathbf{j} + 2\mathbf{k}) \text{ N} \quad \text{and} \quad \mathbf{F}_3 = (3\mathbf{j} + \mathbf{k}) \text{ N}$$

about the point whose position vector is $\mathbf{i} + \mathbf{j} - \mathbf{k}$ given that $\mathbf{F}_1, \mathbf{F}_2$ and $\mathbf{F}_3$ act respectively through points with position vectors **i**, **j** and **k**. (Units of distance in m.)

Solution

The moment of $\mathbf{F}_1$ is given by

$$(-\mathbf{j} + \mathbf{k}) \times (2\mathbf{i} + \mathbf{j}) = \begin{vmatrix} \mathbf{i} & \mathbf{j} & \mathbf{k} \\ 0 & -1 & 1 \\ 2 & 1 & 0 \end{vmatrix} = -\mathbf{i} + 2\mathbf{j} + 2\mathbf{k}$$

The moment of F_2 is given by

$$(-i + k) \times (3i - j + 2k) = \begin{vmatrix} i & j & k \\ -1 & 0 & 1 \\ 3 & -1 & 2 \end{vmatrix} = i + 5j + k$$

The moment of F_3 is given by

$$(-i - j + 2k) \times (3j + k) = \begin{vmatrix} i & j & k \\ -1 & -1 & 2 \\ 0 & 3 & 1 \end{vmatrix} = -7i + j - 3k$$

These three moments add to give $-7i + 8j$

∴   The total moment is $(-7i + 8j)$ Nm.

You should now be able to answer Exercises 15–17 on p. 105.

Systems of forces

Given a system of forces, we can find the resultant by simply finding the vector sum of the separate forces.

Example   A rigid body is acted upon by the following two forces: $(6i + j + k)$ newtons and $(i - j + 4k)$ newtons. What is their resultant force?

Solution $(6i + j + k) + (i - j + 4k) = 7i + 5k$

∴   Resultant force is $(7i + 5k)$ newtons.

Example   A rigid body is acted upon by the following three forces:

$(i - 2j + 3k)$ newtons, $(3i + j - 2k)$ newtons and $(-4i + j - k)$ newtons.

These forces act respectively through the points whose position vectors are

$(i + j)$ metres, k metres and $(j - 2k)$ metres. Find:

(a)   the resultant of the three forces
(b)   the total moment of the three forces about the origin
(c)   the total moment of the three forces about the point whose position vector is $2i + j + 3k$.

Solution   (a) $(i - 2j + 3k) + (3i + j - 2k) + (-4i + j - k) = 0$
∴   The system has a zero resultant force.

(b) $(i + j) \times (i - 2j + 3k) + k \times (3i + j - 2k) + (j - 2k) \times (-4i + j - k)$
= $(3i - 3j - 3k) + (-i + 3j) + (i + 8j + 4k) = 3i + 8j + k$

∴   The total moment about the origin is $(3i + 8j + k)$ Nm.

(c) $(-\mathbf{i} - 3\mathbf{k}) \times (\mathbf{i} - 2\mathbf{j} + 3\mathbf{k}) + (-2\mathbf{i} - \mathbf{j} - 2\mathbf{k}) \times (3\mathbf{i} + \mathbf{j} - 2\mathbf{k})$

$\qquad + (-2\mathbf{i} - 5\mathbf{k}) \times (-4\mathbf{i} + \mathbf{j} - \mathbf{k})$

$\qquad = \quad (-6\mathbf{i} + 2\mathbf{k}) + (4\mathbf{i} - 10\mathbf{j} + \mathbf{k}) + (5\mathbf{i} + 18\mathbf{j} - 2\mathbf{k}) = 3\mathbf{i} + 8\mathbf{j} + \mathbf{k}$

$\therefore$ The total moment about the point with position vector $2\mathbf{i} + \mathbf{j} + 3\mathbf{k}$
is also $(3\mathbf{i} + 8\mathbf{j} + \mathbf{k})$ Nm.

This example illustrates the following:

> If a system of forces has a zero resultant, then the total moment of these
> forces about *any point* will give the same result.
>
> This total moment is known as a *couple*.

And so, in the example above, the system of forces is equivalent to a couple
of $(3\mathbf{i} + 8\mathbf{j} + \mathbf{k})$ Nm.

Example

Two forces $(2\mathbf{i} + \mathbf{j})$ newtons and $(\mathbf{i} + \mathbf{j} + \mathbf{k})$ newtons act on a rigid body at
the points with position vectors $4\mathbf{i}$ metres and $(\mathbf{i} - \mathbf{k})$ metres. The forces are
equivalent to a force $\mathbf{F}$ acting at the point with position vector $2\mathbf{j}$ metres,
together with a couple $\mathbf{G}$. Find $\mathbf{F}$ and $\mathbf{G}$.

Solution

$\qquad (2\mathbf{i} + \mathbf{j}) + (\mathbf{i} + \mathbf{j} + \mathbf{k}) = 3\mathbf{i} + 2\mathbf{j} + \mathbf{k}$

$\therefore$ $\mathbf{F} = (3\mathbf{i} + 2\mathbf{j} + \mathbf{k})$ newtons.

Now take moments about the origin in order to find the couple $\mathbf{G}$

$\therefore$ $4\mathbf{i} \times (2\mathbf{i} + \mathbf{j}) + (\mathbf{i} - \mathbf{k}) \times (\mathbf{i} + \mathbf{j} + \mathbf{k}) = 2\mathbf{j} \times (3\mathbf{i} + 2\mathbf{j} + \mathbf{k}) + \mathbf{G}$

$\therefore$ $(4\mathbf{k}) + (\mathbf{i} - 2\mathbf{j} + \mathbf{k}) = (2\mathbf{i} - 6\mathbf{k}) + \mathbf{G}$

$\therefore$ $\mathbf{G} = (-\mathbf{i} - 2\mathbf{j} + 11\mathbf{k})$ Nm

(It is important to remember that the moment of a couple $\mathbf{G}$ about any
point is, simply, $\mathbf{G}$.)

Example

A system of forces $(2\mathbf{i} + 3\mathbf{j})$ newtons and $(\mathbf{i} - \mathbf{j})$ newtons acts on a rigid
body. The forces act at points with position vectors $\mathbf{i}$ metres and $\mathbf{j}$ metres
respectively, relative to a fixed origin O.

Show that the system is equivalent to a single force $\mathbf{R}$ acting at a point P
whose position vector is $-\frac{2}{3}\mathbf{j}$ metres. Find also the magnitude of $\mathbf{R}$ in
newtons.

Solution $(2\mathbf{i} + 3\mathbf{j}) + (\mathbf{i} - \mathbf{j}) = 3\mathbf{i} + 2\mathbf{j}$

∴ $\mathbf{R} = (3\mathbf{i} + 2\mathbf{j})$ newtons

Taking moments about P we get

$(\mathbf{i} + \tfrac{2}{3}\mathbf{j}) \times (2\mathbf{i} + 3\mathbf{j}) + \tfrac{5}{3}\mathbf{j} \times (\mathbf{i} - \mathbf{j}) = (1\tfrac{2}{3}\mathbf{k}) + (-1\tfrac{2}{3}\mathbf{k}) = 0$

∴   The system of forces has a zero moment about P.

∴   The resultant $\mathbf{R}$ passes through P.

Finally $|\mathbf{R}| = \sqrt{3^2 + 2^2} = \sqrt{13}$

∴ $\mathbf{R}$ has magnitude $\sqrt{13}$ N.

You should now be able to answer Exercises 18–32 on pp. 105–108.

EXERCISES

1 A boy can swim in still water at 1 m s^{-1}. He swims across a river flowing at 0.6 m s^{-1} which is 336 m wide. Given that he travels the shortest possible distance, find:

   (a) the direction in which he swims

   (b) the time he takes to cross the river.

2 Particle A is moving so that at time t seconds its position vector (in m) is given by $t\mathbf{i} + 3t\mathbf{j}$. Particle B is stationary at the point whose position vector is $2\mathbf{i} + \mathbf{j}$.

   (a) What is the position vector of A relative to B?

   (b) For what value of t is A nearest to B?

   (c) What is the shortest distance between A and B?

3 A rifleman on firing practice has to hit a target 200 m away which is moving at a constant speed of 10 m s^{-1} in a direction perpendicular to the line of the man and the target. If the bullet travels at 150 m s^{-1}, find how far in front of the target he must aim.

4 Two ships A and B are sighted at 10 00 hours from a lighthouse, their respective position vectors being given by

$$\mathbf{a} = 6\mathbf{i} + 4\mathbf{j} \qquad \text{and} \qquad \mathbf{b} = -3\mathbf{i} + 6\mathbf{j}$$

where $\mathbf{i}$ and $\mathbf{j}$ are unit vectors each of magnitude 1 km in directions north and west respectively. The velocity of A is given by

$$\mathbf{v}_A = -10\mathbf{i} + 8\mathbf{j},$$

and the velocity of B is

$$\mathbf{v}_B = 15\mathbf{i} + 6\mathbf{j}$$

Find:

(a)   their positions at 10 45 hours,

(b)   how far apart they are at 10 45 hours

(c)   when they are nearest together.

5 At noon two ships A and B have position vectors $(3\mathbf{i} + 2\mathbf{j})$ km and $(-\mathbf{i} + 4\mathbf{j})$ km respectively, referred to an origin O. The velocities of A and B are $(-\mathbf{i} + 5\mathbf{j})$ km h^{-1} and $(2\mathbf{i} + \mathbf{j})$ km h^{-1} respectively. The position vector of A relative to B, at t hours after noon, is $\mathbf{r}$ km. Show that:

(a) $\mathbf{r} = (4 - 3t)\mathbf{i} + (-2 + 4t)\mathbf{j}$

(b) A and B are nearest to each other at 12.48 p.m.

6 The velocity $\mathbf{v}$ m s^{-1} of a particle P at time t seconds is such that

$$\frac{d\mathbf{v}}{dt} + \mathbf{v} = 0$$

Given that $\mathbf{v} = 12\mathbf{i} + 6\mathbf{j}$ at $t = 0$, find $\mathbf{v}$ when $t = \ln 3$.

7 At time t seconds the position vector of a particle P, relative to a fixed origin, is $\mathbf{r}$ metres and its velocity is $\mathbf{v}$ m s^{-1}. The motion of P is such that:

$$\frac{d\mathbf{v}}{dt} = 3\mathbf{v}$$

Given that when $t = 0$, $\mathbf{r} = 3\mathbf{i}$ and $\mathbf{v} = \mathbf{i} - \mathbf{j}$, find $\mathbf{r}$ in terms of t.

8 The velocity $\mathbf{v}$ m s^{-1} at time t seconds of a particle moving in a plane satisfies:

$$\frac{d\mathbf{v}}{dt} = 6\mathbf{v}, \text{ where } \mathbf{v} = (4\mathbf{i} + 2\mathbf{j}) \text{ when } t = 0$$

Given that the particle passes through the point with position vector $(\mathbf{i} + \mathbf{j})$ m when $t = 0$,

(a)   find the position vector of the particle at time t seconds.

(b)   Find, to 2 significant figures, the time t when the magnitude of the acceleration first exceeds 100 m s^{-1}.

9 At time t seconds, the position vector $\mathbf{r}$ metres of a particle P, relative to a fixed origin O, satisfies the vector differential equation:

$$\frac{d^2\mathbf{r}}{dt^2} + 4\frac{d\mathbf{r}}{dt} + 8\mathbf{r} = 0$$

At $t = 0$, $\mathbf{r} = (\mathbf{i} + \mathbf{j})$ and the velocity of P is $(2\mathbf{i} - 4\mathbf{j})$ m s^{-1}.

Find an expression for $\mathbf{r}$ in terms of t.

10 The equation of motion of a particle P, of mass 1 kg, with position vector $\mathbf{r}$ metres at time t seconds is:

$$\frac{d^2\mathbf{r}}{dt^2} + 3\frac{d\mathbf{r}}{dt} + 2\mathbf{r} = 0$$

At $t = 0$ the particle is at the point with position vector $2\mathbf{j}$ metres and its velocity is $(\mathbf{i} + \mathbf{j})$ m s^{-1}. Find $\mathbf{r}$ in terms of t.

11 The position vector $\mathbf{r}$ metres, relative to a fixed origin O, of particle P at time t seconds satisfies the vector differential equation:

$$\frac{d^2\mathbf{r}}{dt^2} - 2\frac{d\mathbf{r}}{dt} + \mathbf{r} = 0$$

Given that when $t = 0$, $\mathbf{r} = \mathbf{i}$ and $\dfrac{d\mathbf{r}}{dt} = \mathbf{j}$, find the distance of P from O when $t = 2$.

12 Points A and B have position vectors $(3\mathbf{i} + \mathbf{j})$ m and $(5\mathbf{i} + 4\mathbf{j} + 2\mathbf{k})$ m respectively. A particle moves from rest at the point A to the point B under the action of a constant force $\mathbf{F}$ newtons only. Given that the work done by the force in moving the bead from A to B is 34 Nm, find $\mathbf{F}$.

13 A smooth cable runs in a straight line from A $(-1, 2, 0)$ to B $(3, 7, 2)$. The units of length on the x-, y- and z-axes are metres. A ring of weight $-5\mathbf{k}$ newtons is moved along the cable under the influence of a constant force $\mathbf{F} = (3\mathbf{i} + \mathbf{j} + 2\mathbf{k})$ newtons and the contact force due to the cable only. Find the increase in the kinetic energy of the ring as it moves from A to B.

14 The point A has position vector $(2\mathbf{i} + \mathbf{j})$ metres and the point B has position vector $(14\mathbf{i} + 4\mathbf{j} + 21\mathbf{k})$ metres. Two constant forces $(\mathbf{i} + 2\mathbf{j} + 3\mathbf{k})$ newtons and $(3\mathbf{i} - \mathbf{j} + 4\mathbf{k})$ newtons act on a particle P, of mass 0.1 kg, causing it to move from rest at A to the point B.

(a) Find the total work done, in joules, by the two forces in moving P from A to B.

Given that no other work is done

(b) find, in m s^{-1} to 1 decimal place, the speed of P at B.

15 Write down in terms of the vector product an expression for the moment of a vector **F** about a point with position vector **p** if **F** acts through a point with position vector **q**.

Evaluate the moment if:

(a) $\mathbf{F} = 2\mathbf{i} + \mathbf{j}$, $\mathbf{p} = 2\mathbf{i} - \mathbf{j}$, $\mathbf{q} = -\mathbf{j} - 2\mathbf{k}$

(b) $\mathbf{F} = 3\mathbf{i} + 2\mathbf{j} + \mathbf{k}$, $\mathbf{p} = 4\mathbf{i} + \mathbf{k}$, $\mathbf{q} = \mathbf{i} + \mathbf{j}$

16 Three forces $(\mathbf{i} + \mathbf{j})$ newtons, $(2\mathbf{j} + \mathbf{k})$ newtons and $(\mathbf{j} - 2\mathbf{k})$ newtons act on a rigid body at the three points with position vectors $2\mathbf{i}$ metres, $3\mathbf{j}$ metres and $(\mathbf{i} + \mathbf{k})$ metres respectively relative to the origin. Find the total moment of these forces about the origin.

17 A force of 6 newtons acts through the point whose position vector is $(4\mathbf{i} - \mathbf{j} + 7\mathbf{k})$ metres. The force acts in the direction $9\mathbf{i} + 6\mathbf{j} - 2\mathbf{k}$.
Find the moment of the force about the point whose position vector is $(\mathbf{i} - 3\mathbf{j} + 2\mathbf{k})$ metres.

18 Three forces $(-\mathbf{i} + \mathbf{j})$ newtons, $(2\mathbf{j} - 2\mathbf{k})$ newtons and **F** newtons act on a rigid body at the three points with position vectors $-17\mathbf{i}$ metres, $\frac{9}{2}\mathbf{i}$ metres and $4\mathbf{j}$ metres respectively relative to the origin. The forces are equivalent to a couple **G**.

(a) Find the force **F**.

(b) Find the magnitude, in Nm, of the couple **G**.

19 A system of four forces $2\mathbf{j}$ newtons, $-\mathbf{i}$ newtons, $-4\mathbf{j}$ newtons, and $3\mathbf{i}$ newtons acts on a rigid body. The forces act at the points with position vectors $-3.5\mathbf{i}$ metres, $-2.5\mathbf{i}$ metres, $(-2.5\mathbf{i} + \mathbf{j})$ metres and $(-3.5\mathbf{i} + \mathbf{j})$ metres, respectively, relative to a fixed origin O.

Show that the system is equivalent to a single resultant force **R** acting at O and find the magnitude of **R** in newtons.

20 A rigid body is free to rotate about a fixed smooth axis through its centre of mass O. A force $\mathbf{F} = (27\mathbf{i} + 16\mathbf{j} - 17\mathbf{k})$ N is applied to the point P of the body where P has position vector $(3\mathbf{i} - 4\mathbf{j} + \mathbf{k})$ m relative to O. The effect of the force is to cause the body to start rotating with angular acceleration of magnitude 4 rad s^{-2}. Find:

(a) the magnitude of the couple, in Nm, acting on the body,

(b) the moment of inertia of the body about the axis.

21 A rigid body is acted on by a force $\mathbf{F}_1$, where $\mathbf{F}_1 = (2\mathbf{i} + \mathbf{j} - 5\mathbf{k})$ newtons.

The moment of $\mathbf{F}_1$ about the origin O is $(3\mathbf{i} - \mathbf{j} + \mathbf{k})$ newton metres.

(a) Find the equation for the line of action of $\mathbf{F}_1$, giving your answer in the form $\mathbf{r} = (\mathbf{c} + t\mathbf{d})$ metres, $t \in \mathbb{R}$.

The force $\mathbf{F}_2$, where $\mathbf{F}_2 = (2\mathbf{i} + \mathbf{j} - \mathbf{k})$ newtons, also acts on the body, through the point H. The position vector of H relative to O is $(k\mathbf{i} + k\mathbf{j} - k\mathbf{k})$ metres, where k is a constant.

The lines of action of $\mathbf{F}_1$ and $\mathbf{F}_2$ meet at a point P.

(b) Show that $k = -1$.

(c) Find the position vector of P.

22 Two forces $4\mathbf{i}$ newtons and $(\mathbf{i} + \mathbf{j} + 2\mathbf{k})$ newtons act on a rigid body at two points with position vectors $0.5\mathbf{j}$ metres and $(\mathbf{j} + \mathbf{k})$ metres respectively to the origin. The forces are equivalent to a resultant $\mathbf{R}$. Find:

(a) the magnitude of $\mathbf{R}$ in newtons

(b) the equation of the line of action of $\mathbf{R}$ in the form $\mathbf{r} = \mathbf{c} + t\mathbf{d}$.

23 A force of $(2\mathbf{i} - \mathbf{j})$ newtons acts on a rigid body at a point whose position vector is $(2\mathbf{j} + \mathbf{k})$ metres. This force is equivalent to a force $\mathbf{R}$ acting at a point whose position vector is $3\mathbf{i}$ metres together with a couple $\mathbf{G}$. Find $\mathbf{R}$ and $\mathbf{G}$.

24 A force of $(3\mathbf{j} + 4\mathbf{k})$ newtons and a couple of $(\mathbf{i} + 4\mathbf{j})$ newton metres acts on a rigid body. The force acts at a point whose position vector is $(\mathbf{i} + \mathbf{k})$ metres. This system is equivalent to a force $\mathbf{R}$ acting at a point whose position vector is $(3\mathbf{j} + \mathbf{k})$ metres together with a couple $\mathbf{G}$. Find $\mathbf{R}$ and $\mathbf{G}$.

25 A force $(2\mathbf{i} + \mathbf{k})$ newtons acts on a rigid body at a point with position vector $3\mathbf{j}$ metres. This force is equivalent to a force $\mathbf{F}$ acting at a point whose position vector is $3\mathbf{k}$ metres together with a couple $\mathbf{G}$. Find:

(a) the magnitude of $\mathbf{F}$ in newtons

(b) the magnitude of $\mathbf{G}$ in newton metres

(c) the equation of the line of action of $\mathbf{F}$ in the form $\mathbf{r} = \mathbf{c} + t\mathbf{d}$

26 A particle, acted on by constant forces $(4\mathbf{i} + \mathbf{j} - 3\mathbf{k})$ newtons and $(3\mathbf{i} + \mathbf{j} - \mathbf{k})$ newtons, is displaced from the point with position vector $(\mathbf{i} + 2\mathbf{j} + 3\mathbf{k})$ metres to the point with position vector $(5\mathbf{i} + 4\mathbf{j} + \mathbf{k})$ metres. Find the work done on the particle.

If the particle has mass 5 kg and starts from rest, what is its final speed?

27 Forces $\mathbf{i} + 3\mathbf{j}$, $-2\mathbf{i} - \mathbf{j}$, $\mathbf{i} - 2\mathbf{j}$ act through the points with position vectors $2\mathbf{i} + 5\mathbf{j}$, $4\mathbf{j}$, $-\mathbf{i} + \mathbf{j}$ respectively. Prove that this system of forces is equivalent to a couple, and calculate the moment of this couple.

28 A particle of mass m moves in a horizontal plane under the action of a variable force $\mathbf{F}$ so that the position vector of the particle at time t is $\mathbf{r} = 4 \cos kt\mathbf{i} + 3 \sin kt\mathbf{j}$, where k is a constant.

Find:

(a) the period of the motion,

(b) the greatest magnitude of $\mathbf{F}$.

(c) If the force $\mathbf{F}$ ceases to act when $t = \dfrac{\pi}{3k}$, find the position vector of the particle when $t = \dfrac{4\pi}{3k}$.

29 The position vectors of the vertices B and C of a triangle ABC are respectively $8\mathbf{i} + 3\mathbf{j} + 5\mathbf{k}$ and $6\mathbf{i} + 4\mathbf{j} + 9\mathbf{k}$. Two forces $3\mathbf{i} + 2\mathbf{j} + \mathbf{k}$ and $4\mathbf{i} + 5\mathbf{j} + 6\mathbf{k}$ act along AB and AC respectively. A third force $\mathbf{F}$ acts through A. If the system of forces is in equilibrium, find:

(a) the magnitude of the force $\mathbf{F}$

(b) the position vector of A

(c) the equation of the line of action of $\mathbf{F}$ in vector form.

30 A particle of mass 3 units is acted on by the forces

$$\mathbf{F}_1 = 2\mathbf{i} + 3\mathbf{j}, \ \mathbf{F}_2 = 3\mathbf{j} + 4\mathbf{k}, \ \mathbf{F}_3 = \mathbf{i} + 2\mathbf{k}$$

and initially it is at rest at the point $\mathbf{i} - \mathbf{j} - \mathbf{k}$. Find the position and the momentum of the particle after 2 seconds. Find also the work done on the particle in this time.

31 Particles A and B start simultaneously from points which have position vectors $-11\mathbf{i} + 17\mathbf{j} - 14\mathbf{k}$ and $-9\mathbf{i} + 9\mathbf{j} - 32\mathbf{k}$ respectively. The velocities of A and B are constant and represented by $6\mathbf{i} - 7\mathbf{j} + 8\mathbf{k}$ and $5\mathbf{i} - 3\mathbf{j} + 17\mathbf{k}$ respectively. Show that A and B will collide.

A third particle C moves so that its velocity relative to A is parallel to the vector $2\mathbf{i} + 3\mathbf{j} + 4\mathbf{k}$ and its velocity relative to B is parallel to the vector $\mathbf{i} + 2\mathbf{j} + 3\mathbf{k}$. Find the velocity of C and its initial position if all three particles collide simultaneously.

32 A force of magnitude $\sqrt{6}$ N acts along the line

$$\mathbf{r} = (s-4)\,\mathbf{i} + (s+1)\,\mathbf{j} + (2s+3)\,\mathbf{k}$$

and a second force of magnitude $\sqrt{14}$ N acts along the line

$$\mathbf{r} = (t-7)\,\mathbf{i} + (2t-3)\,\mathbf{j} + (2-3t)\,\mathbf{k}$$

Show that these two lines meet and find the position vector of their point of intersection P.

Find the magnitude of the resultant of these two forces and the vector equation of its line of action. If these two forces act on a particle of mass 2 kg which is initially at rest at P, find the velocity and the position vector of the particle after 4 seconds.

SUMMARY

You should now be able to:

- tackle relative motion questions using formulae such as
  velocity of A relative to B = velocity of A – velocity of B

- solve the differential equation

  $$\frac{dv}{dt} = kv \,. \quad \text{(Answer is } \mathbf{v} = \mathbf{c}e^{kt})$$

- solve second order vector differential equations such as

  (a) $\dfrac{d^2\mathbf{r}}{dt^2} - 5\dfrac{d\mathbf{r}}{dt} + 6\mathbf{r} = \mathbf{0}$. (Answer is $\mathbf{r} = \mathbf{c}e^{2t} + \mathbf{d}e^{3t}$)

  (b) $\dfrac{d^2\mathbf{r}}{dt^2} - 6\dfrac{d\mathbf{r}}{dt} + 9\mathbf{r} = 0.$ $\left(\text{Answer is } \mathbf{r} = e^{3t}\,(\mathbf{c}t + \mathbf{d})\right)$

  (c) $\dfrac{d^2\mathbf{r}}{dt^2} + 4\dfrac{d\mathbf{r}}{dt} + 13\mathbf{r} = \mathbf{0}.$ $\left(\text{Answer is } \mathbf{r} = e^{-2t}\,(\mathbf{c}\cos 3t + \mathbf{d}\sin 3t)\right)$

- recall and use the result that

  Work done = $\mathbf{F}\,.\,\mathbf{d}$, where $\mathbf{F}$ is the force and $\mathbf{d}$ is the displacement

- recall and use the result that

  $\mathbf{r} \times \mathbf{F}$ is the vector moment of the force $\mathbf{F}$ about O, where $\mathbf{r}$ is the position vector relative to O of any point on the line of action of $\mathbf{F}$.

- recall that the moment of a couple about any point is the same. If the couple is $\mathbf{G}$, then its moment is $\mathbf{G}$.

- reduce a given system of forces to either:

  (a) a single resultant force or
  (b) a couple or
  (c) a force acting through a given point plus a couple.

Kinematics of a particle moving in two dimensions

INTRODUCTION If the position vector of a point in cartesian coordinates is given by $\mathbf{r} = x\mathbf{i} + y\mathbf{j}$, then we know that the velocity vector for the point is $\dfrac{d\mathbf{r}}{dt} = \dfrac{dx}{dt}\mathbf{i} + \dfrac{dy}{dt}\mathbf{j}$ and the acceleration vector for the point is $\dfrac{d^2\mathbf{r}}{dt^2} = \dfrac{d^2x}{dt^2}\mathbf{i} + \dfrac{d^2y}{dt^2}\mathbf{j}$.

But how do we find these vectors if we are working in polar conditions or, indeed, with intrinsic coordinates? This section aims to answer these questions.

When you've finished this section you should be able to find velocities and accelerations using

(a) cartesian coordinates

(b) polar coordinates

(c) intrinsic coordinates.

Some important results

Before embarking upon this section you need to understand what is meant by polar coordinates and intrinsic coordinates. If you have already covered these topics in Module P4, then you can skip the next two pages and move straight on to page 111. However, if they are new to you, or you need a refresher, then read on.

If point P has *polar coordinates* (r, θ) then we have:

Figure 6.1

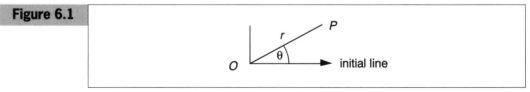

The distance of P from the origin is r and the angle θ is such that $-\pi < \theta \leq \pi$.

If point P has *intrinsic coordinates* (s, ψ) then we have:

Figure 6.2

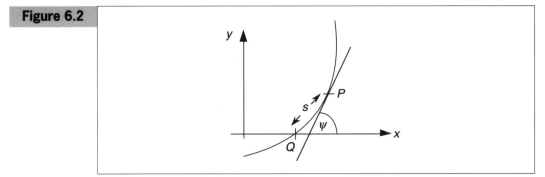

If the curve intercepts the x axis at Q, then the distance QP *along the curve* is s and ψ is such that $\tan \psi$ is the gradient of the tangent at P.

$$\therefore \quad \tan \psi = \frac{dy}{dx} \Rightarrow$$

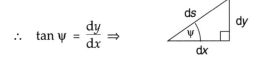

The *radius of curvature* ρ at P is given by $\rho = \dfrac{ds}{d\psi}$

For example, if we have a circle radius a whose centre is the origin, then:

In cartesian coordinates:

Figure 6.3

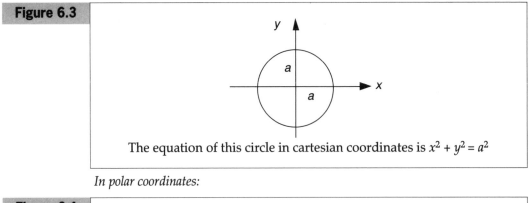

The equation of this circle in cartesian coordinates is $x^2 + y^2 = a^2$

In polar coordinates:

Figure 6.4

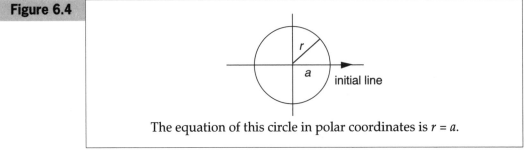

The equation of this circle in polar coordinates is $r = a$.

In intrinsic coordinates:

Figure 6.5

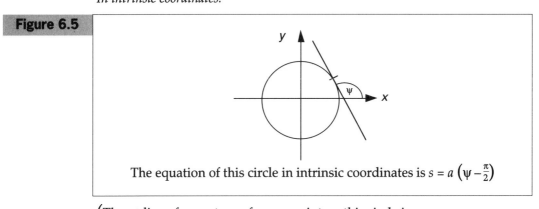

The equation of this circle in intrinsic coordinates is $s = a\left(\psi - \frac{\pi}{2}\right)$

$\bigl($The radius of curvature of every point on this circle is a.

$$\therefore \frac{ds}{d\psi} = a \implies s = a\left(\psi - \frac{\pi}{2}\right),$$

where s is measured from the intercept point $(a,0)$.$\bigr)$

Another look at cartesian coordinates

If we use the notation $\dfrac{dx}{dt} = \dot{x}$ and $\dfrac{d^2x}{dt} = \ddot{x}$ etc, we already know that

$$\mathbf{r} = x\mathbf{i} + y\mathbf{i} \implies \dot{\mathbf{r}} = \dot{x}\mathbf{i} + \dot{y}\mathbf{i} \implies \ddot{\mathbf{r}} = \ddot{x}\mathbf{i} + \ddot{y}\mathbf{j}$$

where $\mathbf{r}$, $\dot{\mathbf{r}}$ and $\ddot{\mathbf{r}}$ are respectively position, velocity and acceleration vectors. We know the methods, then, but at this level, the mathematics can be slightly more complicated.

Example

(a)   Prove that $\dfrac{\cos t - \cos 2t}{\sin 2t - \sin t} = \dfrac{\sin 2t + \sin t}{\cos t + \cos 2t}$

(b)   A particle moves so that its position at time t is given by

$x = 2a \cos t - a \cos 2t$ and $y = 2a \sin t - a \sin 2t$

Show that at any time its velocity is directed towards the point $(3a \cos t, 3a \sin t)$.

Solution

(a)   To prove that $\dfrac{\cos t - \cos 2t}{\sin 2t - \sin t} = \dfrac{\sin 2t + \sin t}{\cos t + \cos 2t}$

is equivalent to proving that

$(\cos t - \cos 2t)(\cos t + \cos 2t) = (\sin 2t - \sin t)(\sin 2t + \sin t)$

i.e. that $\cos^2 t - \cos^2 2t = \sin^2 2t - \sin^2 t$ ... ①

But $\cos^2 t + \sin^2 t = 1$ and $\cos^2 2t + \sin^2 2t = 1$ are well known identities.

∴ Result ① follows.

(b) $x = 2a \cos t - a \cos 2t \implies \dot{x} = -2a \sin t + 2a \sin 2t$

$y = 2a \sin t - a \sin 2t \implies \dot{y} = 2a \cos t - 2a \cos 2t$

If the direction of the velocity is given by the angle α then

$$\tan \alpha = \frac{\dot{y}}{\dot{x}} = \frac{2a \cos t - 2a \cos 2t}{-2a \sin t + 2a \sin 2t}$$

i.e. $\tan \alpha = \dfrac{\cos t - \cos 2t}{\sin 2t - \sin t}$ ... ②

But the gradient of the line joining (x, y) to $(3a \cos t, 3a \sin t)$ is given by:

$$\frac{3a \sin t - (2a \sin t - a \sin 2t)}{3a \cos t - (2a \sin t - a \cos 2t)} = \frac{\sin t + \sin 2t}{\cos t + \cos 2t} \quad ... ③$$

But we saw in (a) that the expressions in ② and ③ are the same.

∴ The result follows.

You should now be able to answer Exercises 1–4 on p. 122.

Differentiation of unit vectors in two dimensions

Look at the diagram in Figure 6.6.

Figure 6.6

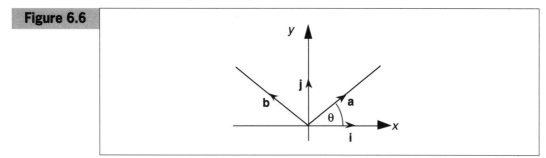

The diagram shows the 'usual' unit vectors **i** and **j** together with another pair of perpendicular unit vectors **a**, **b** where the angle between **a** and **i** is θ.

From the triangle it follows that

$\mathbf{a} = \cos \theta \mathbf{i} + \sin \theta \mathbf{j}$ ... ①

Similarly $\mathbf{b} = -\sin \theta \mathbf{i} + \cos \theta \mathbf{j}$ ... ②

From ① we get

$$\frac{d\mathbf{a}}{dt} = \frac{d\mathbf{a}}{d\theta} \cdot \frac{d\theta}{dt} = (-\sin\theta\,\mathbf{i} + \cos\theta\,\mathbf{j})\,\dot{\theta}$$

Now use ② and this becomes

$$\frac{d\mathbf{a}}{dt} = \dot{\theta}\mathbf{b}$$

Similarly from ② we get

$$\frac{d\mathbf{b}}{dt} = \frac{d\mathbf{b}}{d\theta} \cdot \frac{d\theta}{dt} = (-\cos\theta\,\mathbf{i} - \sin\theta\,\mathbf{j})\,\dot{\theta}$$

Now use ① and this becomes

$$\frac{d\mathbf{b}}{dt} = -\dot{\theta}\mathbf{a}$$

And so:

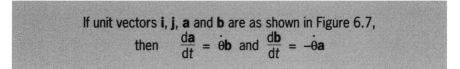

If unit vectors **i**, **j**, **a** and **b** are as shown in Figure 6.7,

then $\dfrac{d\mathbf{a}}{dt} = \dot{\theta}\mathbf{b}$ and $\dfrac{d\mathbf{b}}{dt} = -\dot{\theta}\mathbf{a}$

Figure 6.7

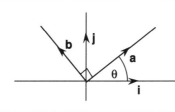

As far as your examination is concerned you will not be expected to prove the above results but you will be expected to know them and to be able to use them.

Velocity and acceleration in polar coordinates

If a point P has polar coordinates $(\mathbf{r}, \theta)$ then we have the situation shown in Figure 6.8.

Figure 6.8

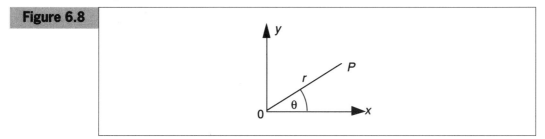

Taking the unit vector **a** as acting along OP and the unit vector **b** at right angles to **a**, we get Figure 6.9.

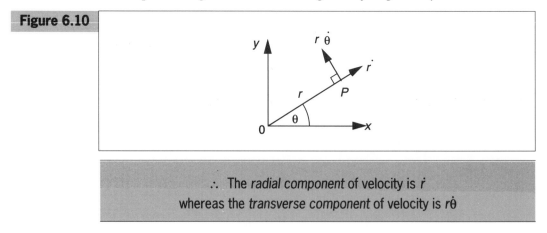

where $\mathbf{r} = \overrightarrow{OP} = r\mathbf{a}$, $\dfrac{d\mathbf{a}}{dt} = \dot{\theta}\mathbf{b}$ and $\dfrac{d\mathbf{b}}{dt} = -\dot{\theta}\mathbf{a}$

And so, beginning with $\mathbf{r} = r\mathbf{a}$ and differentiating as a product we get

$$\dot{\mathbf{r}} = r\,\frac{d\mathbf{a}}{dt} + \dot{r}\mathbf{a}$$

$\Rightarrow \qquad \dot{\mathbf{r}} = r\dot{\theta}\mathbf{b} + \dot{r}\mathbf{a}$ ... ①

Differentiating again we get

$$\ddot{\mathbf{r}} = \dot{r}\dot{\theta}\mathbf{b} + r\ddot{\theta}\mathbf{b} + r\dot{\theta}\,\frac{d\mathbf{b}}{dt} + \dot{r}\,\frac{d\mathbf{a}}{dt} + \ddot{r}\,\mathbf{a}$$

$\Rightarrow \qquad \ddot{\mathbf{r}} = \dot{r}\dot{\theta}\mathbf{b} + r\ddot{\theta}\mathbf{b} - r\dot{\theta}^2\mathbf{a} + \dot{r}\dot{\theta}\mathbf{b} + \ddot{r}\,\mathbf{a}$

$\Rightarrow \qquad \ddot{\mathbf{r}} = (\ddot{r} - r\dot{\theta}^2)\,\mathbf{a} + (r\ddot{\theta} + 2\dot{r}\dot{\theta})\,\mathbf{b}$

$\Rightarrow \qquad \ddot{\mathbf{r}} = (\ddot{r} - r\dot{\theta}^2)\,\mathbf{a} + \dfrac{1}{r}\dfrac{d}{dt}(r^2\dot{\theta})\,\mathbf{b}$ ... ②

$\therefore$ Equation ① gives us the following *velocity diagram in polar coordinates*:

Figure 6.10

$\therefore$ The *radial component* of velocity is $\dot{r}$

whereas the *transverse component* of velocity is $r\dot{\theta}$

Equation ② gives us the following *acceleration diagram in polar coordinates.*

Figure 6.11

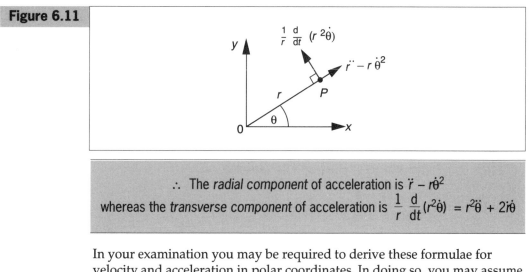

$$\therefore \text{ The } radial \text{ component of acceleration is } \ddot{r} - r\dot{\theta}^2$$

whereas the *transverse component* of acceleration is $\dfrac{1}{r}\dfrac{d}{dt}(r^2\dot{\theta}) = r^2\ddot{\theta} + 2r\dot{r}\dot{\theta}$

In your examination you may be required to derive these formulae for velocity and acceleration in polar coordinates. In doing so, you may assume the differentiation of unit vectors and then simply repeat the explanation above. The formulae themselves are in your formula book, should you need a reminder.

Velocity and acceleration with intrinsic coordinates

If a point P has intrinsic coordinates (s, ψ) then we have:

Figure 6.12

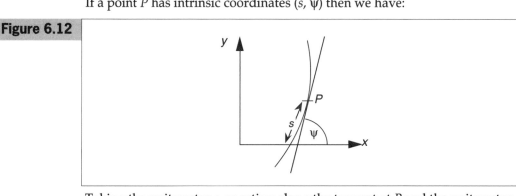

Taking the unit vector **a** as acting along the tangent at P and the unit vector **b** at right angles to **a**, we get Figure 6.8.

Figure 6.13

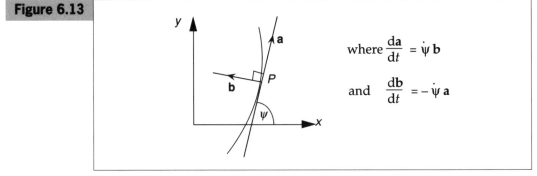

where $\dfrac{d\mathbf{a}}{dt} = \dot{\psi}\,\mathbf{b}$

and $\dfrac{d\mathbf{b}}{dt} = -\dot{\psi}\,\mathbf{a}$

The velocity vector $\mathbf{v}$ of P is such that

$$\mathbf{v} = \dot{s}\mathbf{a} \qquad \ldots ①$$

Differentiating this as a product we get

$$\frac{d\mathbf{v}}{dt} = \dot{s}\,\frac{d\mathbf{a}}{dt} + \ddot{s}\mathbf{a}$$

$$\Rightarrow \qquad \frac{d\mathbf{v}}{dt} = \dot{s}\,\dot{\psi}\mathbf{b} + \ddot{s}\mathbf{a} \qquad \ldots ②$$

But $\quad \dot{\psi} = \dfrac{d\psi}{dt} = \dfrac{d\psi}{ds}\dfrac{ds}{dt} = \dfrac{1}{\rho}\dot{s} \;\left(\text{since the radius of curvature } \rho = \dfrac{ds}{d\psi}\right)$

$\therefore \quad$ Equation ② can be written

$$\frac{d\mathbf{v}}{dt} = \frac{(\dot{s})^2}{\rho}\,\mathbf{b} + \ddot{s}\,\mathbf{a} \qquad \ldots ③$$

Equation ① gives us the following *velocity diagram in intrinsic coordinates*

Figure 6.14

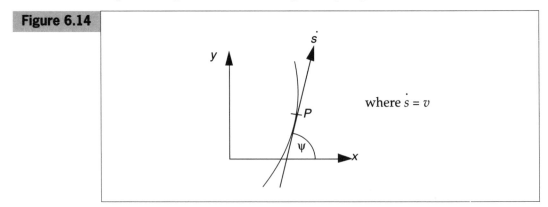

where $\dot{s} = v$

Equation ③ gives us the following *acceleration diagram in intrinsic coordinates*:

Figure 6.15

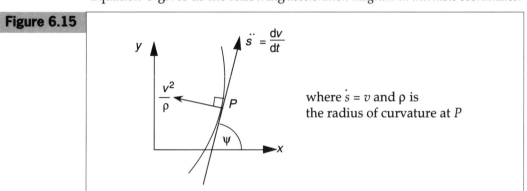

where $\dot{s} = v$ and ρ is
the radius of curvature at P

In your examination you may be required to derive these formulae for velocity and acceleration in intrinsic coordinates. In doing so, you may assume the differentiation of unit vectors and then simply repeat the explanation above. The formulae themselves are often quoted in examination questions, but it would probably be safer to learn them by heart.

Another look at circular motion

You first met circular motion in Module M2. You may like to look back at that to refresh your memory before moving on.

If a particle P describes a circle of radius a

Figure 6.16

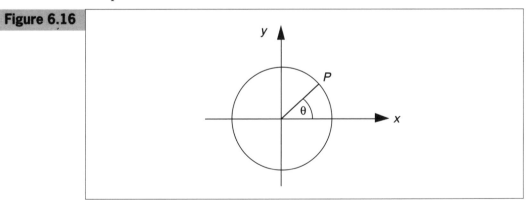

then the polar equation of its path is $r = a$. In this particular case $\dot{r} = 0$, $\ddot{r} = 0$ and

$$\frac{1}{r}\frac{d}{dt}(r^2\,\dot{\theta}) = \frac{1}{a}\frac{d}{dt}(a^2\dot{\theta}) = a\ddot{\theta}$$

And so (adapting Figure 6.10) the velocity diagram for circular motion is given by:

Figure 6.17

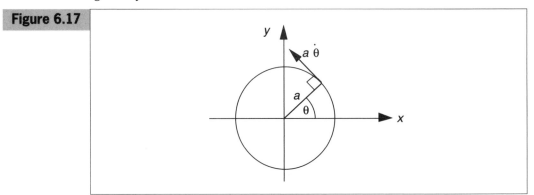

Similarly (adapting Figure 6.11) the acceleration diagram is given by:

Figure 6.18

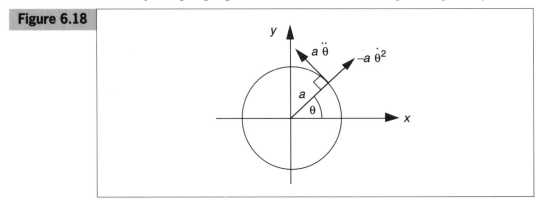

We have not looked at anything new here; however, it is interesting to see how our general work with polar coordinates quickly gave us the standard formulae for velocity and acceleration for circular motion.

Some kinematic examples

We will now go on to work through some kinematic examples involving polar coordinates and intrinsic coordinates. In all of these examples, it will help you to have at your fingertips the velocity and acceleration diagrams for polar coordinates (Figures 6.10 and 6.11) and intrinsic coordinates (Figures 6.14 and 6.15).

Example   At time t, the polar coordinates of a moving particle are given by $r = t^2 + t$, $\theta = \frac{1}{6}(t^3 + 4)$. Find the magnitude of the velocity and the direction of the acceleration when $t = 2$.

Solution

$$r = t^2 + t \implies \dot{r} = 2t + 1 \implies \ddot{r} = 2$$

∴ At $t = 2$, $r = 6$, $\dot{r} = 5$ and $\ddot{r} = 2$ ... ①

$$\theta = \frac{1}{6}(t^3 + 4) \implies \dot{\theta} = \frac{t^2}{2} \implies \ddot{\theta} = t$$

∴ At $t = 2$, $\theta = 2$, $\dot{\theta} = 2$ and $\ddot{\theta} = 2$ ... ②

Finding the velocity components first of all,

$$\dot{r} = 5 \text{ and } r\dot{\theta} = 6 \times 2 = 12 \text{ (from ① and ②)}$$

∴ Magnitude of velocity = $\sqrt{5^2 + 12^2}$ = 13

∴ Magnitude of velocity is 13.

Now for the acceleration components.

$$\ddot{r} - r\dot{\theta}^2 = 2 - 6 \times 2^2 = -22$$

and $\dfrac{1}{r}\dfrac{d}{dt}(r^2\dot{\theta}) = r\ddot{\theta} + 2\dot{r}\dot{\theta} = 6 \times 2 + 2 \times 5 \times 2 = 32$ (from ① and ②)

∴ Our acceleration diagram looks like this:

Figure 6.19

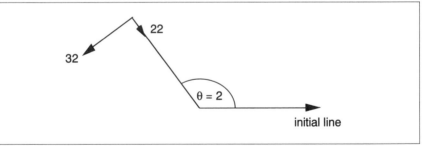

Since $\tan \alpha = \dfrac{32}{22} \implies \alpha = 0.97$ rad, the angle made by the direction of the acceleration vector with the radius vector is $\pi - 0.97 = 2.17$.

The acceleration vector makes an angle of 2.17 radians with the radius vector.

Example

The polar coordinates, at time t, of a particle P of mass m moving in a plane are (r, θ). P moves so that $\dfrac{d\theta}{dt}$ is constant and equal to ω. Prove that the transverse component of the acceleration is $2\dot{r}\omega$.

Solution

$\dot{\theta} = \omega$, a constant $\Rightarrow \ddot{\theta} = 0$

∴   Transverse component of the acceleration

$$= \frac{1}{r}\frac{d}{dt}(r^2\dot{\theta}) = \frac{1}{r}\frac{d}{dt}(r^2\omega) = \frac{\omega}{r}\frac{d}{dt}(r^2) = \frac{\omega}{r} \times 2r\dot{r} = 2\dot{r}\omega$$

∴   The transverse component of the acceleration is $2\dot{r}\omega$.

You should now be able to answer Exercises 5–11 on pp. 122–124.

Example   A particle moves in the curve whose equation is $s = f(\psi)$ in such a way that the tangent rotates uniformly. Prove that the normal acceleration is proportional to the radius of curvature.

Solution

$$v = \frac{ds}{dt} \Rightarrow v = \frac{ds}{d\psi} \times \frac{d\psi}{dt} \Rightarrow v = \rho\dot{\psi} \qquad \qquad \ldots \text{①}$$

But the tangent rotates uniformly ∴ $\dot{\psi} = k$, a constant.

∴   Equation ① gives $v = k\rho$

∴   Normal acceleration $= \dfrac{v^2}{\rho} = \dfrac{(k\rho)^2}{\rho} = k^2\rho$

∴   The normal acceleration is proportional to the radius of curvature.

Example   A particle P of mass m, which is free to move under gravity on the inside of a smooth curve $s = f(\psi)$, fixed in a vertical plane, is shown below.

Figure 6.20

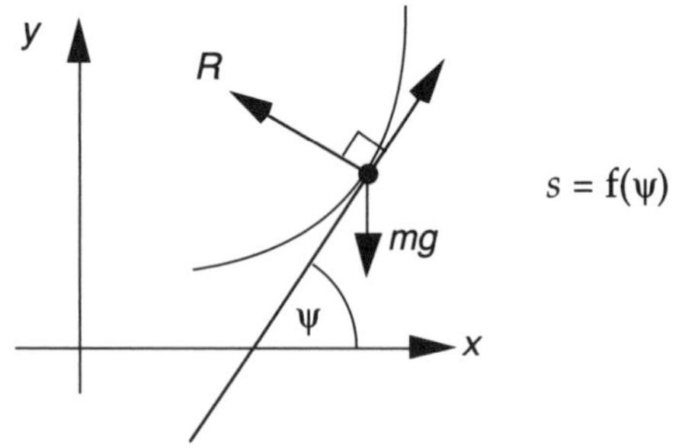

The normal reaction R and the weight mg are also shown.

Set up the equations of motion for the particle.

Solution	The mass acceleration diagram is:

Figure 6.21

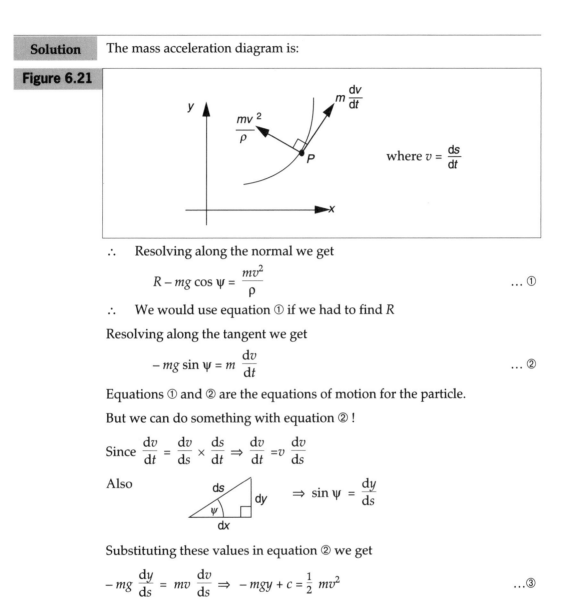

∴   Resolving along the normal we get

$$R - mg \cos \psi = \frac{mv^2}{\rho} \qquad \dots \text{①}$$

∴   We would use equation ① if we had to find R

Resolving along the tangent we get

$$-mg \sin \psi = m \frac{dv}{dt} \qquad \dots \text{②}$$

Equations ① and ② are the equations of motion for the particle.

But we can do something with equation ② !

Since $\dfrac{dv}{dt} = \dfrac{dv}{ds} \times \dfrac{ds}{dt} \Rightarrow \dfrac{dv}{dt} = v \dfrac{dv}{ds}$

Also $\Rightarrow \sin \psi = \dfrac{dy}{ds}$

Substituting these values in equation ② we get

$$-mg \frac{dy}{ds} = mv \frac{dv}{ds} \Rightarrow -mgy + c = \frac{1}{2} mv^2 \qquad \dots \text{③}$$

And this is nothing more than the usual conservation of energy equation.

∴   We would use equation ③ if we had to find v

This 'motion on a smooth curve' should, theoretically, come in the next section on the dynamics of a particle moving in two dimensions, but here it proves a useful link between the two topics.

You should now be able to answer Exercises 12–16 on pp. 125–127.

EXERCISES

1 A particle P, performing damped harmonic motion, moves along a straight line Ox so that its displacement x metres from O at time t seconds is given by

$$x = 3e^{-12t} \cos 5t, \; t \geq 0.$$

(a) Obtain a general expression for the values of t when the particle comes instantaneously to rest.

(b) Show that the distances of P from O at two such consecutive values of t are in the ratio $e^{\frac{12\pi}{5}} : 1$.

2 A particle P is moving in the xy-plane. The acceleration of P is

$$-\lambda^2 (x\mathbf{i} + y\mathbf{j}) \text{ m s}^{-2},$$

where λ is a positive constant and (x, y) are the coordinates of P. The particle is projected, at time $t = 0$, with velocity $(\lambda a\mathbf{j})$ m s^{-1} from the point A with position vector $(2a\mathbf{i})$ m, where a is a positive constant.

(a) Show that the equation of the path of P is

$$\frac{x^2}{4a^2} + \frac{y^2}{a^2} = 1.$$

(b) Show also that P first return to A after a time $\left(\frac{2\pi}{\lambda}\right)$ seconds.

3 A particle P of mass M kilograms moves in a horizontal plane. Its position vector at time t seconds is $\mathbf{r} = (x\mathbf{i} + y\mathbf{j})$ metres. P is moving under the action of a resultant force $-6 \, Mx\mathbf{j}$ newtons. At time $t = 0$ the particle is at the origin and its velocity is $(u\mathbf{i} + u\mathbf{j})$ m s^{-1}, where u is a positive constant.

(a) Find the cartesian equation of the path of the particle

(b) Sketch the path of the particle.

4 The components of acceleration of a particle at time t are given by $\ddot{x} = ft, \ddot{y} = 0$ where f is a constant. At time $t = 0$ the particle is passing through the origin with a velocity whose components parallel to the x- and y-axes are u and v respectively. Prove that the equation of the path is given by $6xv^3 = fy^3 + 6uv^2y$.

5 At time t, the polar coordinates of a moving particle are given by $r = e^{-t}, \theta = t^2 - 1$. Find the value of t when the velocity and acceleration vectors are perpendicular.

6 A particle P of mass m moves in a plane. At time t its position is given by polar coordinates (r, θ) relative to an origin O and a fixed line in the plane. The path of P is the spiral with polar equation

$r = ke^{\theta}$, where k is a positive constant.

The particle moves so that the angular speed of OP is constant and equal to ω.

Show that the resultant force acting on P is of magnitude $2mr\omega^2$ and acts in a direction perpendicular to OP.

7 A particle P is moving in a horizontal plane. The path of P, relative to a fixed origin O and a fixed line in the plane, has polar equation $r = a(1 + \cos \theta)$, where a is a positive constant, r is the distance OP and θ is the angle OP makes with the fixed line. Given that $\dfrac{d\theta}{dt} = \omega$, where ω is constant,

(a) show that the radial component of the acceleration of P is $-a\omega^2 (1 + 2 \cos \theta)$.

(b) Find an expression for the magnitude, f, of the acceleration of P.

(c) Show that the maximum value of f as θ varies is $3a\omega^2$.

8 A particle P moves in a horizontal plane along the curve with polar equation

$r = d(2 + \cos \theta),$

where d is a positive constant, so that the radius vector $\overrightarrow{OP}$ is rotating at constant angular speed ω.

Show that when $\theta = \dfrac{\pi}{2}$,

(a) the speed of P is $d\omega\sqrt{5}$,

(b) the magnitude of the radial component of the acceleration of P is $2d\omega^2$.

9 A particle P moves in a plane. At time t, P is at the point with polar coordinates (r, θ) referred to the pole O.

(a) Derive an expression for the component of the acceleration of P perpendicular to the radius vector $\overrightarrow{OP}$.

Given that the motion of P is such that $r^2 \dfrac{d\theta}{dt}$ is constant,

(b) state what can be deduced about the resultant force acting on P.

10

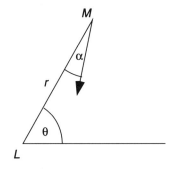

L is the fixed position of a light. A moth M moves in a plane containing L. At time t the moth is at the point with polar coordinates (r, θ) relative to L and a fixed line in the plane. The moth flies so that its velocity always makes a constant angle α $(0 < \alpha < \frac{\pi}{2})$ with ML , as shown in the above figure. When t= 0 the moth is at the point with polar coordinates $(R, 0)$. By considering the radial and transverse components of the velocity of M,

(a)   show that $\dfrac{dr}{d\theta} = -r \cot \alpha.$

(b)   Find the polar equation of the path of M.

11   The polar coordinates, at time t, of a particle P of mass m moving in a plane are (r, θ). P moves so that $\dfrac{d\theta}{dt}$ is constant and equal to ω.

The radial component of the force acting on P is directed away from the pole O and has magnitude $3mr\omega^2$. Initially P is at the point with polar coordinates $(2a, 0)$ and has zero radial velocity.

(a)   Show that r satisfies the differential equation

$$\frac{d^2r}{dt^2} - 4\omega^2r = 0.$$

(b)   Find r in terms of α, ω and t.

(c)   Hence find the polar equation of the curve described by P.

12 The figure on the right shows a sketch of the catenary with intrinsic equation

$$s = c \tan \psi$$

where c is a positive constant.

A particle P describes this curve with constant speed u. Show that the magnitude of the acceleration of P at the point on the curve where $\psi = \frac{\pi}{4}$ is $\frac{u^2}{2c}$.

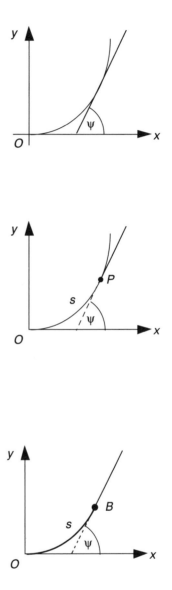

13 A bead P of mass m can slide along a smooth wire bent into the form of part of a cycloid which is held with its vertex, O, downwards and its axis vertical as shown on the right.

The intrinsic equation of the part cycloid is $s = 4a \sin \psi$, $0 \le \psi < \frac{\pi}{2}$, where a is a positive constant. The particle is released from rest from any point P on the curve. Show that the time for the particle to reach O is independent of the position of P.

14 A bead B, of mass m, can slide along a smooth wire bent into the form of part of a cycloid which is held with its vertex, O, downwards and its axis vertical as shown in the figure. The length of the arc OB is s. The intrinsic equation of the part cycloid is $s = 4a \sin \psi$, $0 \le \psi \le \frac{\pi}{4}$, where a is a positive constant.

The bead is projected from the point O with speed $\sqrt{(3ag)}$ along the wire.

(a) Find the speed of B when $\psi = \frac{\pi}{4}$.

(b) Show that the magnitude of the normal contact force when $\psi = \frac{\pi}{4}$ is $\frac{3}{4} mg \sqrt{2}$.

[It may be assumed that the tangential and normal components of acceleration are $\dot{v}$ and $\frac{v^2}{\rho}$ respectively, where $v = \dot{s}$ and $\rho = \frac{ds}{d\psi}$.]

15

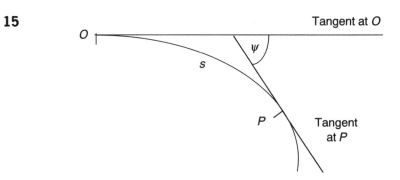

The above figure shows the uniform vertical cross section of a smooth surface. The cross section is the curve with intrinsic equation

$$s = k \sin \psi, \ 0 \leq \psi \leq \frac{\pi}{2}, \qquad \text{where } k \text{ is a positive constant.}$$

A small bead B, of mass m, is placed on the surface at O and projected horizontally from O, in the plane of the cross section, with speed u, where $u^2 < kg$.

At time t the bead is at the point P on the surface where s is the length of the arc OP and ψ is the angle between the tangent at P and the tangent at O, which is horizontal.

(a)   Show that: $\dfrac{d^2s}{dt^2} = \dfrac{g}{k} s.$

Given that $u^2 = \frac{1}{2} gk$,

(b)   find the value of ψ at the point where B leaves the surface.

16

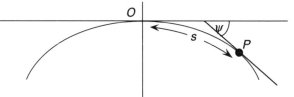

A bead B slides on a smooth wire which is in the shape of one arch of a cycloid. the vertex O of the arch is at the highest point and the axis of the arch is vertical. B is initially at O and moving with horizontal speed u, where $u^2 = \frac{1}{2} ga$ and a is a positive constant. When B has moved a distance s along the wire, it is at the point P and has speed v. The tangent to the wire at P makes an angle ψ with the horizontal, as shown in the above figure. The intrinsic equation of the cycloid is $s = a \sin \psi$.

(a)   show that $v^2 = \dfrac{g}{2a} (2s^2 + a^2).$

Continued on page 127

At the point P, the force exerted by the wire on the bead is of magnitude N.

(b)   Show that $N = \dfrac{mg}{2 \cos \psi} (1 - 4 \sin^2 \psi)$.

(c)   Hence find the distance travelled by B along the wire before N becomes zero.

$\left[\text{It may be assumed at the tangential and normal components of acceleration are } \dot{v} \text{ and } \dfrac{v^2}{\rho} \text{ respectively, where } v = \dot{s} \text{ and } \rho = \dfrac{ds}{d\psi}.\right]$

SUMMARY

You should now know, be able to prove and use, the following velocity and acceleration formulae:

Polar coordinates

VELOCITIES

ACCELERATIONS

Intrinsic coordinates

VELOCITIES

ACCELERATIONS

where $\rho = \dfrac{ds}{d\psi}$ and

You should also be able to tackle the motion of a particle on a smooth curve given intrinsically. The relevant equations are:

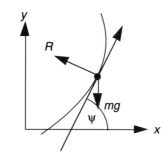

$$R - mg \cos \psi \ = \ \frac{mv^2}{\rho}$$

$$- mg \sin \psi \quad = m \frac{dv}{dt}$$

$$\tfrac{1}{2} \, mv^2 + mgy \ = \text{constant}$$

Dynamics of a particle moving in two dimensions

INTRODUCTION   In this section we'll be building on the ideas involved in earlier work. We begin by looking (again) at the motion of a particle on a smooth curve and then move on to consider motion under a central force (i.e. planetary orbits). Finally, our earlier work on the motion of projectiles will be extended to include projectiles on inclined planes.

When you've finished this section you should be able to:

- solve problems involving the motion of a particle on a smooth curve

- set up, and solve, the equations of motion of a particle moving under the action of a central force

- tackle projectile problems involving inclined planes.

Relevant results from P3 and P4

Before embarking upon this section you need to have met radius of curvature and hyperbolic functions. If you have already covered these topics in Modules P3 and P4, then you can skip the following summary and move straight on to page 130. However, if they are new to you, or you need a refresher, then read on.

- We have already used the formula $\rho = \dfrac{d\psi}{ds}$ for the radius of curvature.

  It can also be shown (and the formula is given in your formula book) that

  $$\rho = \frac{\left[1 + \left(\frac{dy}{dx}\right)^2\right]^{\frac{3}{2}}}{\frac{d^2y}{dx^2}}.$$

  We'll be using this formula in this section.

- Hyperbolic functions sinh x and cosh x occur in the worked example on pages 132 to 134. You need to know that:

  (a) sinh x and cosh x are defined by

  $$\sinh x = \frac{e^x - e^{-x}}{2} \text{ and } \cosh x = \frac{e^x + e^{-x}}{2}$$

  (b) $1 + \sinh^2 x = \cosh^2 x$ (easily proved by direct substitution)

  (c) $y = \sinh f \Rightarrow \dfrac{dy}{dx} = f' \cosh f$

  $y = \cosh f \Rightarrow \dfrac{dy}{dx} = f' \sinh f$ (again, easily proved by direct substitution)

Motion of a particle on a smooth curve

If we are working in cartesian coordinates then we have:

Figure 7.1

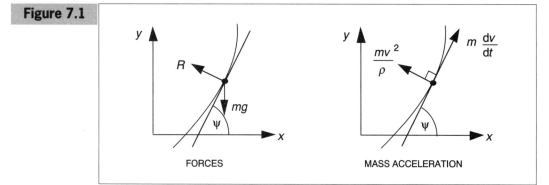

FORCES   MASS ACCELERATION

(The particle of mass m is at point P on the curve. The gradient of the tangent at P is tan ψ. The normal reaction at P is R. There is no frictional force since the curve is smooth.)

The equations of motion are:

$$\leftarrow \quad : \quad R \sin \psi = -m\ddot{x} \qquad \qquad \dots ①$$

$$\uparrow \quad : \quad R \cos \psi - mg = m\ddot{y} \qquad \dots ②$$

Angle ψ is given by $\tan \psi = \dfrac{dy}{dx} \Rightarrow$

Just as we saw in the example on page 120, there is something else which can be derived from these equations.

Eliminating R we get:

$$mg \sin \psi = -m\ddot{x} \cos \psi - m\ddot{y} \sin \psi$$

$$\Rightarrow \quad mg \frac{dy}{ds} = -m\ddot{x} \frac{dx}{ds} - m\ddot{y} \frac{dy}{ds}$$

$$\Rightarrow \quad mg \, dy = -m\ddot{x} \, dx - m\ddot{y} \, dy$$

$$\Rightarrow \quad mg \frac{dy}{dt} = -m\ddot{x} \frac{dx}{dt} - m\ddot{y} \frac{dy}{dt}$$

$$\Rightarrow \quad mgy = -\frac{1}{2} m\dot{x}^2 - \frac{1}{2} m\dot{y}^2 + \text{constant}$$

$$\Rightarrow \quad \frac{1}{2} m \, (\dot{x}^2 + \dot{y}^2) + mgy = \text{constant}$$

And so we have the usual conservation of energy equation.

∴   When working with cartesian coordinates we have
- the equations of motion given by ① and ② above
- the conservation of energy equation.

That's the end of the mechanics – the rest is 'just' a matter of pure mathematics.

As for intrinsic coordinates, we've already looked at that problem (see Section 6). Once again we get two equations of motion, together with an energy equation. And so:

Figure 7.2

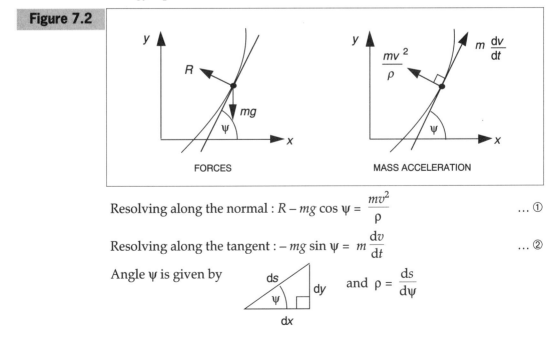

Resolving along the normal : $R - mg \cos \psi = \dfrac{mv^2}{\rho}$ ... ①

Resolving along the tangent : $- mg \sin \psi = m \dfrac{dv}{dt}$ ... ②

Angle ψ is given by 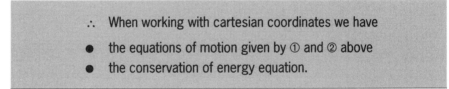 and $\rho = \dfrac{ds}{d\psi}$

Equation ② leads to the conservation of energy equation

$$\frac{1}{2}mv^2 + mgy = \text{constant (refer back to page 121 if necessary)} \qquad \ldots \text{③}$$

∴   When working with intrinsic coordinates we have:

● the equations of motion given by ① and ②.
● the conservation of energy equation ③.

Equation ① is only required if we need to find R.
The conservation of energy equation ③ is used if we need to find v.

Once again, that's the end of the mechanics and the rest is a matter of pure mathematics.

If you have a choice, you'll find intrinsic coordinates easier to use.

Example   A particle slides down a smooth curve in the downwards form of the catenary $y = c \cosh \dfrac{x}{c}$, the y-axis being vertically downwards. With the usual notations, the curve is sketched below.

Figure 7.3

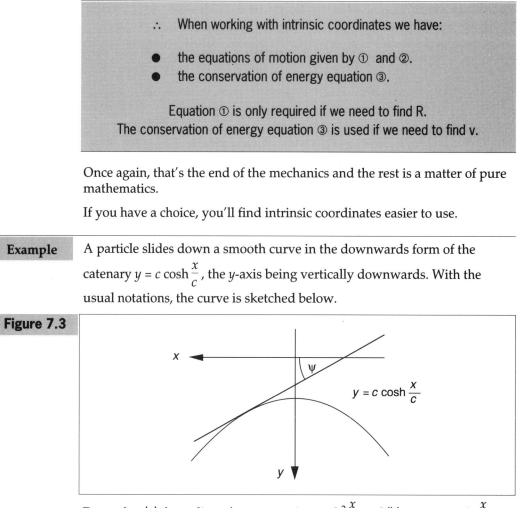

$$y = c \cosh \frac{x}{c}$$

Prove that (a) the radius of curvature is $c \cosh^2 \dfrac{x}{c}$ and (b) $\cos \psi = \operatorname{sech} \dfrac{x}{c}$

If the particle is slightly disturbed from rest at the highest point, show that it leaves the surface at the point where the tangent makes an angle of 60° with the horizontal.

Solution

(a) $y = c \cosh \dfrac{x}{c} \Rightarrow \dfrac{dy}{dx} = \sinh \dfrac{x}{c} \Rightarrow \dfrac{d^2y}{dx^2} = \dfrac{1}{c} \cosh \dfrac{x}{c}$

$$\therefore \; \rho = \frac{\left[1 + \left(\dfrac{dy}{dx}\right)^2\right]^{\frac{3}{2}}}{\dfrac{d^2y}{dx^2}} = \frac{\left[1 + \sinh^2 \dfrac{x}{c}\right]^{\frac{3}{2}}}{\dfrac{1}{c} \cosh \dfrac{x}{c}} = c \cosh^2 \dfrac{x}{c}, \text{ as required}$$

(b) $\tan \psi = \dfrac{dy}{dx} \Rightarrow \tan \psi = \sinh \dfrac{x}{c}$

Figure 7.4

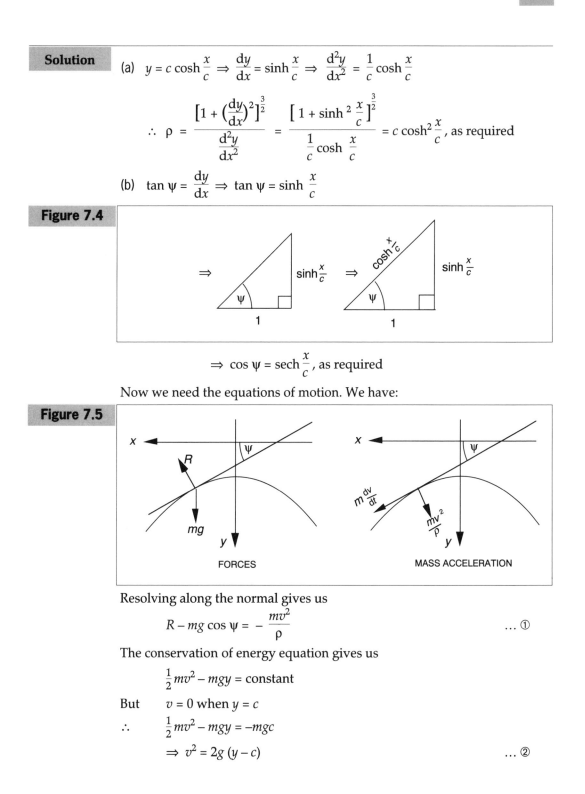

$$\Rightarrow \cos \psi = \operatorname{sech} \frac{x}{c}, \text{ as required}$$

Now we need the equations of motion. We have:

Figure 7.5

FORCES   MASS ACCELERATION

Resolving along the normal gives us

$$R - mg \cos \psi = -\frac{mv^2}{\rho} \qquad \qquad \ldots \text{①}$$

The conservation of energy equation gives us

$$\frac{1}{2}mv^2 - mgy = \text{constant}$$

But $v = 0$ when $y = c$

$\therefore$ $\dfrac{1}{2}mv^2 - mgy = -mgc$

$$\Rightarrow v^2 = 2g(y - c) \qquad \qquad \ldots \text{②}$$

The particle leaves the surface when $R = 0$

$\therefore$ Equations ① and ② give us

$$g \cos \psi = \frac{2g\,(y - c)}{\rho}$$

Now we substitute for y and ρ to get

$$g \cos \psi = \frac{2g\,(\cosh \frac{x}{c} - 1)}{\cosh^2 \frac{x}{c}}$$

and then using (b) this becomes

$$g \operatorname{sech} \frac{x}{c} = \frac{2g\,\left(\cosh \frac{x}{c} - 1\right)}{\cosh^2 \frac{x}{c}}$$

$\Rightarrow$ $\cosh \dfrac{x}{c} = 2$

$\Rightarrow$ $\sinh \dfrac{x}{c} = \sqrt{3}$

$\Rightarrow$ $\tan \psi = \sqrt{3}$

$\Rightarrow$ $\psi = 60°$

$\therefore$ The tangent makes an angle of 60° with the horizontal, as required.

Example   A small bead of mass m slides on a smooth wire bent in the form of the parabola $y = 4x^2$. The bead is released from rest from the point whose coordinates are (1, 4). Find the reaction of the wire on the bead when the bead reaches the origin of coordinates.

Solution   We have (for the curve $y = 4x^2$):

Figure 7.6

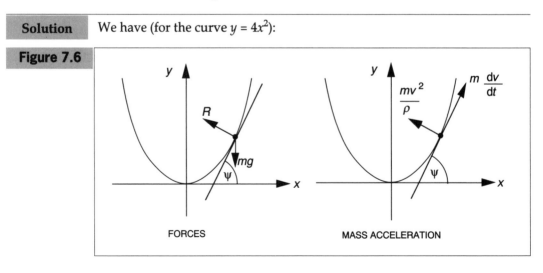

FORCES   MASS ACCELERATION

$$y = 4x^2 \implies \frac{dy}{dx} = 8x$$

$$\implies \quad \rho = \frac{\left[1 + \left(\frac{dy}{dx}\right)^2\right]^{\frac{3}{2}}}{\frac{d^2y}{dx^2}} = \frac{\left(1 + 64x^2\right)^{\frac{3}{2}}}{8}$$

$\therefore$ At the origin $\rho = \frac{1}{8}$.

If v is the velocity of the particle at the origin, then conservation of energy gives:

$$\frac{1}{2}mv^2 = mg\,4 \implies v^2 = 8g \qquad\qquad \dots \text{①}$$

resolving vertically at the origin we get

$$R - mg = \frac{mv^2}{\rho} \implies R = mg + \frac{mv^2}{\rho}$$

Now use equation ① and $\rho = \frac{1}{8}$ to get

$$R = mg + \frac{m \times 8g}{\frac{1}{8}} \implies R = 65mg.$$

$\therefore$ The reaction at the origin is $65mg$.

You should now be able to answer Exercises 1–6 on pp. 146–147.

Motion of a particle under a central force

We are now going to look at the motion of a particle under the action of a *central force*, by which is meant a force directed towards (or away from) some fixed point O. Practical examples of this kind of force most frequently occur in outer space.

Newton was the first to consider this, when he studied the motion of planets round the sun, by modelling planets as particles and the sun as a fixed point.

In more recent times scientists have built and launched space probes: relative to the centre of the earth, the force of attraction between a satellite and the earth is also a central force.

With problems involving a central force, polar coordinates come into play. We have:

Figure 7.7

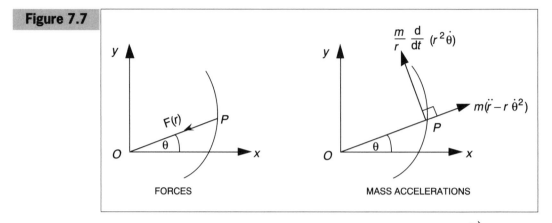

FORCES   MASS ACCELERATIONS

(The central force F(r) is a function of r and acts in the direction $\overrightarrow{PO}$. The acceleration components are as found in the previous section.)

There is no transverse force and so the transverse acceleration must be zero.

$$\therefore \quad \frac{1}{r}\frac{d}{dt}(r^2\dot{\theta}) = 0 \implies r^2\dot{\theta} = h, \text{ a constant.}$$

Note: In these sort of problems, h is the conventional letter for the constant of integration.

Radially we get $-F(r) = m\,(\ddot{r} - r\dot{\theta}^2)$

Using $r^2\dot{\theta} = h$ this becomes $-F(r) = m\left(\ddot{r} - \frac{h^2}{r^3}\right)$

Multiplying by $\dot{r}$ and integrating we get:

$$-\int F(r)\,dr = m\left(\frac{1}{2}\dot{r}^2 + \frac{h^2}{2r^2}\right) + \text{constant}$$

$$\implies \quad -\int F(r)\,dr = m\left(\frac{1}{2}\dot{r}^2 + \frac{1}{2}r^2\dot{\theta}^2\right) + \text{constant} \quad (\text{using } r^2\dot{\theta} = h)$$

$$\implies \quad -\int F(r)\,dr = \frac{1}{2}m\,(\dot{r}^2 + (r\dot{\theta})^2) + \text{constant}$$

But $\dot{r}$ and $r\dot{\theta}$ are the radial and transverse components of the velocity v, so that $v^2 = \dot{r}^2 + (r\dot{\theta})^2$

$$\therefore \quad -\int F(r)\,dr = \frac{1}{2}mv^2 + \text{constant}$$

This is called the **energy equation.** If we know F(r) and the initial conditions, we can use this to find the speed at any subsequent position.

To summarise:

> If a central force F(r) acts towards the origin then
>
> - $r^2\dot{\theta} = h$
>
> - $-F(r) = m\,(\ddot{r} - r\dot{\theta}^2)$
>
> Useful results derived from these equations are
>
> - $-F(r) = m\left(\ddot{r} - \dfrac{h^2}{r^3}\right)$
>
> - $-\displaystyle\int F(r)\,dr = \dfrac{1}{2}mv^2 + \text{constant}$

Example

A particle moves round the curve $r = 3 + 2\cos\theta$ under a central force acting towards the origin O. When $\theta = 0$ the particle has speed $4\ \text{m s}^{-1}$.

Find the time taken to move from $\theta = 0$ to $\theta = \dfrac{\pi}{3}$.

Solution

In order to find the time, we are only interested in the equation $r^2\dot{\theta} = h$.

Therefore we need to find h. To do this we work out the value of $r^2\dot{\theta}$ when $\theta = 0$.

Now $r = 3 + 2\cos\theta \Rightarrow \dot{r} = -2\sin\theta\,\dot{\theta}$

$\therefore\quad \theta = 0 \Rightarrow \dot{r} = 0$

But the initial speed is $4\ \text{m s}^{-1}$

$\therefore\quad$ initially $r\dot{\theta} = 4$ ... ①

Also, when $\theta = 0$, $r = 5$ ... ②

$\therefore\quad \theta = 0 \Rightarrow r^2\dot{\theta} = r \times r\dot{\theta} = 5 \times 4 = 20$ (using ① and ②)

$\therefore\quad r^2\dot{\theta} = 20$ at all points.

Substituting for r we get

$$(3 + 2\cos\theta)^2\,\dot{\theta} = 20$$

$$\Rightarrow \int_0^{\pi/3} \left[9 + 12\cos\theta + 4\cos^2\theta\right]\,d\theta = \int_0^t 20\,dt$$

$$\Rightarrow \int_0^{\pi/3} \left[11 + 12\cos\theta + 2\cos 2\theta\right] d\theta = \left[20t\right]_0^t$$

(using $2\cos^2\theta = 1 + \cos 2\theta$)

$$\Rightarrow \left[11\theta + 12\sin\theta + \sin 2\theta\right]_0^{\pi/3} = \left[20t\right]_0^t$$

$$\Rightarrow 22.78 = 20t \Rightarrow t = 1.14 \text{ (2 d.p.)}$$

∴ The required time is 1.14 seconds.

[The important point to notice in this solution is that everything follows once $r^2\dot\theta$ has been found.]

Example

A particle of mass in kg is moving under a central force of $\dfrac{10m}{r^2}$ newtons acting towards the origin.

At time t the position of the particle is given by polar coordinates (r, θ).
Initially $\mathbf{r} = 2\mathbf{i}$ metres and $\dot{\mathbf{r}} = 3\mathbf{j}$ metres per second. Find:

(a) the speed when the magnitude of $\mathbf{r}$ is 4 metres

(b) the magnitude of $\mathbf{r}$ when the speed is 0.5 metres per second.

Solution

Since we are given $F(r)$ we could use the equation $-F(r) = m(\ddot{r} - r\dot\theta^2)$ and integrate it. However, it is much quicker to use the (derived) energy equation

$$-\int F(r)\,dr = \frac{1}{2}mv^2 + \text{constant}$$

Now when $\theta = 0$ we have $r = 2$, $\dot{r} = 0$ and $r\dot\theta = 3$

∴ Using the energy equation we have:

(a) $$-\int_2^4 \frac{10m}{r^2}\,dr = \left[\frac{1}{2}mv^2\right]_3^v$$

$$\Rightarrow \left[\frac{10}{r}\right]_2^4 = \frac{1}{2}v^2 - \frac{9}{2} \Rightarrow v^2 = 4 \Rightarrow v = 2$$

∴ The speed is 2 metres per second.

(b) $$-\int_2^r \frac{10m}{r^2}\,dr = \left[\frac{1}{2}mv^2\right]_3^{0.5}$$

$$\Rightarrow \left[\frac{10}{r}\right]_{2}^{r} = -4.375 \Rightarrow r = 16$$

∴ **r** has magnitude 16 metres at this moment.

[In this question we went straight to the energy equation because we knew the central force and we were interested in velocities.]

You should now be able to answer Exercises 7–13 on p. 147–150.

Projectiles revisited

We first met projectile questions in Module M1. We'll now look at this topic in a little more detail and then move on to consider projectiles on inclined planes.

Example	A particle of mass m, initially at the origin, is projected with initial velocity vector $u \cos \alpha \mathbf{i} + u \sin \alpha \mathbf{j}$. Ignoring air resistance, set up the equations of motion. Hence find the equation of the path of the projectile.

Solution	We have:

Figure 7.8	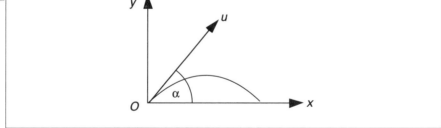

Using cartesian coordinates, this gives us:

Figure 7.9	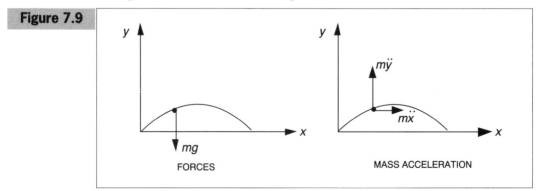

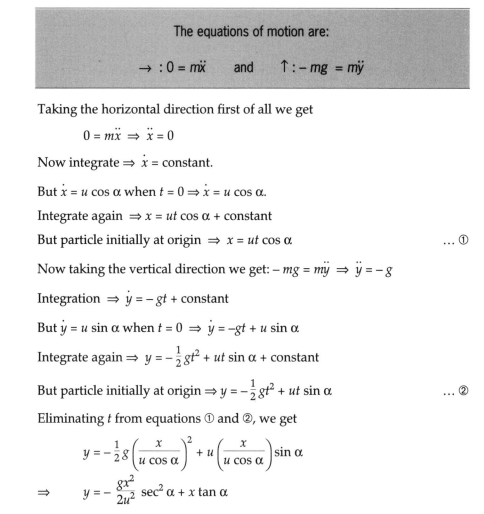

The equations of motion are:

$$\rightarrow \; : 0 = m\ddot{x} \qquad \text{and} \qquad \uparrow : -mg = m\ddot{y}$$

Taking the horizontal direction first of all we get

$$0 = m\ddot{x} \Rightarrow \ddot{x} = 0$$

Now integrate $\Rightarrow \dot{x} = $ constant.

But $\dot{x} = u \cos \alpha$ when $t = 0 \Rightarrow \dot{x} = u \cos \alpha$.

Integrate again $\Rightarrow x = ut \cos \alpha + $ constant

But particle initially at origin $\Rightarrow x = ut \cos \alpha$ ... ①

Now taking the vertical direction we get: $-mg = m\ddot{y} \Rightarrow \ddot{y} = -g$

Integration $\Rightarrow \dot{y} = -gt + $ constant

But $\dot{y} = u \sin \alpha$ when $t = 0 \Rightarrow \dot{y} = -gt + u \sin \alpha$

Integrate again $\Rightarrow y = -\frac{1}{2}gt^2 + ut \sin \alpha + $ constant

But particle initially at origin $\Rightarrow y = -\frac{1}{2}gt^2 + ut \sin \alpha$ ... ②

Eliminating t from equations ① and ②, we get

$$y = -\frac{1}{2}g\left(\frac{x}{u \cos \alpha}\right)^2 + u\left(\frac{x}{u \cos \alpha}\right)\sin \alpha$$

$$\Rightarrow \qquad y = -\frac{gx^2}{2u^2}\sec^2 \alpha + x \tan \alpha$$

$$\Rightarrow \qquad y = -\frac{g}{2u^2}(1 + \tan^2 \alpha)x^2 + x \tan \alpha,$$

the required equation of the path of the projectile.

(Sometimes this path of the projectile is referred to as the *trajectory* of the particle.)

There are two important points to note here.

● The solution involved integration (rather than relying on $s = ut + \frac{1}{2}at^2$ etc). We'll regularly use this technique from now on.
● The equation of the path is a parabola.

When it comes to firing projectiles up (or down) an inclined plane, it is often useful to choose axes along and perpendicular to the plane. Suppose, then, that we have:

Figure 7.10

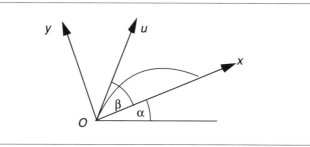

[The initial velocity u of the particle is inclined at β to the line of greatest slope of the plane, which is itself inclined at α to the horizontal.]

The acceleration of the particle is $-g \sin \alpha$ in the direction of the x-axis and $-g \cos \alpha$ in the direction of the y-axis.

∴ The equations of motion are:

Up the plane:	$m\ddot{x} = -mg \sin \alpha$
Perpendicular to the plane:	$m\ddot{y} = -mg \cos \alpha$

Taking up the plane first of all we get (using integration and not forgetting the initial conditions)

$$\ddot{x} = -g \sin \alpha$$

$$\Rightarrow \quad \dot{x} = -gt \sin \alpha + u \cos \beta$$

$$\Rightarrow \quad x = -\frac{1}{2} gt^2 \sin \alpha + ut \cos \beta$$

Now taking perpendicular to the plane we get (again using integration and not forgetting the initial conditions)

$$\ddot{y} = -g \cos \alpha$$

$$\Rightarrow \quad \dot{y} = -gt \cos \alpha + u \sin \beta$$

$$\Rightarrow \quad y = -\frac{gt^2}{2} \cos \alpha + ut \sin \beta$$

The particle hits the plane again when $y = 0$

$$\Rightarrow \quad 0 = t \left(-\frac{gt}{2} \cos \alpha + u \sin \beta \right)$$

$$\Rightarrow \quad t = \frac{2u \sin \beta}{g \cos \alpha}$$

∴ The first bounce takes a time of $\dfrac{2u \sin \beta}{g \cos \alpha}$

The range of this first bounce is given by the value of x at this time.

$$\therefore \quad x = -\frac{1}{2}g\left(\frac{2u \sin \beta}{g \cos \alpha}\right)^2 \sin \alpha + u\left(\frac{2u \sin \beta}{g \cos \alpha}\right)\cos \beta$$

$$= \frac{2u^2 \sin \beta}{g \cos^2 \alpha}\left(-\sin \beta \sin \alpha + \cos \beta \cos \alpha\right)$$

$$= \frac{2u^2 \sin \beta \cos (\alpha + \beta)}{g \cos^2 \alpha}$$

This can be rewritten as:

$$x = \frac{u^2}{g \cos^2 \alpha}\left[\sin (\alpha + 2\beta) - \sin \alpha\right] \quad *$$

∴ For the range of the first bounce to be as big as possible, we will have to choose β so that $\sin (\alpha + 2\beta) = 1$, i.e. $\alpha + 2\beta = \dfrac{\pi}{2}$

In other words, for maximum range up the plane, the direction of projection must bisect the angle between Ox and the vertical.

The velocity of the particle just before impact will be given by $\dot{x}$ and $\dot{y}$ where:

$$\dot{x} = -gt \sin \alpha + u \cos \beta$$

$$= -g\left(\frac{2u \sin \beta}{g \cos \alpha}\right)\sin \alpha + u \cos \beta$$

$$= u \cos \beta - \frac{2u \sin \beta \sin \alpha}{\cos \alpha}$$

and $\quad \dot{y} = -gt \cos \alpha + u \sin \beta$

$$= -g\left(\frac{2u \sin \beta}{g \cos \alpha}\right)\cos \alpha + u \sin \beta$$

$$= -u \sin \beta \text{ (as expected?)}$$

As the particle rebounds from the plane, this component of the particle's velocity will be reversed and multiplied by e, the coefficient of restitution between the particle and the plane.

∴ After impact, the velocity situation is given by:

Figure 7.11

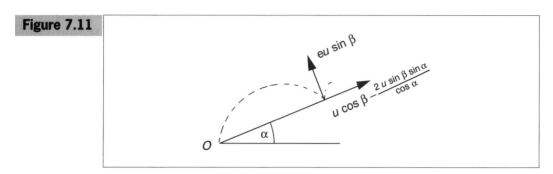

and, so off we go again … or we could do, anyway!

When tackling these types of problem, I suggest that you always write down the equations of motion and then integrate. There is no need to learn any general results by heart.

$*\Big[$Using the standard formula for sin $(A + B)$ and sin $(A – B)$ it follows that

$$\sin (A + B) – \sin (A – B)$$
$$= (\sin A \cos B + \cos A \sin B) – (\sin A \cos B – \cos A \sin B)$$

∴ $\sin (A + B) – \sin (A – B) = 2 \cos A \sin B$

Putting $A + B = P$ and $A – B = Q$, this gives us

$$\text{Sin } P – \sin Q = 2 \cos \left(\frac{P + Q}{2}\right) \sin \left(\frac{P - Q}{2}\right)$$

∴   As a special case of this we have

$$\sin (\alpha + 2\beta) – \sin \alpha = 2 \cos (\alpha + \beta) \sin \beta\Big]$$

Example   A ball is thrown with a speed of 28 m s⁻¹ at an angle of projection of $\tan^{-1}2$. Find:

(a)   the greatest height reached

(b)   its vertical height when the direction of motion is inclined at 45° to the horizontal. (Take g as 9.8 m s⁻²).

Solution

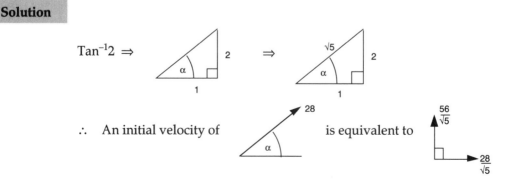

∴   An initial velocity of   is equivalent to

Now write down the equations of motion and integrate them. Taking the x and y axes as horizontal and vertical respectively, we get:

$\uparrow: \quad \ddot{y} = -g \qquad\qquad$ and $\rightarrow: \quad \ddot{x} = 0$

$\dot{y} = -gt + \dfrac{56}{\sqrt{5}} \qquad\qquad\qquad \dot{x} = \dfrac{28}{\sqrt{5}}$

$y = -\dfrac{gt^2}{2} + \dfrac{56}{\sqrt{5}}t \qquad\qquad\quad x = \dfrac{28}{\sqrt{5}}t$

(a) Greatest height reached when $\dot{y} = 0 \quad \Rightarrow t = \dfrac{56}{g\sqrt{5}}$

$\Rightarrow x = \dfrac{28}{\sqrt{5}} \cdot \dfrac{56}{g\sqrt{5}} = \dfrac{1568}{5g} = 32$

∴ The greatest height reached in 32 m

(b) Direction of motion inclined at $45° \quad \Rightarrow \dfrac{\dot{y}}{\dot{x}} = \tan 45°$

$\Rightarrow \dfrac{\dot{y}}{\dot{x}} = 1 \quad \Rightarrow \dot{y} = \dot{x}$

$\Rightarrow -gt + \dfrac{56}{\sqrt{5}} = \dfrac{28}{\sqrt{5}}$

$\Rightarrow t = \dfrac{28}{g\sqrt{5}}$

$\Rightarrow y = \dfrac{-g}{2}\left(\dfrac{28}{g\sqrt{5}}\right)^2 + \dfrac{56}{\sqrt{5}}\left(\dfrac{28}{g\sqrt{5}}\right) = \dfrac{235.2}{g} = 24$

∴ The required height is 24m.

Example A shot is fired from a gun in a horizontal direction with a velocity of 300 m s⁻¹. The gun is on the side of a hill of inclination $\tan^{-1}\dfrac{4}{5}$ to the horizontal. Find:

(a) how far along the hill the shot will strike

(b) determine its velocity then in magnitude and direction.

(Take g as 9.8 m s⁻² and give your answers correct to 3 significant figures.)

Solution

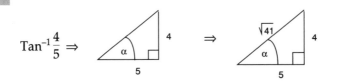

$\mathrm{Tan}^{-1}\dfrac{4}{5} \Rightarrow$

∴   An initial velocity of 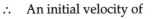 is equivalent to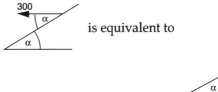

Now write down the equations of motion and integrate them. Taking the x and y axes as down and perpendicular to the plane respectively, we get:

Down the plane: $\ddot{x} = \dfrac{4g}{\sqrt{41}}$ Perpendicular to the plane: $\ddot{y} = -\dfrac{5g}{\sqrt{41}}$

$$\dot{x} = \frac{4gt}{\sqrt{41}} + \frac{1500}{\sqrt{41}} \qquad\qquad \dot{y} = -\frac{5gt}{\sqrt{41}} + \frac{1200}{\sqrt{41}}$$

$$x = \frac{2gt^2}{\sqrt{41}} + \frac{1500t}{\sqrt{41}} \qquad\qquad y = -\frac{5gt^2}{2\sqrt{41}} + \frac{1200t}{\sqrt{41}}$$

(a) Shot strikes hill when $y = 0$ $\Rightarrow$ $\dfrac{-5gt^2}{2\sqrt{41}} + \dfrac{1200t}{\sqrt{41}} = 0$

$$\Rightarrow \quad t = \frac{480}{g}$$

$$\Rightarrow \quad x = \frac{2g}{\sqrt{41}}\left(\frac{480}{g}\right)^2 + \frac{1500}{\sqrt{41}}\left(\frac{480}{g}\right)$$

$$= 18800 \text{ (to 3 s.f.)}$$

∴   Shot strikes hill at a distance of 18.8 km away.

(b) When the shot strikes the hill, its velocity components are

$$\dot{x} = \frac{4g}{\sqrt{41}} \cdot \frac{480}{g} + \frac{1500}{\sqrt{41}} \quad\text{and}\quad \dot{y} = -\frac{5g}{\sqrt{41}} \cdot \frac{480}{g} + \frac{1200}{\sqrt{41}}$$

$$= \frac{3420}{\sqrt{41}} \qquad\qquad\qquad = -\frac{1200}{\sqrt{41}}$$

∴   The shot lands with velocity components given by

Figure 7.12

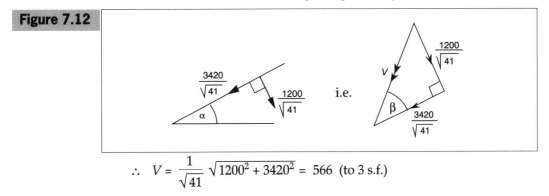

∴ $V = \dfrac{1}{\sqrt{41}}\sqrt{1200^2 + 3420^2} = 566$ (to 3 s.f.)

and $\tan \beta = \dfrac{1200}{3420} \Rightarrow \beta = 19.3°$

∴   The angle the shell makes with the horizontal is
   $\alpha + \beta = 58.0°$ (to 3 s.f.)

∴   The shell strikes the hill with velocity 566 m s^{-1} at an angle of 58°
   to the horizontal.

You should now be able to answer Exercises 14–21 on pp. 150–151.

EXERCISES

1 An object of mass m near the surface of the earth is projected
   horizontally from a point O. The resistance, mR, of the atmosphere has
   a direction opposite to that of the velocity v of the object. If, at a
   subsequent instant, ψ is the angle which the direction of motion makes
   with the horizontal, ρ the radius of curvature of the trajectory at that
   point and s the length of the trajectory traversed from O (see figure
   below), show that:

$$g \cos \psi = \frac{v^2}{\rho} \quad \text{and} \quad g \sin \psi - R = v\frac{dv}{ds}$$

   Hence show that $\tan \psi - \dfrac{R}{g \cos \psi} = \dfrac{1}{v} \cdot \dfrac{dv}{d\psi}$

2 A particle of mass m slides on a smooth cycloid $s = 4a \sin \psi$ which is
   held fixed with axis vertical and vertex downwards. If the particle is
   released from rest at a point whose distance from the vertex, measured
   along the arc, is c, prove that it passes through the vertex with speed
   $c\sqrt{\left(\dfrac{g}{4a}\right)}$ and that the thrust on the curve is then
   $mg\left(1 + \dfrac{c^2}{16a^2}\right).$

3 A particle slides under gravity down a smooth cycloid $s = 4b \sin \psi$ starting from rest at height h above the vertex. Show that the vertical component of the motion is simple harmonic, of amplitude $\frac{1}{2}h$ and period $2\pi\sqrt{\left(\dfrac{b}{g}\right)}$.

4 A small bead moves on a smooth wire in the shape of one branch of the rectangular hyperbola $y^2 - x^2 = a^2$. The wire is held with its real axis vertical and its vertex downwards and the bead is released from rest at a point where $y = \dfrac{3a}{2}$. Prove that when the bead passes through the vertex, the magnitude of the reaction between the bead and the wire is twice the weight of the bead.

5 A small bead moves on a smooth wire in the shape of the curve $y = \cos x$ from $x = 0$ to $x = \frac{1}{2}\pi$, the wire being held in a vertical coordinate plane in which the axis of y is vertical. The bead is displaced slightly from rest at $x = 0$. Calculate the speed of the bead when it reaches the point $\left(\frac{1}{2}\pi, 0\right)$ and the reaction of the wire on the bead there.

6 Show that the radius of curvature at the point t of the parabola $x = 2at$, $y = at^2$ is

$$2a(1 + t^2)^{3/2}$$

A smooth rigid wire bent into the form of this parabola is fixed with the y-axis vertical and the vertex at the lowest point. A bead of mass m threaded on the wire is released from rest at the point $t = t_0$. Show that when the bead reaches the point $t = t_1$ in the subsequent motion its speed is $\left\{ 2ga\left(t_0^2 - t_1^2\right) \right\}^{1/2}$, and prove that the force exerted by the wire on the bead is

$$mg\,\frac{1 + t_0^2}{\left(1 + t_1^2\right)^{3/2}}$$

7 A particle moves round the curve $r = 4 + \sin 4\theta$ under a central force acting towards O. Sketch the orbit. If the particle takes 20 seconds to move once round the orbit, how long does it take to move from $\theta = 0$ to $\theta = \dfrac{\pi}{4}$?

8 The path of a particle of unit mass is given parametrically by the equations $r = t$, $\theta = \dfrac{6\pi}{t}$. Find the velocity and acceleration vectors in terms of their radial and transverse components, and show that this motion is consistent with motion under a central force. Find this force when $t = 2$.

9 A particle of mass m kg is moving under a central force of $\dfrac{5m}{r^2}$ newtons acting towards the origin. Initially $\mathbf{r} = 5\mathbf{i}$ metres and $\dot{\mathbf{r}} = (0.6\mathbf{i} + 0.8\mathbf{j})$ metres per second. Find the speed of the particle on the two occasions when it is moving at right angles to the direction of the central force.

10 A particle moves under a central force of $k^2 r$ per unit mass directed towards the origin. Prove that $v^2 + k^2 r^2$ is a constant .

The diameter OA of a circle has length $2k$. A particle is projected with speed V from A perpendicular to OA, and moves round the circle under the action of a central force directed towards O. (See diagram below.)

Prove that the time taken to move from A to P, where $A\hat{O}P = \theta$, is $\dfrac{k}{V}$ ($\theta + \sin \theta \cos \theta$).

Find the time T taken by the particle to reach O.

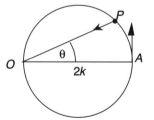

Show further that the perpendicular distance from O to the tangent at P is $k (1 + \cos 2\theta)$. Hence show that the speed of the particle at P is $2V (1 + \cos 2\theta)^{-1}$. By showing that the speed can also be written as $4k^2 V r^{-2}$, and using the energy equation, prove that the central force is inversely proportional to r^5.

11 A particle P of mass m is attracted to a fixed point O by a central force

$$\mathbf{F} = -mf(r)\,\hat{\mathbf{r}},$$

where r is the distance of P from O and $\hat{\mathbf{r}}$ is a unit vector in the direction of OP. Show that the motion of P lies in a fixed plane through O. Write down the radial and tangential components of the equations of motion for P, and show that they may be put in the form

$$r^2\dot{\theta} = h, \quad \ddot{r} = \frac{h^2}{r^3} - f(r), \quad \text{where } h \text{ is a constant.}$$

Using the relation $\dfrac{d}{dt} = \dot{\theta}\,\dfrac{d}{d\theta}$, prove that

$$\dot{r} = -h\,\frac{d}{d\theta}\left(\frac{1}{r}\right), \quad \ddot{r} = -\frac{h^2}{r^2}\,\frac{d^2}{d\theta^2}\left(\frac{1}{r}\right).$$

Hence show that $u = \dfrac{1}{r}$ satisfies the equation

$$\frac{d^2u}{d\theta^2} + u = \frac{1}{h^2 u^2}\, f\!\left(\frac{1}{u}\right)$$

P is projected from the point $r = a$ on the line $\theta = 0$ with a speed $v > \dfrac{u^{\frac{1}{2}}}{a}$

in a direction perpendicular to the radius vector OP. Show that if the central force is

$$f(r) = \frac{\mu}{r^3}$$

then the path of P is

$$r = a \sec k\theta, \qquad \text{where } k^2 = 1 - \frac{\mu}{v^2 a^2}.$$

12 A satellite S, of mass m, is orbiting about Venus in a plane through the centre O of Venus which may be regarded as stationary. The only force on the satellite has magnitude F and acts along SO.

At time t, OS is of length r and is rotating about O with angular speed $\dot{\theta}$. When $t = 0$, $r = a$ and the satellite is moving with speed U in a direction perpendicular to OS. Show that:

$$r^2\dot{\theta} = aU.$$

Given that $F = \dfrac{2maU^2}{r^2}$, show that

$$\ddot{r} = \frac{aU^2(a - 2r)}{r^3}$$

Hence show that

$$\dot{r}^2 = \frac{U^2(4ar - a^2 - 3r^2)}{r^2}$$

13 A particle moves on the curve $r^2 \cos 2\theta = c^2$ under the action of a central force directed away from the origin. Find the law determining the force. [Very hard]

14 A ball is thrown from a point distance a from a smooth vertical wall against the wall, and returns to the point of projection. Prove that the velocity u of projection and the elevation α of projection are connected by the equation

$$u^2 \sin 2\alpha = ag \left(\frac{1+e}{e} \right),$$

where e is the coefficient of restitution between the ball and the wall.

15 A projectile is fired from a fixed point O at an elevation α and hits a stationary target A, where OA is horizontal. Find the speed V of projection, neglecting air resistance.

On another occasion the target starts to rise vertically from A with uniform speed U at the same instant as a projectile is fired from O with elevation α. If the moving target is to be hit, show that the speed of projection must be increased to W, where W is the positive root of the equation

$$W^2 - WU \operatorname{cosec} \alpha = V^2$$

16 A particle is projected from a point on an inclined plane with a velocity which is the resultant of u along a line of greatest slope and v vertically upward. Prove that its range on the plane is $\dfrac{2uv}{g}$.

17 A particle is projected from a point on a plane of angle α so that the range R up the plane is as great as possible. If the time of flight is T, show that $2R = gT^2$.

18 From a point in a plane inclined to the horizontal at an acute angle β a particle is projected in a vertical plane perpendicular to the inclined plane. The initial velocity of the particle is V in a direction making an angle α with the upward direction of the line of greatest slope of the plane.

Show that the particle will strike the plane perpendicularly if $2 \tan \alpha = \cot \beta$. Show also that if this condition is satisfied, the greatest range of the particle on the plane for different values of β is $\dfrac{V^2}{g\sqrt{3}}$.

19 A particle is projected with speed u from a point A in a plane of angle α. The direction of projection makes an angle ψ ($> \alpha$) with the horizontal, and the motion takes place in the vertical plane containing the line of greatest slope through A. The particle strikes the plane at right angles at B. Prove:

(a) $\cot (\psi - \alpha) = 2 \tan \alpha$

(b) $AB = \dfrac{u^2 \{ \sin (2\psi - \alpha) - \sin \alpha \}}{g \cos^2\alpha}$

20 A ball is projected from a point P on a plane inclined at an angle α to the horizontal, the direction of projection lying in a vertical plane through a line of greatest slope and making an angle β ($\beta < \frac{1}{2}\pi - \alpha$) with the upward direction of that line. The coefficient of restitution between ball and plane is e. Show that the condition that the ball returns to P on the nth impact with the plane is $(1 - e^n) \tan \alpha \tan \beta = 1 - e$.

21 A particle is projected with a velocity of 90 m s^{-1} at an elevation of 60° from the foot of a plane of inclination 30°. The motion being in the vertical plane through a line of greatest slope of the plane, find the range on the plane and the time of flight. (Take g as 9.8 m s^{-2} and give your answers correct to 3 s.f.)

SUMMARY   You should now be able to:

- set up and solve the equations of motion for a particle moving on a smooth curve:

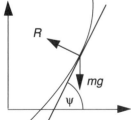
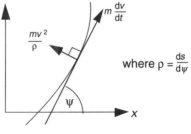

FORCES   MASS ACCELERATION

normally: $R - mg \cos \psi = \dfrac{mv^2}{\rho}$

tangentially: $-mg \sin \psi = m \dfrac{dv}{dt}$

This second equation integrates to give the energy equation $\frac{1}{2}mv^2 + mgy = c$

- tackle questions involving a central force:

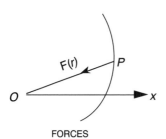 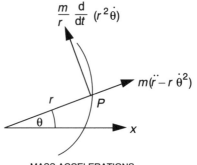

FORCES   MASS ACCELERATIONS

It follows that

$$r^2\dot\theta = h, \text{ a constant}$$

and $-F(r) = m(\ddot r - r\dot\theta^2)$

Useful results derived from these equations are

$$-F(r) = m\left(\ddot r - \frac{h^2}{r^3}\right)$$

and $-\int F(r) = \frac{1}{2}mv^2 + \text{constant, the energy equation}$

- interpret the equation $r^2\dot\theta = h$ as a conservation of angular momentum:

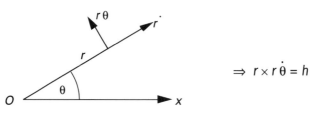

$$\Rightarrow r \times r\dot\theta = h$$

- solve problems involving projectiles and inclined planes – choose your axes along and perpendicular to the plane and then use integration.

General motion of a rigid body

In Section 2 we studied the motion of a rigid body about a *fixed* smooth horizontal axis. In this section we are going to look at the *free* motion of a rigid body.

When you have finished this section you should be able to:
- set up and solve the equations resulting from an impulse on an unconstrained rigid body.
- set up and solve the equations of motion of a freely moving rigid body
- decide whether a body is rolling or slipping.

The momentum system for a freely moving rigid body

If a rigid body is rotating about a *fixed*, smooth horizontal axis through its centre of mass G, and suddenly an impulse J is applied then, using the methods of Section 2, we have:

Figure 8.1

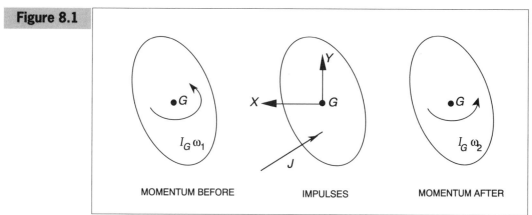

MOMENTUM BEFORE   IMPULSES   MOMENTUM AFTER

(ω_1 is the angular velocity of the body *before* the impulse, J is the impulse itself and X and Y are the impulsive reactions at the smooth axis; ω_2 is the angular velocity of the body *after* the impulse.)

If the axis through G is now free to move in the vertical plane, then the momentum system of the rigid body of mass M is given by

Figure 8.2

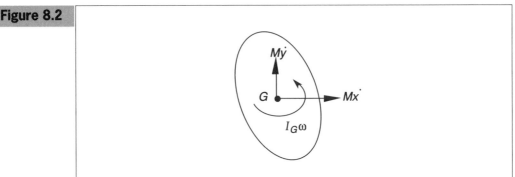

(where $\dot{x}$, $\dot{y}$ are the components of velocity of G and ω is the angular velocity of the body about the axis through G).

And so, if an impulse J is suddenly applied to the rigid body of mass M we get:

Figure 8.3

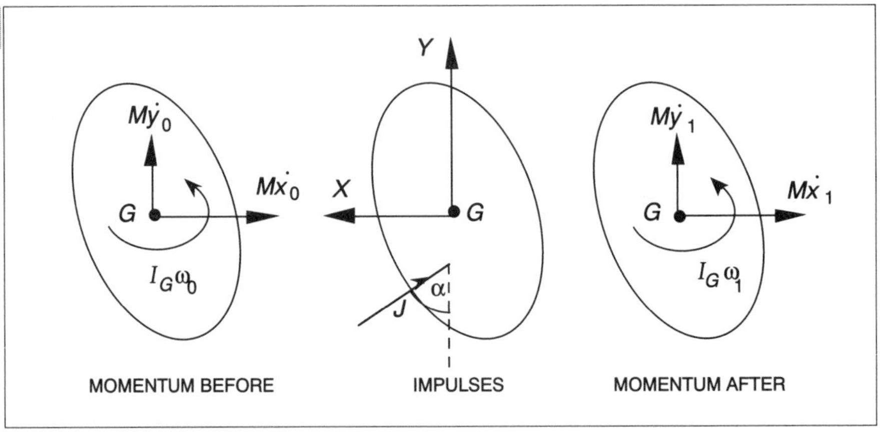

MOMENTUM BEFORE   IMPULSES   MOMENTUM AFTER

(Before the impulse, ω_0 is the angular velocity of the body about the axis through G and $\dot{x}_0$, $\dot{y}_0$ are the velocity components of G. J is the impulse itself and X and Y are the impulsive reactions of the smooth axis through G. After the impulse, ω_1 is the angular velocity of the body about the axis through G and $\dot{x}_1$, $\dot{y}_1$ are the velocity components of G.)

From this situation we can get *three equations*. If we take moments about the axis through G we get:

G $\circlearrowleft$: $I_G\omega_1 - I_G\omega_0 = Jd$ (where d is the perpendicular distance of the line of action of J from the axis). We would use this equation if we wanted to find the impulse J.

If we resolve in two directions we also get:

$\uparrow: M\dot{y}_1 - M\dot{y}_0 = Y + J\cos\alpha$

$\rightarrow: M\dot{x}_1 - M\dot{x}_0 = J\sin\alpha - X.$

We would use these latter two equations if we needed to find the impulsive reactions X and Y.

The above three equations are sufficient to solve problems involving freely moving rigid bodies to which an impulse has been applied. However, *it is also necessary to be able to write down the velocity component of any point P of the rigid body.* And so, if we are given:

Figure 8.4

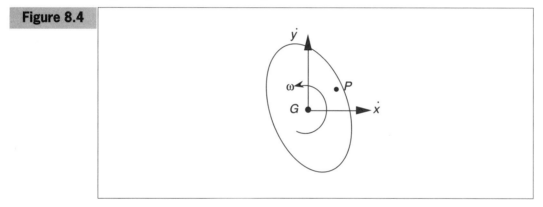

(the velocity components of G are $\dot{x}, \dot{y}$ and the rigid body is spinning about the axis through G with angular velocity ω).

Then, if P is any point on the rigid body, the velocity of P is shown in the diagram below.

Figure 8.5

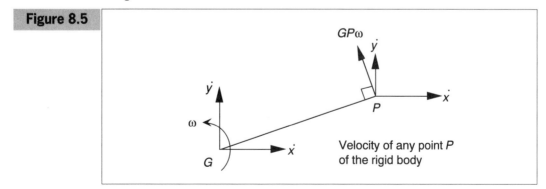

Velocity of any point P of the rigid body

(The velocity of P is the velocity of G plus the velocity of P relative to G.)

Example   A thin uniform rod *AB* of length 4*a* and mass *m* is at rest on a smooth horizontal table. An impulse *P* is then applied to the rod. The direction of *P* is perpendicular to *AB* and its point of impact is at a distance *a* from the centre of mass of the rod. Find the velocities of both ends of the rod immediately after impact.

Solution   There is no momentum 'before' and so we only have the two diagrams as shown:

Figure 8.6

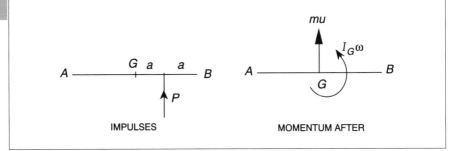

IMPULSES   MOMENTUM AFTER

[After impact, the motion of the rod is reduced to the motion of *G* together with a couple.]

The impulse is at right angles to the rod and so, initially, *G* will move off in that direction. *u* is this initial velocity and ω the initial angular velocity. The moment of inertia I_G is given by:

$$I_G = \frac{1}{3} m\,(2a)^2 \text{ i.e. } I_G = \frac{4}{3} ma^2$$

We therefore get two equations:

↑: $P = mu$ and G ⟲   : $Pa = I_G \omega$

Using $I_G = \frac{4}{3} ma^2$, these equations give us

$$u = \frac{P}{m} \text{ and } \omega = \frac{3P}{4ma} \qquad \qquad \dots ①$$

To find the velocity of *B* we have:

Figure 8.7

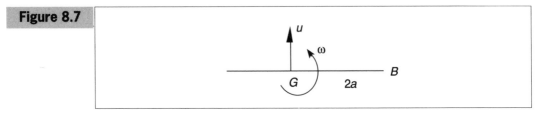

∴   Velocity of $B = u + 2a\omega$

$$= \frac{P}{m} + \frac{3P}{2m} \text{ (using the results in ①)}$$

$$= \frac{5P}{2m}.$$

To find the velocity of A we have

Figure 8.8

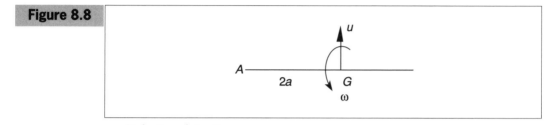

∴ Velocity of $A = 2a\omega - u$

$$= \frac{3P}{2m} - \frac{P}{m} \text{ (using the results in ①)}$$

$$= \frac{P}{m}$$

∴ The velocities of the end points of the rod are as shown below:

Figure 8.9

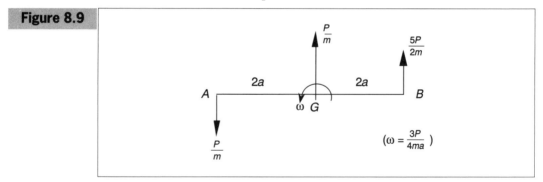

Example   A thin uniform rod AB, of mass $9m$ and length $2a$, is lying at rest on a smooth horizontal table. A particle Q, of mass m, moving on the table with speed u in a direction perpendicular to AB strikes the rod at the end A. The coefficient of restitution between the rod and the particle is $\frac{1}{4}$.

(a)   Show that the rod begins to rotate with angular velocity $\frac{15u}{52a}$.

(b)   Show that the speed of Q after impact is $\frac{7u}{52}$

| **Solution** | Begin by setting up the three separate diagrams: |

Figure 8.10

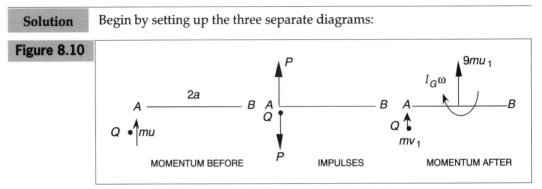

[P is the impulse on the rod at A and the equal and opposite impulse on the particle of mass m. After impact, the centre of mass of the rod moves off in the direction of P. u_1 is the initial velocity of this centre of mass, ω the initial angular velocity and v_1 the initial velocity of the particle after impact.]

The moment of inertia I_G is given by:

$$I_G = \frac{1}{3}(9m)\,a^2 \quad \text{i.e.} \quad I_G = 3ma^2$$

This time we have *three* unknowns to find (u_1, v_1 and ω), and so *we need three equations*. Two of these equations come from resolving and taking moments and the third requires Newton's Experimental Law. And so:

Conservation of linear momentum for the *whole system* (or, if you prefer, resolving ↑ for the *whole system*) gives us:

$$\uparrow : 9\,mu_1 + mv_1 - mu = 0$$

$$\therefore \quad 9u_1 + v_1 = u \qquad\qquad \dots \text{①}$$

Moments about A for the *whole system* gives us:

$$\overset{A}{\curvearrowright} : -I_G\omega + 9mau_1 - 0 = 0$$

But $I_G = 3ma^2$

$$\therefore \quad -3ma^2\omega + 9mau_1 = 0$$

$$\therefore \quad -a\omega + 3u_1 = 0 \qquad\qquad \dots \text{②}$$

After impact, the velocity of A is $u_1 + a\omega$

$\therefore$ Newton's Experimental Law gives us:

$$(u_1 + a\omega) - v_1 = -\frac{1}{4}(0 - u)$$

$$\therefore \quad u_1 + a\omega - v_1 = \frac{1}{4}u \qquad\qquad \dots \text{③}$$

Equations ② and ③ lead to $4u_1 - v_1 = \dfrac{1}{4}u$

Now solve simultaneously with equation ① to get:

$$u_1 = \frac{5u}{52} \text{ and } v_1 = \frac{7u}{52}$$

∴ (from equation ②), $\omega = \dfrac{15u}{52a}$, as required.

∴ The speed of Q after impact is $\dfrac{7u}{52}$ (i.e. v_1).

Example Two particles A and B of mass $2m$ and m are connected by a light rod and lie on a smooth horizontal table. The mass A is struck a horizontal blow at $\tan^{-1}\dfrac{4}{3}$ with AB. Find the ratio of the initial velocities of A and B.

Solution Begin by setting up two diagrams:

Figure 8.11

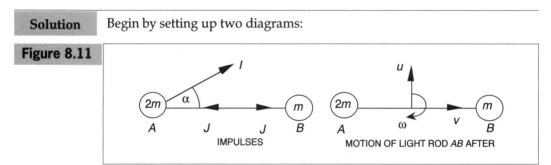

(I is the resulting impulse at A inclined at α to AB and J is the impulsive reaction in the light rod AB. After impact, u and v are the initial velocity components of the centre of mass of AB and ω is the initial angular velocity.)

The velocities of A and B immediately after impact are:

Figure 8.12

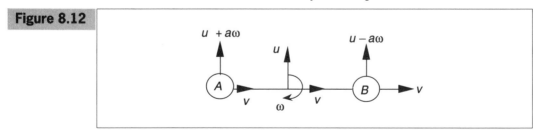

Since we need to find *three unknowns* (u, v and ω) we need *three equations*. These can be found by resolving twice and taking moments.

Resolving $\uparrow$ for the *whole system* gives us:

$\uparrow$: $2m(u + a\omega) + m(u - a\omega) = I \sin \alpha$

∴ $3mu + ma\omega = I \sin \alpha$ ... ①

Resolving → for the *whole system* gives us:

→ : $2\,mv + mv = I\cos\alpha$

∴ $3mv = I\cos\alpha$ ... ②

Moments about A for the *whole system* gives us

A) : $0 = m(u - a\omega)\cdot 2a$

∴ $u = a\omega$ ... ③

Equations ① and ③ give $u = \dfrac{I\sin\alpha}{4m}$ and equation ② gives $v = \dfrac{I\cos\alpha}{3m}$

But $\tan\alpha = \dfrac{4}{3}$ ⇒

∴ $u = \dfrac{I}{5m}$ and $v = \dfrac{I}{5m}$ and $a\omega = \dfrac{I}{5m}$

∴   Velocities of A and B after impact are given by

Figure 8.13

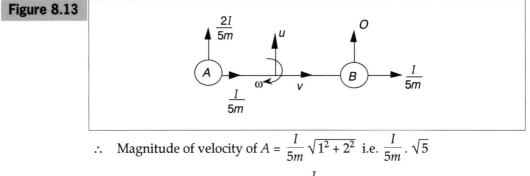

∴   Magnitude of velocity of $A = \dfrac{I}{5m}\sqrt{1^2 + 2^2}$ i.e. $\dfrac{I}{5m}\cdot\sqrt{5}$

But the magnitude of velocity of $B = \dfrac{I}{5m}$.

∴   The ratio of the initial velocities of A and B is $\sqrt{5} : 1$.

You should now be able to answer Exercises 1–11 on pp. 168–169.

The mass acceleration system for a freely moving rigid body

If a rigid body of mass M is spinning about a smooth horizontal axis through its centre of mass G and if that axis is itself moving in a vertical plane, then we have:

Figure 8.14

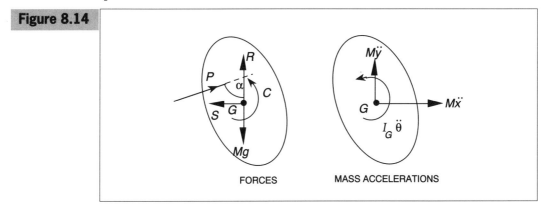

FORCES   MASS ACCELERATIONS

(R and S are the forces at the axis, P is some external force and C some external couple. The acceleration components of G are $\ddot{x}$ and $\ddot{y}$ and the rigid body is spinning about the axis through G with angular acceleration $\ddot{\theta}$).

From this situation we can get *three equations*. If we take moments about the axis through G we get:

G ⟲ : $I_G\ddot{\theta} = C - Pd$ (where d is the perpendicular distance of the line of action of P from the axis). If P and C are constant then this leads to the usual energy equation.

If we resolve in two directions we get:

↑ : $M\ddot{y} = R + P \cos \alpha - Mg$

→ : $M\ddot{x} = P \sin \alpha - S$

We would use these equations if we needed to find the forces. The above three equations (together with the deduced energy equation) are sufficient to solve problems involving freely moving rigid bodies. However, it *is also necessary to understand about rolling and slipping* and so we will look at that now.

Rolling and slipping

Suppose that a wheel is moving along a horizontal surface. If the angular velocity of the wheel is ω and the velocity of the centre of the wheel is u, then we have:

Figure 8.15

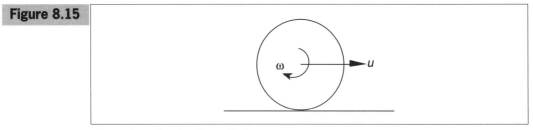

Does the wheel roll or slip?

If the wheel is moving very fast along the surface and yet only turning very slowly, then we'll get sliding (or slipping or skidding, whichever you prefer).

On the other hand, if the wheel is moving very slowly along the surface and yet spinning very fast there will once again be skidding.

Somewhere between these two situations, then, is a happy medium, namely, the wheel will roll.

Whether it slips or rolls all depends on the velocity of the contact point A.

Figure 8.16

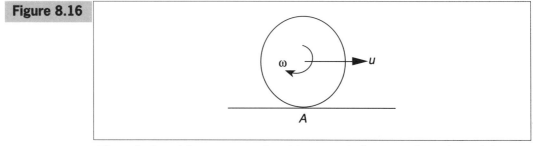

The velocity of the contact point A is $u - a\omega$ (where a is the radius of the wheel).

If $u - a\omega$ is zero, then we'll get rolling. In that case we will have (with the usual notations):

Figure 8.17

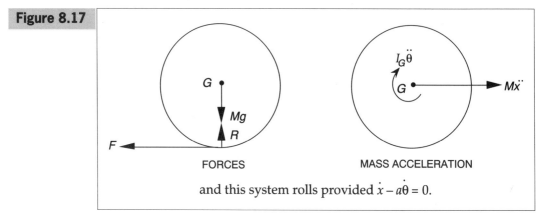

FORCES   MASS ACCELERATION

and this system rolls provided $\dot{x} - a\dot{\theta} = 0$.

The equations of motion are:

$\rightarrow:\quad -F = M\ddot{x}$

$\uparrow:\quad R - Mg = 0$

$\overset{\curvearrowleft}{G}:\quad Fa = I_G\ddot{\theta}$

The frictional force F is against the direction of motion and $F < \mu R$.

If $u - a\omega$ is not zero, then we'll get *skidding*.

We might then have:

Figure 8.18

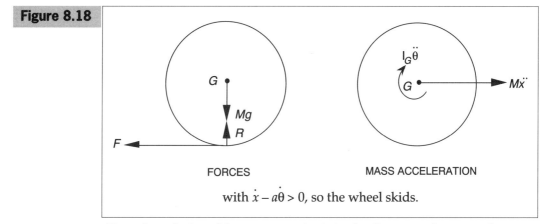

FORCES   MASS ACCELERATION

with $\dot{x} - a\dot{\theta} > 0$, so the wheel skids.

Since the velocity of the contact point is in the direction of motion, the frictional force F will be in the opposite direction from this (as shown).

The equations of motion are:

$\rightarrow:\quad -F = M\ddot{x}$

$\uparrow:\quad R - Mg = 0$

$\overset{\curvearrowleft}{G}:\quad Fa = I_G\ddot{\theta}$

And the frictional force $F = \mu R$

Alternatively we might have $\dot{x} - a\dot{\theta} < 0$, so the wheel still skids – and yet there is an important difference from the previous case. The velocity of the contact point will have a direction *opposite* to the direction of motion and so the frictional force F will have to be in the direction of motion. This gives:

Figure 8.19

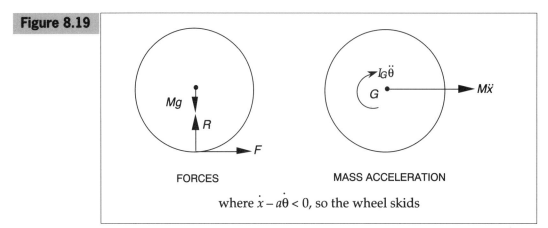

FORCES   MASS ACCELERATION

where $\dot{x} - a\dot{\theta} < 0$, so the wheel skids

The equations of motion are:

$\rightarrow$: $F = M\ddot{x}$

$\uparrow$: $R - Mg = 0$

$\overset{\frown}{G}$: $Fa = -I_G\ddot{\theta}$

And the frictional force $F = \mu R$

In summary, then:

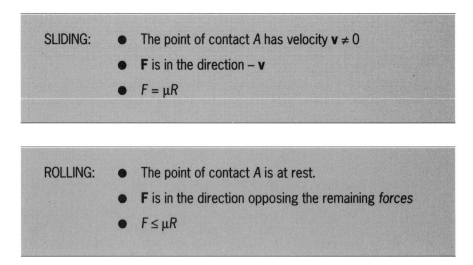

SLIDING: • The point of contact A has velocity $\mathbf{v} \neq 0$

   • $\mathbf{F}$ is in the direction $-\mathbf{v}$

   • $F = \mu R$

ROLLING: • The point of contact A is at rest.

   • $\mathbf{F}$ is in the direction opposing the remaining *forces*

   • $F \leq \mu R$

Example   A uniform sphere mass m of radius a rolls down an inclined plane of inclination α. Set up the equations of motion for the sphere. How long will it take for the sphere to roll a distance $30a$ down the plane from rest?

Solution   With the usual notations we have:

Figure 8.20

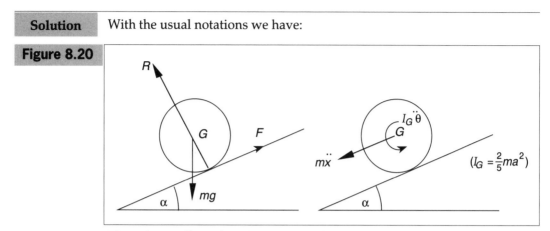

The sphere rolls and so the velocity of the contact point is zero.

$$\therefore \ \dot{x} - a\dot{\theta} = 0 \qquad \qquad \dots \text{①}$$

The three equations of motion are:

Down the plane: $mg \sin \alpha - F = m\ddot{x}$ $\qquad \qquad \dots \text{②}$

Normal to the plane: $R - mg \cos \alpha = 0$ $\qquad \qquad \dots \text{③}$

$\overset{\curvearrowleft}{G}$: $Fa = I_G \ddot{\theta} = \dfrac{2ma^2}{5}\ddot{\theta}$ $\qquad \qquad \dots \text{④}$

Equations ② and ④ give $g \sin \alpha - \dfrac{2}{5} a\ddot{\theta} = \ddot{x}$

Integrating this equation (and using the initial conditions) gives us

$$gt \sin \alpha - \frac{2}{5} a\dot{\theta} = \dot{x}$$

Now using equation ① this becomes $gt \sin \alpha - \dfrac{2}{5}\dot{x} = \dot{x}$

$$\Rightarrow \ \dot{x} = \frac{5}{7} gt \sin \alpha$$

$$\Rightarrow \ x = \frac{5gt^2}{14} \sin \alpha \ \text{(having integrated and used the initial conditions } x = 0$$
when $t = 0$.)

$$\therefore \quad x = 30a \Rightarrow 30a = \frac{5gt^2 \sin \alpha}{14} \Rightarrow t = \sqrt{\frac{84a}{g \sin \alpha}}$$

$\therefore$ The required time is $\sqrt{\dfrac{84\,a}{g \sin \alpha}}$

$$= \frac{2ma^2}{6}\ddot{\theta}$$

Example

A uniform cylinder mass m of base radius a and height h is projected up the line of greatest slope of a plane of inclination α. The axis of the cylinder is always at right angles to this line of slope. Initially the cylinder has an angular velocity of $\dfrac{u}{a}$ with the velocity of its centre $5u$ along the line of greatest slope (see diagram below).

(a) Show that the cylinder initially skids

(b) Set up the equations of motion for the cylinder

(c) Prove that the cylinder stops skidding after a time of

$$\frac{4u}{g(3\mu \cos \alpha + \sin \alpha)} \text{ , where } \mu \text{ is the coefficient of friction between the}$$
cylinder and plane.

Solution

Figure 8.21

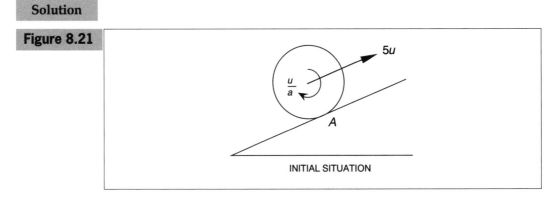

INITIAL SITUATION

(a) The velocity of contact point A is initially $5u - a \times \dfrac{u}{a}$ i.e. $4u$

Since $4u > 0$, the cylinder will initially skid and the frictional force F will be down the plane.

Figure 8.22

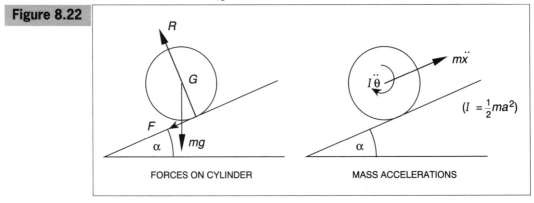

FORCES ON CYLINDER

MASS ACCELERATIONS

$(I = \tfrac{1}{2}ma^2)$

(b) The equations of motion are:

Down the plane: $F + mg \sin \alpha = -m\ddot{x}$ ... ①

Normal to the plane: $R - mg \cos \alpha = 0$ ... ②

$\overset{\curvearrowleft}{\widehat{G}}$: $Fa = I_G \ddot{\theta}$ ... ③

Skidding ∴ $F = \mu R$ ... ④

(c) Equations ② and ④ give $F = \mu mg \cos \alpha$ ... ⑤

∴ Equation ③ gives $\mu g \cos \alpha = \dfrac{a}{2} \ddot{\theta}$

∴ Integrating (and using the initial condition that $\dot{\theta} = \dfrac{u}{a}$ when $t = 0$), we get

$$\mu g t \cos \alpha = \frac{a}{2} \dot{\theta} - \frac{u}{2}$$

$$\Rightarrow a\dot{\theta} = u + 2\mu g t \cos \alpha \qquad ⑥$$

Equations ① and ⑤ give

$$\ddot{x} = -\mu g \cos \alpha - g \sin \alpha$$

∴ Integrating (and using the initial condition that $\dot{x} = 5u$ when $t = 0$), we get

$$\dot{x} = -gt (\mu \cos \alpha + \sin \alpha) + 5u \qquad ⑦$$

Skidding stops when the velocity of the contact point is zero,

i.e. when $\dot{x} - a\dot{\theta} = 0$

∴ Equations ⑥ and ⑦ give

$$-gt (\mu \cos \alpha + \sin \alpha) + 5u = u + 2\mu g t \cos \alpha$$

$$\therefore \ t = \frac{4u}{g(3\mu \cos \alpha + \sin \alpha)}$$

You should now be able to answer Exercises 12–24 on pp. 169–171.

1 A thin uniform rod AB of length $6a$ and mass $2m$ is at rest on a smooth horizontal table. An impulse P is then applied to the rod. The direction of P is perpendicular to AB and its point of impact is at a distance $2a$ from the centre of mass of the rod. Show how the initial angular velocity of the rod is $\dfrac{P}{3ma}$ and find the velocity of the end point of the rod nearer to the point of impact.

2 A thin uniform rod AB, of mass $4\,m$ and length $6a$, is lying at rest on a smooth horizontal table. A particle Q, of mass m, moving on the table with speed u in a direction perpendicular to AB strikes the rod at the end B. The coefficient of restitution between the rod and the particle is $\dfrac{1}{2}$.

(a) Show that the rod begins to rotate with angular velocity $\dfrac{3u}{16a}$.

(b) Show that the speed of Q after impact is $\dfrac{u}{4}$.

3 A uniform rod, of length $2a$, moving with speed u perpendicularly to its length without rotation, receives a blow in the same direction at one end, which increases the speed of its centre by half its value. Find the angular velocity of the rod after the blow, and show that its kinetic energy has been trebled.

4 A uniform rod of mass m and length $2a$ rests on a smooth horizontal table. It receives an impulse J perpendicular to it, in the plane of the table at one end. Find the initial speed of the other end of the rod.

5 A uniform rod AB, of mass m and length $2a$, lies at rest on a smooth horizontal table. A horizontal impulse P, making an angle β with AB, is applied to the end A. Find the kinetic energy generated by the impulse.

6 A uniform rod of mass m and length $2a$ lying on a smooth horizontal table is struck a horizontal blow of impulse P perpendicular to its length at one end. Find the velocities with which the ends of the rod begin to move.

7 A circular ring of radius a lies on a smooth horizontal table when a point on the circumference is made to move in the direction of the tangent at the point with speed u. Prove that the initial angular velocity of the ring is $\dfrac{u}{2a}$.

8 A circular *disc* of radius a lies on a smooth horizontal table. A point P of its rim is made to move along the tangent at P to the disc with speed u. Prove that the angular velocity with which the disc begins to turn is $\dfrac{2u}{3a}$.

9 $ABCD$ is a square lamina lying on a smooth horizontal table. The corner A is made to move with speed u along BA. Show that the initial angular velocity of the lamina is $\dfrac{3u}{8a}$.

10 A thin uniform rod AB of mass m and length $2L$ is at rest on a smooth horizontal surface. A particle P of mass m is moving along the surface with speed u in a direction perpendicular to the rod. The particle P collides with the rod at the point a distance $\dfrac{2L}{3}$ from B and immediately adheres to it. The centre of mass of the combined body is at the point G on the rod AB and the body starts to rotate with an angular velocity ω.

(a) Show that the moment of inertia of the combined body about the vertical axis through G is $\dfrac{7}{18}mL^2$.

(b) Find ω.

(c) Show that $\dfrac{3}{7}$ of the kinetic energy is lost in the collision.

11 A thin uniform rod AB, of mass $5m$ and length $2L$, is lying at rest on a smooth horizontal table. A particle P, of mass m, moving on the table with speed u in a direction perpendicular to AB strikes the rod at the end B. The coefficient of restitution between the rod and the particle is $\dfrac{1}{3}$.

(a) Show that the rod begins to rotate with angular speed $\dfrac{4u}{9L}$.

(b) Find the speed of P after the impact.

12 A uniform circular disc rolls down a plane whose inclination to the horizontal is α. Calculate its acceleration and the least value of the coefficient of friction to prevent sliding.

13 A uniform solid cylinder is placed with its axis horizontal on a rough plane making an angle α with the horizontal. If there is no sliding, and the cylinder takes t sec to roll down the plane, find the length of the plane.

14 A uniform circular disc of mass m and radius a rolls down a plane inclined at α to the horizontal. If the coefficient of friction is μ and a constant braking couple of moment G is applied to the disc, prove that it will continue to roll down the plane if $\mu > \frac{1}{3}\tan\alpha + \dfrac{2G\sec\alpha}{3\,mag}$.

15 A vertical uniform circular disc of radius a rolls without slipping up a line of greatest slope of a plane inclined at α to the horizontal. If the initial angular velocity is ω, show that the disc will roll a distance $\dfrac{3a^2\omega^2}{4g\sin\alpha}$ up the plane before coming instantaneously to rest.

16 A uniform disc, of mass m and radius r, is placed on a rough plane inclined at an angle α to the horizontal. The plane of the disc is vertical and the disc is released from rest so as to move along a line of greatest slope of the inclined plane. The disc rolls without slipping down the plane.

(a) Show that the frictional force is $\frac{1}{3}mg\sin\alpha$.

(b) Find, in terms of α, the smallest possible value of the coefficient of friction between the rim of the disc and the plane.

17 A uniform circular hoop of radius a and mass m has a particle of mass m attached to it. Initially the particle is at the highest point when it is slightly displaced. If the hoop rolls without slipping, show that its angular velocity when the radius to the particle makes an angle θ with the vertical is given by

$$\omega^2 = \frac{g}{a} \times \frac{1-\cos\theta}{2+\cos\theta}$$

18 A uniform circular hoop is rotating about a horizontal axis through its centre perpendicular to its plane with angular speed Ω when it is placed gently on a horizontal plane whose coefficient of friction is μ. Show that the hoop will slide for a time $\dfrac{a\Omega}{2\mu g}$.

19 A uniform circular disc of radius a and rotating with angular velocity Ω is placed gently on a rough horizontal table whose coefficient of friction is μ. Show that there will be slipping for a time $\dfrac{a\Omega}{3\mu g}$, after which the disc will roll along the plane with angular speed $\frac{1}{3}\Omega$.

20 A sphere, of mass m and radius a is spinning about a horizontal axis through its centre with angular speed Ω. The spinning sphere is gently lowered on to a rough horizontal plane and released. The coefficient of friction between the sphere and the plane is μ.

Show that for a time T, where T is given by $T = \dfrac{2\Omega a}{7\mu g}$, the sphere is slipping.

21 A uniform rod is held inclined at 30° to the vertical with its lower end in contact with a rough horizontal plane; if the rod is released from rest and falls under gravity, show that it will not immediately slip on the plane if the coefficient of friction exceeds $\dfrac{27^{\frac{1}{2}}}{13}$, and find in this case the initial reaction on the plane.

22 A uniform circular hoop, of mass m and radius r, starts from rest and rolls, without slipping and with its plane vertical, down a line of greatest slope of a fixed plane which is inclined at an angle α to the horizontal.

Show that the acceleration of the centre of the hoop is $\frac{1}{2} g \sin \alpha$.

23 Two particles A and B, of mass m and $2m$ respectively, are connected by a light rigid rod of length $2a$ and lie on a smooth horizontal table. A horizontal impulse of magnitude I is applied to A in a direction making an angle α with the line BA produced. Determine, in terms of m, I and α, the initial speed of each particle and find the kinetic energy generated by the impulse.

24 A uniform sphere, of radius a, is rotating about a horizontal diameter with angular speed Ω. The sphere is gently placed on a rough plane which is inclined at an angle α to the horizontal, the sense of rotation being such as to tend to cause the sphere to move up the plane along a line of greatest slope. Given that the coefficient of friction between the sphere and the plane is $\tan \alpha$, show that the centre of the sphere will remain at rest for a time

$$\frac{2a\Omega}{5g \sin \alpha}$$

You should now know that (with the usual notations)

- the momentum system for a freely moving rigid body is given by

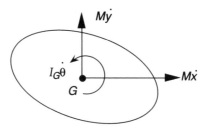

- the mass acceleration system for a freely moving rigid body is given by

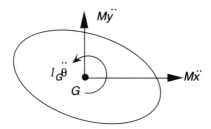

- if the centre of mass G is moving, then P has a velocity given by

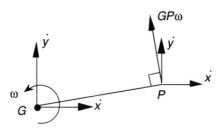

- rolling occurs on a surface if the velocity of the contact point is zero

  for example: rolls $\Rightarrow u - a\omega = 0$

- slipping occurs on a surface if the velocity v of the contact point is non-zero. In that case the frictional force F has the direction of $-v$ and $F = \mu R$.

Stability

Imagine a particle resting at the bottom of a hemispherical bowl.

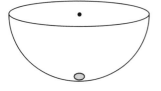

It is in *equilibrium*.

If the particle is then moved up one side of the bowl and released from rest, it will eventually return to its original position under gravity. If all the surfaces are smooth, then the particle will oscillate about the equilibrium position. In such situations the particle is said to be originally in a state of *stable equilibrium*.

If the hemispherical bowl is inverted and the particle is placed on top of the bowl, then we still have equilibrium.

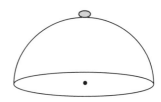

However, if the particle is now displaced from this position it will not return to its original position but, instead, it will fall to the ground. In this case the particle is said to be in *unstable equilibrium*.

In this section we'll be looking more closely at these two types of equilibrium.

When you've finished this section you should be able to:

● find positions of stable and unstable equilibrium
● work out the period of small oscillations about a position of stable equilibrium.

Finding positions of stable and unstable equilibrium

In the position of stable equilibrium described in the Introduction, the potential energy (PE) of the particle was at a minimum. On the other hand, when we had unstable equilibrium, the potential energy of the particle was at a maximum. This illustrates the following important result.

- Stationary values of PE determine positions of equilibrium.

- If the PE takes a minimum value, then the equilibrium is stable.

- If the PE takes a maximum value, then the equilibrium is unstable.

However, *this only applies when there is a total conservation of energy* i.e. when the system is conservative.

Example   The graph below shows the PE of a conservative system plotted as a function of a parameter θ. *A*, *B* and *C* are stationary points. What can you say about the system at the corresponding values of θ?

Figure 9.1

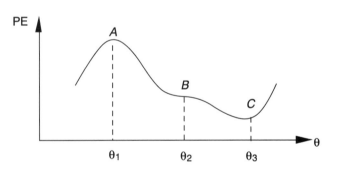

Solution   (a) At *A* the PE is a maximum

∴ when θ = θ$_1$, the system is in unstable equilibrium.

(b) At *B* there is a point of inflection.

If you regard the graph in terms of a switchback railway at a funfair, then *B* will be an unstable point of equilibrium. Clearly it is unstable to the right of *B* and if the carriage is released to the left of *B* it will arrive at *B* with a velocity which would carry it over to the right.

∴ when θ = θ$_2$, the system is in unstable equilibrium

(c) At *C* the PE is a minimum

∴ when θ = θ$_3$, the system is in stable equilibrium.

Example

Figure 9.2

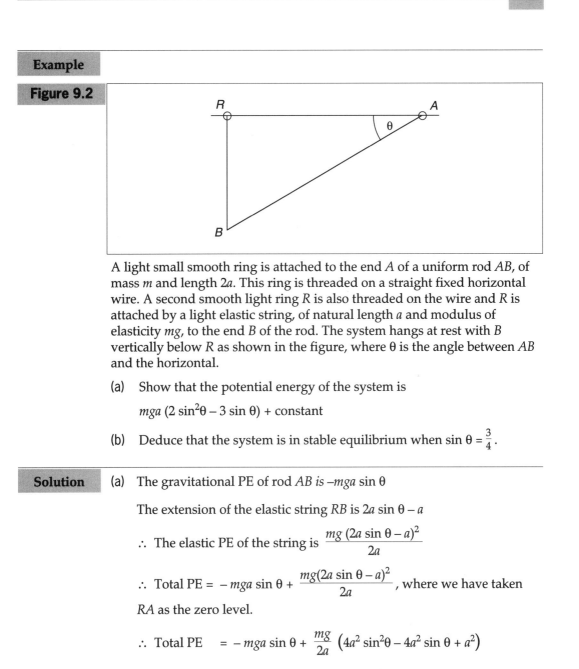

A light small smooth ring is attached to the end A of a uniform rod AB, of mass m and length $2a$. This ring is threaded on a straight fixed horizontal wire. A second smooth light ring R is also threaded on the wire and R is attached by a light elastic string, of natural length a and modulus of elasticity mg, to the end B of the rod. The system hangs at rest with B vertically below R as shown in the figure, where θ is the angle between AB and the horizontal.

(a) Show that the potential energy of the system is

$mga\,(2\sin^2\theta - 3\sin\theta) + \text{constant}$

(b) Deduce that the system is in stable equilibrium when $\sin\theta = \dfrac{3}{4}$.

Solution

(a) The gravitational PE of rod AB is $-mga\sin\theta$

The extension of the elastic string RB is $2a\sin\theta - a$

$\therefore$ The elastic PE of the string is $\dfrac{mg\,(2a\sin\theta - a)^2}{2a}$

$\therefore$ Total PE $= -mga\sin\theta + \dfrac{mg(2a\sin\theta - a)^2}{2a}$, where we have taken RA as the zero level.

$\therefore$ Total PE $= -mga\sin\theta + \dfrac{mg}{2a}\left(4a^2\sin^2\theta - 4a^2\sin\theta + a^2\right)$

$= -3\,mga\sin\theta + 2\,mga\sin^2\theta + \dfrac{mga}{2}$

$= -3\,mga\sin\theta + 2\,mga\sin^2\theta + \text{constant}$

$\therefore$ The total PE is given by

$$V = -3\,mga\sin\theta + 2\,mga\,\sin^2\theta + \text{constant}$$

(b)   Differentiating we get

$$\frac{dV}{d\theta} = -3\,mga\,\cos\theta + 4\,mga\,\sin\theta\,\cos\theta$$

The equilibrium position is therefore found from the equation

$$-3\,mga\,\cos\theta + 4\,mga\,\sin\theta\,\cos\theta = 0$$

$$\Rightarrow\ \cos\theta\,(4\sin\theta - 3) = 0$$

$$\Rightarrow\ \cos\theta = 0\ \ \text{or}\ \ \sin\theta = \frac{3}{4}$$

To decide on stability (or otherwise) we differentiate again

$$\therefore \qquad \frac{d^2V}{d\theta^2} = mga\,(3\sin\theta - 4\sin^2\theta + 4\cos^2\theta)$$

If $\sin\theta = \frac{3}{4}$ then we have

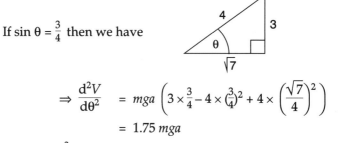

$$\Rightarrow\ \frac{d^2V}{d\theta^2} = mga\left(3\times\frac{3}{4} - 4\times\left(\tfrac{3}{4}\right)^2 + 4\times\left(\frac{\sqrt{7}}{4}\right)^2\right)$$

$$= 1.75\,mga$$

∴ Since $\dfrac{d^2V}{d\theta^2}$ is positive, the PE is a minimum, and equilibrium is stable.

∴ The system is in stable equilibrium when $\sin\theta = \frac{3}{4}$.

$$\left[\text{If } \cos\theta = 0 \text{ then } \frac{d^2V}{d\theta^2} = -mga < 0\right.$$

and, therefore, the equilibrium position with $\theta = \dfrac{\pi}{2}$ is unstable.$\Big]$

And so, when tackling stability questions, the procedure is:

● Find an expression for the total PE, usually written as *V*.

● Find the stationary values of *V* by solving the equation $\dfrac{dV}{d\theta} = 0$

● If the stationary value is a maximum $\left(\text{usually tested by } \dfrac{d^2V}{d\theta^2} < 0\right)$, then the equilibrium is unstable.

● If the stationary value is a minimum $\left(\text{usually tested by } \dfrac{d^2V}{d\theta^2} > 0\right)$, then the equilibrium is stable.

As for your examination question on this topic, you will almost certainly be asked to derive a *given* expression for the potential energy V. In other words, even if you can't quite manage to derive the formula for V yourself, you can still go on to differentiate V and so discuss the stability. That is known as examination technique!

You should now be able to answer Exercises 1–6 on pp. 181–184.

Small oscillations about a point of stable equilibrium

When we considered small oscillations before (e.g. with the compound pendulum in Section 2, p. 25), we obtained our results directly from the equations of motion. However, it is sometimes easier to find an expression for the *total* energy (which must be constant) and then to differentiate that.

Example   A fixed uniform rod AB of mass m and length $2a$ is smoothly hinged to a fixed point at its end A. C is a fixed point at a height $2a$ *vertically above* A, and an elastic string of natural length $2a$ and modulus of elasticity $\frac{4}{3}mg$ joins C to the other end B of the rod. The system hangs at rest as shown in the figure below, and θ is the angle made by AB with the downward vertical.

Figure 9.3

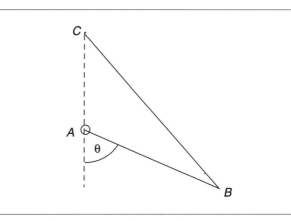

(a)   Show that the potential energy of the system is:

$$\frac{2\,mga}{3}\left(5\cos^2\tfrac{1}{2}\theta - 8\cos\tfrac{1}{2}\theta\right) + \text{constant}$$

(b)   Deduce that the system is in stable equilibrium when $\cos\frac{1}{2}\theta = \frac{4}{5}$

(c)   Find the period of small oscillations about this position of stable equilibrium.

Solution   (a)   The PE of rod AB is $-mga \cos\theta$ (where we have taken the horizontal through A as the fixed level)

The distance CB is $4a \cos\frac{1}{2}\theta$.

∴ The elastic PE of the string is $\dfrac{\frac{4}{3}mg\left(4a\cos\frac{1}{2}\theta - 2a\right)^2}{4a}$

which simplifies to $\frac{4}{3}mga\left(4\,\cos^2\frac{1}{2}\theta - 4\cos\frac{1}{2}\theta + 1\right)$

∴ The total potential energy V is given by

$$V = -mga\cos\theta + \frac{4}{3}mga\left(4\cos^2\frac{1}{2}\theta - 4\cos\frac{1}{2}\theta + 1\right)$$

$$= -mga\left(2\cos^2\frac{1}{2}\theta - 1\right) + \frac{4}{3}mga\left(4\cos^2\frac{1}{2}\theta - 4\cos\frac{1}{2}\theta + 1\right)$$

$$= \frac{2\,mga}{3}\left(5\cos^2\frac{1}{2}\theta - 8\cos\frac{1}{2}\theta\right) + \frac{7}{3}mga$$

∴ the total potential energy V is given by

$$V = \frac{2\,mga}{3}\left(5\cos^2\frac{1}{2}\theta - 8\cos\frac{1}{2}\theta\right) + \text{constant}$$

(b)   Differentiating we get

$$\frac{dV}{d\theta} = \frac{2\,mga}{3}\left(-5\cos\frac{1}{2}\theta\,\sin\frac{1}{2}\theta + 4\sin\frac{1}{2}\theta\right)$$

and $$\frac{d^2V}{d\theta^2} = \frac{2\,mga}{3}\left(-\frac{5}{2}\cos^2\frac{1}{2}\theta + \frac{5}{2}\sin^2\frac{1}{2}\theta + 2\cos\frac{1}{2}\theta\right)$$

∴ $$\frac{dV}{d\theta} = 0 \Rightarrow \sin\frac{1}{2}\theta\left(4 - 5\cos\frac{1}{2}\theta\right) = 0$$

$$\Rightarrow \sin\frac{1}{2}\theta = 0 \text{ or } \cos\frac{1}{2}\theta = \frac{4}{5}$$

∴ One of the equilibrium positions is given by

$$\cos\frac{1}{2}\theta = \frac{4}{5} \Rightarrow$$

$$\Rightarrow \frac{d^2V}{d\theta^2} = \frac{2\,mga}{3}\left(-\frac{5}{2}\left(\tfrac{4}{5}\right)^2 + \frac{5}{2}\times\left(\tfrac{3}{5}\right)^2 + 2\times\tfrac{4}{5}\right)$$

$$= 0.6\,mga$$

∴ Since $\dfrac{d^2V}{d\theta^2}$ is positive, the potential energy is a minimum and so there is stable equilibrium when $\cos\frac{1}{2}\theta = \frac{4}{5}$.

(c)   The KE of the (light) string is zero.

The KE of the rod AB about the horizontal axis through A is

$$\frac{1}{2}\left(\frac{4}{3}ma^2\right)\dot{\theta}^2 \text{ i.e. } \frac{2}{3}ma^2\,\dot{\theta}^2$$

∴   the total energy E of the system is given by

$$E = KE + PE$$

$$= \frac{2}{3}ma^2\dot{\theta}^2 + \frac{2}{3}mga\left(5\cos^2\frac{1}{2}\theta - 8\cos\frac{1}{2}\theta\right) + \text{constant}$$

But E is itself a constant ∴ $\dfrac{dE}{dt} = 0$

$$\Rightarrow \frac{4}{3}ma^2\,\dot{\theta}\,\ddot{\theta} + \frac{2}{3}mga\left(-5\cos\frac{1}{2}\theta\sin\frac{1}{2}\theta + 4\sin\frac{1}{2}\theta\right)\dot{\theta} = 0$$

$$\Rightarrow 2a\ddot{\theta} = \left(-4g\sin\frac{1}{2}\theta + 5g\cos\frac{1}{2}\theta\sin\frac{1}{2}\theta\right) \qquad \ldots \text{①}$$

The position of stable equilibrium was given by $\frac{1}{2}\theta = \alpha$, i.e. by $\theta = 2\alpha$, where α was given by the following triangle:

We now put $\theta = 2\alpha + \psi$ where ψ is very small

i.e. we put $\frac{1}{2}\theta = \alpha + \frac{1}{2}\psi$.

Since ψ is small we have $\sin\frac{1}{2}\psi \approx \frac{1}{2}\psi$ and $\cos\frac{1}{2}\psi \approx 1$

Also $\sin\frac{1}{2}\theta = \sin\left(\alpha + \frac{1}{2}\psi\right)$

$$= \sin\alpha\cos\frac{1}{2}\psi + \cos\alpha\sin\frac{1}{2}\psi$$

$$\approx \frac{3}{5}\times 1 + \frac{4}{5}\times\frac{1}{2}\psi$$

$$= \frac{3}{5} + \frac{2}{5}\psi$$

and $\cos\frac{1}{2}\theta = \cos\left(\alpha + \frac{1}{2}\psi\right)$

$$= \cos\alpha\cos\frac{1}{2}\psi - \sin\alpha\sin\frac{1}{2}\psi$$

$$\approx \frac{4}{5}\times 1 - \frac{3}{5}\times\frac{1}{2}\psi$$

$$= \frac{4}{5} - \frac{3}{10}\psi$$

Moreover $\dot{\theta} = \dot{\psi}$ and $\ddot{\theta} = \ddot{\psi}$

∴ Equation ① becomes

$$2a\ \ddot{\psi} \approx \left(-4g\left(\tfrac{3}{5} + \tfrac{2}{5}\psi\right) + 5g\left(\tfrac{4}{5} - \tfrac{3}{10}\psi\right)\left(\tfrac{3}{5} + \tfrac{2}{5}\psi\right)\right)$$

$$\Rightarrow \quad 2a\ \ddot{\psi} \approx -\frac{9g}{10}\psi \quad \text{(ignoring terms in } \psi^2\text{)}$$

$$\therefore \qquad \ddot{\psi} \approx -\frac{9g}{20a}\psi$$

The oscillations are therefore approximately simple harmonic, and the

period is $2\pi\sqrt{\dfrac{20a}{9g}}$

And so, when tackling small oscillations about a position of stable equilibrium, the procedure is:

- Find the position of stable equilibrium $\theta = \theta_0$

- Find the *total* energy E of the system and put $\dfrac{dE}{dt} = 0$

- Put $\theta = \theta_0 + \psi$ and, using suitable approximations, substitute this into the equation $\dfrac{dE}{dt} = 0$

- The equations will reduce to $\ddot{\psi} \approx -\omega^2\psi$, which is approximately simple harmonic with period $\dfrac{2\pi}{\omega}$.

You should now be able to answer Exercises 7–10 on pp. 184–185.

1

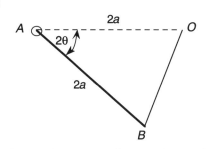

The figure shows a uniform rod AB, of mass m and length $2a$, which is attached at the end A to a fixed smooth pivot. O is a fixed point at the same horizontal level as A where $OA = 2a$. A light elastic string of natural length a and modulus $\dfrac{mg}{2\sqrt{3}}$ has one end attached to O and the other to B. The rod can rotate in the vertical plane containing AO and in a general position $\hat{OAB} = 2\theta$ as indicated, B being below AO. Show that, apart from an additive constant, the potential energy of the system is

$$-\frac{mga}{\sqrt{3}}\ (\sqrt{3}\sin 2\theta + 2\cos 2\theta + 2\sin\theta)$$

provided that the string is not slack.

Hence, or otherwise, *verify* that there is a position of equilibrium in which $\theta = 30°$ and determine whether this position is stable or unstable.

Show also that there is another position of equilibrium in which $\theta = \alpha$, where $90° < \alpha < 120°$.

2 A uniform rod OA of weight W and length $2a$ is freely pivoted to a fixed point at O; the end A is attached to a light inextensible string of length > $6a$) which passes over a small fixed smooth pulley at B, at a distance $4a$ vertically above O. The other end of the string is attached to a weight kW hanging vertically. Show that, when $\hat{AOB} = \theta$, the potential energy V of the system is

$$Wa\left[\cos\theta + 2k(5 - 4\cos\theta)^{\frac{1}{2}}\right] + \text{constant}$$

Hence, or otherwise, show that, in addition to the equilibrium positions given by $\theta = 0°$ and $\theta = 180°$, there is another position of equilibrium for a value of θ between $0°$ and $180°$, provided that $\dfrac{1}{4} < k < \dfrac{3}{4}$.

If $k = \dfrac{1}{4}\sqrt{3}$, determine the stability of the equilibrium positions.

3

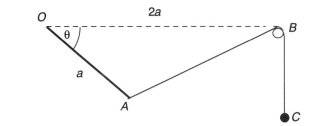

The diagram shows a uniform rod OA of length a and mass m, smoothly hinged at the end O to a fixed point. The other end A is attached by a long inextensible string to a particle C of mass M. The string passes over a smooth small pulley B fixed at the same level as O and at a distance $2a$ from it. In a general position $\angle AOB = \theta$ (A lying in the vertical plane containing OB), and the particle is hanging freely with the string taut.

If $M = \frac{1}{4} m$, prove that the potential energy of the system is

$$\frac{1}{4} mag \left[-2 \sin \theta + (5 - 4 \cos \theta)^{\frac{1}{2}}\right] + \text{constant}.$$

Hence, or otherwise, show that in this case the values of θ corresponding to positions of equilibrium satisfy the equation

$$x^3 - 3x^2 + 2 = 0,$$

where $x = 2 \cos \theta$.

Deduce that there are only two positions of equilibrium and find the corresponding values of θ.

Determine the stability of these equilibrium positions.

4   A light elastic string of natural length l and modulus λ is stretched to a length $(l + e)$. Prove that the potential energy stored in the string is

$$\frac{\lambda e^2}{2l}.$$

AC is a uniform rod of weight W and length a which can rotate in a vertical plane about the fixed point A. The point B vertically above A is such that $AB = 2a$. A light elastic string of natural length a and modulus $\frac{1}{2} W$ joins B and C. Find the potential energy of the system in terms of θ, where θ is the angle ($0 \le \theta \le \pi$) made by AC with the upward vertical at A.

Prove that the rod is in equilibrium if, and only if,

$$\cos \theta = \frac{1}{4}, \text{ or } 1, \text{ or } -1.$$

Distinguish between the stable and unstable positions.

5

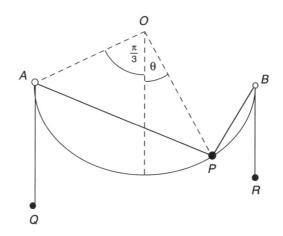

The diagram shows a smooth rigid wire shaped in the form of an arc AB of a circle, centre O and radius a with angle $AOB = \dfrac{2\pi}{3}$. The wire is fixed with the plane AOB vertical, the wire being below the level of the chord AB which is horizontal. A small bead P of mass m is threaded on the wire and has two long inextensible strings attached to it, one string passing through a small smooth ring at A and supporting a particle Q of mass km hanging freely, and the second string passing through a small smooth ring at B and supporting a particle R, also of mass km hanging freely. In a general position the radius to the bead makes an angle θ with the downward vertical at O, the strings being taut and the segments outside the wire vertical. Show that the potential energy of the system is

$$mag \left(2k \cos \frac{\theta}{2} - \cos \theta\right) + \text{constant}$$

Hence, or otherwise, determine the values of θ in the range $-\dfrac{\pi}{3} < \theta < \dfrac{\pi}{3}$ for which equilibrium is possible.

Determine also whether the equilibrium positions are stable or unstable for small displacements of the bead from an equilibrium position in the case $k = 1.8$.

183

6 A uniform rod AB has weight W and length $2a$. The upper end A is attached to a small light ring which can slide on a fixed smooth vertical wire; the end B is attached to a small light ring which can slide on a fixed smooth horizontal wire which intersects the vertical wire at O, below A. One end of a light inextensible string, of length greater than $\frac{3a}{2}$, is attached to the rod at a point C where $BC = \frac{1}{2}a$; the string passes over a small smooth pulley at O and, at its other end, carries a particle of weight $\frac{1}{2}W$ which hangs freely. Show that the potential energy of the system is

$$\tfrac{1}{4}W a \left[4 \cos \theta + (1 + 8 \ \sin^2\theta)^{\frac{1}{2}}\right] + \text{constant}$$

where $\theta \left(0 < \theta < \frac{\pi}{2}\right)$ is the angle OAB.

Show that there is a position of equilibrium in which the rod is inclined to the vertical and determine whether it is stable or unstable.

7 The upper end A of a uniform rod AB of mass m and length $2a$ is freely pivoted to a fixed point. A bead C of mass $\frac{1}{12}m$ slides on a smooth horizontal wire passing through A, the bead being connected to B by a light inextensible string of length $2a$. In a general position the rod makes an angle θ with the downward vertical at A, the string is taut, and B is vertically below the mid-point of AC. Prove that, if the system is in motion, then

$$2a \left(\frac{d\theta}{dt}\right)^2 (1 + \cos^2\theta) = 3g \cos \theta + \text{constant}.$$

(a) Initially the rod is vertical and the system is in motion, the bead having speed $(6ag)^{\frac{1}{2}}$ along the wire. Find the angle turned through by the rod before it first comes to instantaneous rest.

(b) Initially the rod is vertical and the bead is slightly displaced from its equilibrium position and released from rest. Show that the resulting motion is approximately simple harmonic, having period $4\pi \sqrt{\left(\dfrac{2a}{3g}\right)}$.

8 The end A of uniform rod AB of mass m and length $2a$ is freely pivoted to a fixed point. A small bead C of mass $\frac{1}{2}m$ slides on a smooth vertical wire passing through A, the bead being connected to B by a light rod of length $2a$. In a general position the bead is below A and $B\hat{A}C = \theta$. If the system is in motion under gravity only, in a vertical plane, prove that:

$$2a\dot{\theta}^2(1 + 6\sin^2\theta) = 9g\cos\theta + \text{constant}$$

Using this equation, or otherwise, prove the following results.

(a) If the rod AB is released from rest when $\theta = \alpha$, then the stress in the light rod when AB first passes through the vertical position is $\frac{1}{2}mg(19 - 18\cos\alpha)$.

(b) If in (a) α is small, then AB first passes through the vertical position after a time $\frac{1}{3}\pi\sqrt{(a/g)}$ approximately.

9 Two beads of equal mass, free to slide on a smooth vertical circular wire, are joined by a light rod of length $2a\sin\alpha$, where a is the radius of the circle. Show that the period of small oscillations about the stable position of equilibrium is $2\pi\sqrt{(a/g\cos\alpha)}$.

10 A uniform beam AB of mass m can pivot about a horizontal axis through A, and is kept in a horizontal position by the tension of a vertical spring, of natural length l and elastic constant λ, attached to the beam at B. Show that if slightly disturbed from this position, the period of oscillations will be $2\pi\sqrt{(ml/3\lambda)}$.

SUMMARY

You should now know that:

- positions of stable and unstable equilibrium are found by solving the equation $\frac{dV}{d\theta} = 0$, where V is the potential energy of the system.
- if V has a minimum value then the equilibrium is stable
- If V has a maximum value then the equilibrium is unstable
- the period of small oscillations about a position of stable equilibrium $\theta = \theta_0$ is found by substituting $\theta = \theta_0 + \psi$, where ψ is small, into the equation $\frac{dE}{dt} = 0$, where E is the *total* energy of the system. Small approximations should then reduce this equation to $\ddot{\psi} = -\omega^2\psi$ so that the period is $\frac{2\pi}{\omega}$.

Solutions

Section 1

1 (a) $\frac{1}{3}ma^2 + 2m \times a^2 = \frac{7}{3}ma^2$

(b) $\frac{4}{3}ma^2 + 2m \times (2a)^2 = \frac{28}{3}ma^2$

2 (a) $\frac{1}{2}mr^2$

(b) The cylinder is made up of a series of discs, one upon the other, radius r. $\therefore$ MI $= \frac{1}{2}Mr^2$

3 Moment of inertia about an axis through its centre and perpendicular to its plane is Ma^2. The parallel axis theorem gives $Ma^2 + Ma^2 = 2\,Ma^2$.

4 Moment of inertia about an axis through its centre parallel to a side is $\frac{1}{3}Ma^2$.

$\therefore$ Moment of inertia about an axis through its centre perpendicular to the plane of the lamina is $\frac{1}{3}Ma^2 + \frac{1}{3}Ma^2 = \frac{2}{3}Ma^2$.

$\therefore$ Moment of inertia about a parallel axis through a corner is $\frac{2}{3}Ma^2 + M(a\sqrt{2})^2 = \frac{8}{3}Ma^2$.

5 Using symmetry and the perpendicular axis theorem, $Ma^2 = I + I$ $\therefore$ $I = \frac{1}{2}Ma^2$.

6 Use the answer to question 5 and the parallel axis theorem

$\therefore$ MI $= \frac{1}{2}Ma^2 + Ma^2 \Rightarrow$ MI $= \frac{3}{2}Ma^2$

$\Rightarrow$ MI $= M\left(a\sqrt{\frac{3}{2}}\right)^2$

$\therefore$ Radius of gyration is $a\sqrt{\frac{3}{2}}$.

7 Moment of inertia $= \frac{5}{4}Ma^2$
(see earlier example on pp. 8–9)

$\therefore$ MI $= M\left(\frac{\sqrt{5}}{2}a\right)^2$

$\therefore$ Radius of gyration is $\frac{a\sqrt{5}}{2}$.

8 The cube is made up of a series of squares, one upon the other, side $2a$. Using the answer to question 4, the result follows.

9 (a) MI $= \frac{1}{2}mr^2$ $\quad + \quad mr^2$

$\qquad\qquad\quad\uparrow\qquad\qquad\qquad\uparrow$

$\qquad$ standard result $\quad$ parallel axis theorem

$\therefore$ MI $= \frac{3}{2}mr^2$ $\quad \therefore k = r\sqrt{\frac{3}{2}}$.

(b) For a rectangle whose sides are b and c, the moment of inertia about an axis through its centre perpendicular to its plane is

$\frac{1}{3}m\left(\frac{b}{2}\right)^2 + \frac{1}{3}m\left(\frac{c}{2}\right)^2$ or $\frac{m}{12}(b^2 + c^2)$

But the cube is made up of a series of these rectangles, one upon the other.

$\therefore$ MI $= \frac{m}{12}(b^2 + c^2)$ $\therefore$ $k = \sqrt{\frac{b^2 + c^2}{12}}$.

(c)  Let mass of each wire be $\frac{m}{4}$.

Assume the perpendicular axis passes through A.

$\therefore$ required moment of inertia is the sum of the following:

For AB : $\frac{4}{3}\left(\frac{m}{4}\right)a^2 = \frac{m}{3}a^2$

For AD : $\frac{4}{3}\left(\frac{m}{4}\right)a^2 = \frac{m}{3}a^2$

For BC : $\frac{1}{3}\left(\frac{m}{4}\right)a^2 + \frac{m}{4}(5a^2) = \frac{4}{3}ma^2$

(Use the parallel axis theorem here.)

For CD : $\frac{1}{3}\left(\frac{m}{4}\right)a^2 + \frac{m}{4}(5a^2) = \frac{4}{3}ma^2$

$\therefore$ MI $= \frac{m}{3}a^2 + \frac{m}{3}a^2 + \frac{4}{3}ma^2 + \frac{4}{3}ma^2$

$\therefore$ MI $= \frac{10}{3}ma^2$ $\therefore$ $k = a\sqrt{\frac{10}{3}}$.

10 The moment of inertia about the axis through its centre perpendicular to its plane is
$$\tfrac{1}{3} ma^2 + \tfrac{1}{3} ma^2 = \tfrac{2}{3} ma^2.$$

Using symmetry and the perpendicular axes theorem gives the required answer as
$$\tfrac{1}{2} \times \tfrac{2}{3} ma^2 \text{ or } \tfrac{1}{3} ma^2 .$$

11 Required moment of inertia is the sum of the following:

Left hand sphere: $\tfrac{2}{5} (5m)r^2 + (5m)(5r)^2 = 127mr^2$

Uniform rod: $\tfrac{1}{3} (6m)(3r)^2 + (6m)(r)^2 = 24mr^2$

Right hand sphere: $\tfrac{2}{5} (5m) r^2 + (5m)(3r)^2 = 47mr^2$

∴ Total moment of inertia = $198mr^2$

12 $\tfrac{1}{2} mr^2 + M \left(\tfrac{r}{2}\right)^2 = (2m + M) \tfrac{r^2}{4}$

13 For the rod: $\tfrac{4}{3} \left(\tfrac{3m}{2}\right) r^2 = 2mr^2$

For the sphere: $\tfrac{2}{5} (5m) r^2 + (5m)(3r)^2 = 47mr^2$

∴ The total moment of inertia = $49mr^2$ as required.

Section 2

1

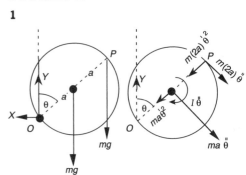

MI of disc about axis through $O = \tfrac{1}{2} ma^2 + ma^2$

MI of particle about axis through $O = m(2a)^2$

∴ Total MI $= 5\tfrac{1}{2} ma^2$

Conservation of energy gives:

$$\tfrac{1}{2} \left(5\tfrac{1}{2} ma^2\right) \dot\theta^2 + mga \cos \theta + mg\, 2a \cos \theta$$
$$= mga + 2mga$$

∴ $11 a\dot\theta^2 = 12g (1 - \cos \theta)$

When P is vertically beneath O

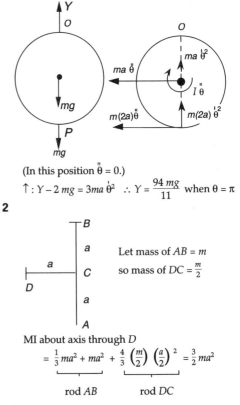

(In this position $\ddot\theta = 0$.)

$\uparrow : Y - 2 mg = 3ma\, \dot\theta^2$ ∴ $Y = \dfrac{94\, mg}{11}$ when $\theta = \pi$

2

Let mass of $AB = m$

so mass of $DC = \dfrac{m}{2}$

MI about axis through D

$$= \underbrace{\tfrac{1}{3} ma^2 + ma^2}_{\text{rod } AB} + \underbrace{\tfrac{4}{3} \left(\tfrac{m}{2}\right) \left(\tfrac{a}{2}\right)^2}_{\text{rod } DC} = \tfrac{3}{2} ma^2$$

Conservation of energy (at $\theta = 0$ and $\theta = \frac{\pi}{2}$)

gives

$0 = \frac{1}{2}\left(\frac{3}{2}ma^2\right)\omega^2 - \left(\frac{m}{2}\right)\left(\frac{ga}{2}\right) - mga$

$\therefore 3a\omega^2 = 5g$

3   Part (a) is 'book work'.

MI $= \frac{1}{3}ml^2 + ml^2 = \frac{4}{3}ml^2$.

(b) MI about axis through A

$= \frac{4}{3}ml^2 + M(2l)^2 = l^2\left(\frac{4m}{3} + 4M\right)$

Conservation of energy gives

$\frac{1}{2} \times l^2\left(\frac{4m}{3} + 4M\right)\omega^2 + 0 = 0 + mgl + Mg \times 2l$

$\therefore \omega^2 = \frac{3(m + 2M)}{2(m + 3M)} \times \frac{g}{l}$

4   MI about axis through axle

$= \frac{1}{2}M(1.2)^2 + M(0.1)^2 = 0.73M$

ω is greatest when centre of mass of disc is vertically beneath the point of suspension.

Conservation of energy gives

$Mg(0.1) = \frac{1}{2}(0.73M)\omega^2 - Mg(0.1)$

$\therefore \omega \approx 2.32$ rad / second

5   Part (a) is 'book work'.

MI $= \frac{1}{2}Ma^2$

(b) MI about axis through centre

$= \frac{1}{2}Ma^2 + m\left(\frac{a}{2}\right)^2 = \left(\frac{M}{2} + \frac{m}{4}\right)a^2$

Maximum ω of $\sqrt{\frac{g}{4a}}$ when particle vertically beneath the point of suspension.

Least ω of $\sqrt{\frac{g}{8a}}$ when particle vertically above the point of suspension.

$\therefore$ Conservation of energy gives:

$\frac{1}{2}\left(\frac{M}{2} + \frac{m}{4}\right)a^2\left(\frac{g}{4a}\right) - mg \times \frac{a}{2}$

$= \frac{1}{2}\left(\frac{M}{2} + \frac{m}{4}\right)a^2\left(\frac{g}{8a}\right) + mg \times \frac{a}{2}$

$\therefore 63\,m = 2M$

6

MI about axis through pivot

$= \frac{1}{3}m(a^2 + b^2) + ma^2$

$= \frac{m}{3}(4a^2 + b^2)$

Conservation of energy gives:

$0 = \frac{1}{2} \times \frac{m}{3}(4a^2 + b^2)\omega^2 - mga$ $\therefore \omega = \sqrt{\frac{6ga}{4a^2 + b^2}}$

7

MI about axis through A

$= \frac{1}{2}ma^2 + ma^2 + \underbrace{\quad}_{\text{disc}}$

$m(2a)^2 = 5\frac{1}{2}ma^2$

$\underbrace{\quad}_{\text{particle}}$

Conservation of energy gives

$O = \frac{1}{2}\left(5\frac{1}{2}ma^2\right)\omega^2 - mga - mg2a$

$\therefore a\omega = \sqrt{\frac{12ga}{11}}$

But speed of $B = 2a\omega$

$\therefore$ Speed of $B = \sqrt{\frac{48ga}{11}}$ or $4\sqrt{\frac{3ga}{11}}$.

8

MI about axis through pivot $=$

$\frac{1}{3}ml^2 + ml^2 = \frac{4}{3}ml^2$

$\underbrace{\quad}_{\text{rod}}$ $\underbrace{\quad}_{\text{particle}}$

Conservation of energy gives

$\frac{1}{2}\left(\frac{4}{3}ml^2\right)\omega^2 - mgl = 0$

$\therefore l\omega = \sqrt{\frac{3gl}{2}}$, the speed of B.

9

MI about axis through centre of disc

$= \frac{1}{2}Ma^2 + ma^2 = \frac{a^2}{2}(M + 2m)$

$\underbrace{\quad}_{\text{disc}}$ $\underbrace{\quad}_{\text{particle}}$

Conservation of energy gives

$mga\cos 60° = \frac{1}{2} \times \frac{a^2}{2}(M + 2m)\omega^2 - mga$

$\therefore \omega = \sqrt{\frac{6\,mg}{a(M + 2m)}}$.

10

MI about axis through centre of disc $=$

$\frac{1}{2}Ma^2 + ma^2 = \frac{a^2}{2}(M + 2m)$

Conservation of energy gives

$\frac{1}{2} \times \frac{a^2}{2}(M + 2m)\omega_1^{\,2} + mga$

$= \frac{1}{2} \times \frac{a^2}{2}(M + 2m)\omega_2^{\,2} - mga$

$\therefore a(M + 2m)(\omega_2^{\,2} - \omega_1^{\,2}) = 8mg$

11

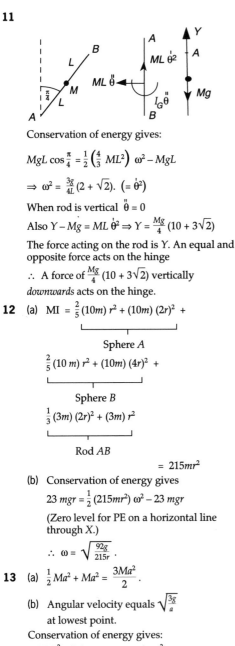

Conservation of energy gives:

$$MgL \cos\frac{\pi}{4} = \frac{1}{2}\left(\frac{4}{3} ML^2\right)\omega^2 - MgL$$

$$\Rightarrow \omega^2 = \frac{3g}{4L}(2 + \sqrt{2}). \ (= \dot\theta^2)$$

When rod is vertical $\ddot\theta = 0$

Also $Y - Mg = ML\dot\theta^2 \Rightarrow Y = \frac{Mg}{4}(10 + 3\sqrt{2})$

The force acting on the rod is Y. An equal and opposite force acts on the hinge

∴ A force of $\frac{Mg}{4}(10 + 3\sqrt{2})$ vertically *downwards* acts on the hinge.

12 (a) MI $= \underbrace{\frac{2}{5}(10m)\, r^2 + (10m)\,(2r)^2\ +}_{\text{Sphere } A}$

$\underbrace{\frac{2}{5}(10\,m)\, r^2 + (10m)\,(4r)^2\ +}_{\text{Sphere } B}$

$\underbrace{\frac{1}{3}(3m)\,(2r)^2 + (3m)\, r^2}_{\text{Rod } AB}$

$= 215mr^2$

(b) Conservation of energy gives

$23\, mgr = \frac{1}{2}(215mr^2)\,\omega^2 - 23\, mgr$

(Zero level for PE on a horizontal line through X.)

∴ $\omega = \sqrt{\dfrac{92g}{215r}}$.

13 (a) $\frac{1}{2} Ma^2 + Ma^2 = \dfrac{3Ma^2}{2}$.

(b) Angular velocity equals $\sqrt{\dfrac{3g}{a}}$ at lowest point.

Conservation of energy gives:

$$\frac{1}{2}\left(\frac{3Ma^2}{2}\right)\left(\frac{3g}{a}\right) - Mga = \frac{1}{2}\left(\frac{3Ma^2}{2}\right)\omega^2 + Mga$$

∴ $\omega = \sqrt{\dfrac{g}{3a}}$.

14 MI about axis through centre of disc

$= \frac{1}{2} m\, 1^2 + (2m)\,(0.5)^2 = m.$

Angular velocity ω is a maximum when the particle is vertically beneath the point of suspension.

Conservation of energy gives

$$\frac{1}{2}(m)\,\omega^2 - 2m \times g \times (0.5) = 0 + (2m) \times g \times (0.5)$$

∴ $\omega = \sqrt{4g} = 2\sqrt{g}$

15 MI about axis through end of rod

$= \frac{4}{3} m\left(\frac{l}{2}\right)^2 = \frac{1}{3} ml^2$

Let ω be the angular velocity at the highest point

∴ $\frac{1}{2}\left(\frac{ml^2}{3}\right)\left(\frac{6g}{l}\right) - mg\frac{l}{2} = \frac{1}{2}\left(\frac{ml^2}{3}\right)\omega^2 + mg\frac{l}{2}$

∴ $\omega = 0$ ∴ Complete circles are *just* described

16

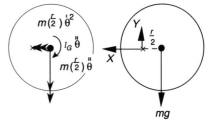

MI of disc about axis $= \frac{1}{2} mr^2 + m\left(\frac{r}{2}\right)^2 = \frac{3}{4} mr^2$

When the centre of mass is in a horizontal line with the pivot we have:

$\downarrow : mg - Y = m\left(\frac{r}{2}\right)\ddot\theta$

$\leftarrow : X = m\left(\frac{r}{2}\right)\dot\theta^2$

pivot$\curvearrowright$: $\left(\frac{3}{4} mr^2\right)\ddot\theta = mg\frac{r}{2}$.

Energy equation: $\frac{1}{2}\left(\frac{3}{4} mr^2\right)\dot\theta^2 = mg\frac{r}{2}$.

∴ $\dot\theta^2 = \frac{4g}{3r} \Rightarrow X = \frac{2}{3} mg$ and $Y = \frac{2}{3} mg$

∴ Magnitude of resultant force

$= \sqrt{X^2 + Y^2} = \frac{2\sqrt{2}}{3} mg$

17

MI about horizontal axis through $P = \frac{1}{2} Ma^2 + Ma^2$

$= \frac{3}{2} Ma^2$

∴ $P\curvearrowleft$: $- Mga \sin\theta = \frac{3}{2} Ma^2\ddot\theta$

Putting $\sin\theta = \theta$ this reduces to $\ddot\theta = \left(\frac{-2g}{3a}\right)\theta$

∴ Period $= 2\pi \sqrt{\dfrac{3a}{2g}}$.

18

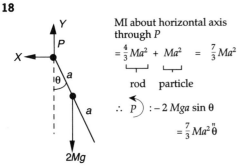

MI about horizontal axis through P

$$= \tfrac{4}{3} Ma^2 + Ma^2 = \tfrac{7}{3} Ma^2$$

rod   particle

$\therefore \curvearrowleft P) : -2\, Mga \sin\theta$

$$= \tfrac{7}{3} Ma^2 \ddot\theta$$

Putting $\sin\theta = \theta$ this reduces to $\ddot\theta = -\left(\tfrac{6g}{7a}\right)\theta$

$\therefore$ Period $= 2\pi \sqrt{\dfrac{7a}{6g}}$

19

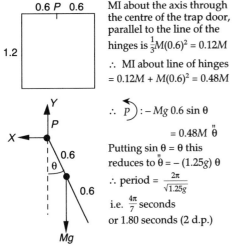

MI about the axis through the centre of the trap door, parallel to the line of the hinges is $\tfrac{1}{3} M (0.6)^2 = 0.12M$

$\therefore$ MI about line of hinges

$= 0.12M + M(0.6)^2 = 0.48M$

$\therefore \curvearrowleft P) : - Mg\, 0.6 \sin\theta$

$$= 0.48M\, \ddot\theta$$

Putting $\sin\theta = \theta$ this reduces to $\ddot\theta = -(1.25g)\,\theta$

$\therefore$ period $= \dfrac{2\pi}{\sqrt{1.25g}}$

i.e. $\tfrac{4\pi}{7}$ seconds

or 1.80 seconds (2 d.p.)

20 MI of system about axis through centre of disc

$$= \tfrac{1}{2} Ma^2 + Ma^2 = \tfrac{3}{2} Ma^2$$

disc   particle

$\therefore \curvearrowleft P) : - Mga \sin\theta = \tfrac{3}{2} Ma^2 \ddot\theta$

Putting $\sin\theta = \theta$ this reduces to $\ddot\theta = -\left(\tfrac{2g}{3a}\right)\theta$

$\therefore$ Period $= 2\pi \sqrt{\dfrac{3a}{2g}}$

But period of a simple pendulum $= 2\pi \sqrt{\dfrac{l}{g}}$

$\therefore l = \dfrac{3a}{2}$, as required.

21 MI of system about horizontal axis through point of suspension

$$= \tfrac{1}{2} Mr^2 + \left(\tfrac{M}{2}\right) r^2 = Mr^2$$

disc   particle

$\therefore \curvearrowleft P) : - \dfrac{Mg}{2} r \sin\theta = Mr^2 \ddot\theta$

Putting $\sin\theta = \theta$ this reduces to $\ddot\theta = -\left(\dfrac{g}{2r}\right)\theta$

$\therefore$ Period $= 2\pi \sqrt{\dfrac{2r}{g}}$

22 MI of system about horizontal axis through centre

$$= (2)(0.3)^2 + (0.03)(0.3)^2 = 0.1827$$

Wheel   particle

[Remember: the moment of inertia of a circular *ring* about the central axis perpendicular to its plane is ma^2 – it needs to be a solid *disc* before it becomes $\tfrac{1}{2} ma^2$.]

$\therefore \curvearrowleft P) : - 0.03g \times 0.3 \sin\theta$

$$= 0.1827\, \ddot\theta$$

Putting $\sin\theta = \theta$ this reduces to $\ddot\theta = -(0.4828)\,\theta$

$\therefore$ Period $= \dfrac{2\pi}{\sqrt{0.4828}}$

or 9 seconds

23 (a) MI $= \tfrac{4}{3} M \left(\tfrac{3L}{2}\right)^2 + \tfrac{1}{2}(5M)L^2 + (5M)(3L)^2$

rod   disc

$$= 50.5\, ML^2$$

(b)

$\therefore \curvearrowleft O) : - Mg \times \dfrac{3L}{2} \sin\theta - 5\, Mg \times 3L \sin\theta$

$$= 50.5\, ML^2 \ddot\theta$$

Putting $\sin\theta = \theta$ this reduces to $\ddot\theta = -\left(\dfrac{33g}{101L}\right)\theta$

$\therefore$ Period $= 2\pi \sqrt{\dfrac{101L}{33g}}$.

24 $\text{MI} = \frac{4}{3} m (6r)^2 + \frac{1}{2}(2m)(2r)^2 + (2m)(9r)^2$

       ⎣———┬———⎦ ⎣————————┬————————⎦
           rod   disc

                       $= 214\, mr^2$

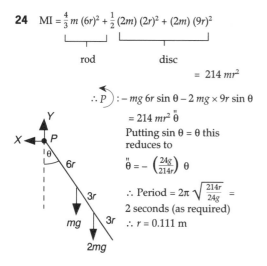

$\therefore \overset{\curvearrowleft}{P} : -mg\,6r \sin\theta - 2\,mg \times 9r \sin\theta$

           $= 214\, mr^2\, \ddot{\theta}$

Putting $\sin\theta = \theta$ this reduces to

           $\ddot{\theta} = -\left(\frac{24g}{214r}\right)\theta$

$\therefore$ Period $= 2\pi \sqrt{\dfrac{214r}{24g}} =$
2 seconds (as required)

$\therefore r = 0.111$ m

$\therefore$ The pendulum is 1.34 m long and the disc has a radius of 22.3 cm.

Affecting factors might include:

- Central bar will not be thin but will have a width. A rectangular lamina might have been more realistic.

- Bolts connecting the bar and disc have been ignored.

- The point of suspension will not be perfectly smooth. The consequent frictional couple has been ignored.

No doubt you can think of some more.

25   Conservation of energy: $mga = \frac{1}{2}\left(\frac{4}{3}ma^2\right)\omega^2$

$\therefore \ \omega = \sqrt{\dfrac{3g}{2a}}$

$\overset{\curvearrowleft}{A} : \left(\frac{4}{3}ma^2\right)\omega = I \times 2a \ \therefore I = m\sqrt{\dfrac{2ga}{3}}$,
the impulse required.

26   Conservation of energy to find angular velocity ω before impact:

$\frac{1}{2}\left(\frac{4}{3}ma^2\right)\omega^2 - mga = 0 \ \therefore \ \omega = \sqrt{\dfrac{3g}{2a}}$.

Let ω' be the angular velocity after impact *in the same direction as* ω.

$\overset{\curvearrowleft}{\text{end}} : \left(\frac{4}{3}ma^2\right)\omega' - \left(\frac{4}{3}ma^2\right)\omega = Ia$, where I is the impulse.

But $\omega' = -\frac{\omega}{2} \ \therefore I = m\sqrt{6\,ga}$ as required

27   Let I be the impulse and ω the initial angular velocity. For simplicity let $l = 2a$.

$\overset{\curvearrowleft}{\text{end}} : I \times 2a = \left(\frac{4}{3}ma^2\right)\omega \ \Rightarrow \ I = \frac{2\,ma\omega}{3}$

Then conservation of energy

$\frac{1}{2}\left(\frac{4}{3}ma^2\right)\omega^2 - mga = 0 + mga \Rightarrow a\omega^2 = 3g$

Eliminate ω to get $I = m\sqrt{\dfrac{4ga}{3}}$

$\therefore$ The impulse is $m\sqrt{\dfrac{2gl}{3}}$.

28   Let I be the impulse and ω the initial angular velocity.

$\overset{\curvearrowleft}{A} : I \times 2a = \left(\frac{3}{2}Ma^2\right)\omega \Rightarrow I = \frac{3Ma\omega}{4}$

Then conservation of energy

$\frac{1}{2}\left(\frac{3}{2}Ma^2\right)\omega^2 - Mga = -\dfrac{Mga}{2} \Rightarrow \omega^2 = \dfrac{2g}{3a}$.

Eliminate ω to get $I = M\sqrt{\dfrac{3ga}{8}}$ or $\dfrac{M}{2}\sqrt{\dfrac{3ga}{2}}$.

29   Set up the three separate diagrams

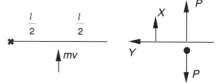

MOMENTUM BEFORE   IMPULSES

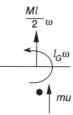

MOMENTUM AFTER

(X, Y are the impulsive reactions at the hinge. P represents the impulse on the rod and the equal and opposite impulse on the particle. ω is the angular velocity of the rod and u the velocity of the particle after impact.)

For the particle: $mu - mv = -P$ ... ①

The velocity of the centre is $\frac{l}{2}\omega$.

$\therefore$ Newton's law gives: $\dfrac{l\omega}{2} - u = \dfrac{-1}{2}(0 - v)$

$\Rightarrow \dfrac{l\omega}{2} - u = \frac{1}{2}\,v$ ... ②

Moments about the hinge for the gate gives:

$$\overset{\curvearrowleft}{\text{hinge}}): \left(\tfrac{1}{8}ml^2\right)\omega - 0 = \tfrac{Pl}{2} \qquad \dots \text{③}$$

Solve equations ①, ② and ③ to get $\omega = \dfrac{2v}{l}$

and $u = \dfrac{v}{2}$.

$\therefore$ Angular velocity is $\dfrac{2v}{l}$ and the speed of the

particle is $\dfrac{v}{2}$.

30 $\overset{\curvearrowleft}{A}): Px = \left(\tfrac{4}{3}Ma^2\right)\omega + mb^2\omega$

$\Rightarrow \omega = \dfrac{3Px}{4Ma^2 + 3mb^2}$

31 Conservation of energy: $mga = \tfrac{1}{2}\left(\tfrac{4}{3}ma^2\right)\omega^2$

$\Rightarrow 2a\omega^2 = 3g.$

$\overset{\curvearrowleft}{A}): \left(\tfrac{4}{3}ma^2\right)\omega = Pb$

Eliminate ω and get $P = \dfrac{2ma}{b}\sqrt{\tfrac{2}{3}ga}$ as required.

32 A useful summary:

Quantity	Units
MI	$J\,s^2$
Angular momentum	$J\,s$
Energy	J
Work done	$J\,s^{-1}$

Section 3

1 (a) $m\dfrac{dv}{dt} = mg - kv^2$. Putting $mg = kV^2$ this

becomes $\dfrac{V^2}{g}\dfrac{dv}{dt} = V^2 - v^2$

$\therefore \dfrac{dv}{V^2 - v^2} = \dfrac{g}{V^2}\,dt$

$\therefore \dfrac{1}{2V}\ln\left(\dfrac{V+v}{V-v}\right) = \dfrac{gt}{V^2}\;(c = 0)$

$\therefore t = \dfrac{V}{2g}\ln\left(\dfrac{V+v}{V-v}\right)$

(b) $\dfrac{V^2}{g} \times v\dfrac{dv}{ds} = V^2 - v^2$

$\therefore \dfrac{v\,dv}{V^2 - v^2} = \dfrac{g}{V^2}\,ds$

$\therefore -\tfrac{1}{2}\ln(V^2 - v^2) = \dfrac{g}{V^2}s - \tfrac{1}{2}\ln V^2$

$\therefore s = \dfrac{V^2}{2g}\ln\left(\dfrac{V^2}{V^2 - v^2}\right)$.

2 $-mv\dfrac{dv}{dx} = mg\dfrac{v^2}{k^2} + mg \quad \therefore \dfrac{-v\,dv}{g + \frac{gv^2}{k^2}} = dx$

$\therefore \dfrac{-k^2}{2g}\ln\left(g + \dfrac{gv^2}{k^2}\right) = x - \dfrac{k^2}{2g}\ln\left(g + \dfrac{gu^2}{k^2}\right)$

And $v = 0 \Rightarrow x = \dfrac{k^2}{2g}\ln\left(1 + \dfrac{u^2}{k^2}\right)$

3 $\dfrac{dv}{dt} = A - 0.1v$

$\Rightarrow -10\ln(A - 0.1v) = t - 10\ln A$

$\Rightarrow v = 10A(1 - e^{-0.1t})$

But $v = 3$ when $t = 10 \Rightarrow A = 0.475$ (3 d.p.)

$\therefore \dfrac{dx}{dt} = 4.75(1 - e^{-0.1t})$

$\Rightarrow x = 4.75(t + 10e^{-0.1t}) - 47.5$

$\therefore t = 10 \Rightarrow x = 17.5$ (3 s.f.) as required.

4 $g - kv = \dfrac{dv}{dt} \Rightarrow -\dfrac{1}{k}\ln(g - kv) = t - \dfrac{1}{k}\ln g$

$\Rightarrow v = \dfrac{g}{k}(1 - e^{-kt}) \le \dfrac{g}{k}$ as required.

5 $-\dfrac{dv}{dt} = g + \dfrac{gv^2}{k^2} \Rightarrow \dfrac{dv}{1 + \frac{v^2}{k^2}} = -g\,dt$

$\Rightarrow k\tan^{-1}\dfrac{v}{k} = -gt + k\tan^{-1}\dfrac{U}{k}$

$\therefore v = 0 \Rightarrow t = \dfrac{k}{g}\tan^{-1}\dfrac{U}{k}$ as required.

6 $mg - mkv^2 = mv \dfrac{dv}{dx} \Rightarrow \dfrac{v\,dv}{g - kv^2} = dx$

$\Rightarrow -\dfrac{1}{2k} \ln(g - kv^2) = x - \dfrac{1}{2k} \ln g$

$\Rightarrow \ln\left(\dfrac{g - kv^2}{g}\right) = -2kx$

$\Rightarrow kv^2 = g(1 - e^{-2kx})$

Then put $v = V$ and $x = h$.

7 $\uparrow : -mv \dfrac{dv}{dx} = mg + mkv^2 \Rightarrow x = \dfrac{1}{2k} \ln$

$\left(\dfrac{g + kV^2}{g + kv^2}\right)$

$\therefore v = 0 \Rightarrow x = \dfrac{1}{2k} \ln\left(1 + \dfrac{kV^2}{g}\right)$, the greatest

height

$\downarrow : mv \dfrac{dv}{dx} = mg - mkv^2 \Rightarrow x = \dfrac{1}{2k} \ln\left(\dfrac{g}{g - kv^2}\right)$

But $v = V_1$ when $x = \dfrac{1}{2k} \ln\left(1 + \dfrac{kV^2}{g}\right)$

$\Rightarrow \dfrac{1}{2k} \ln\left(1 + \dfrac{kV^2}{g}\right) = \dfrac{1}{2k} \ln\left(\dfrac{g}{g - kV_1^{\,2}}\right)$

$\Rightarrow 1 + \dfrac{kV^2}{g} = \dfrac{g}{g - kV_1^{\,2}}$

$\Rightarrow \left(1 + \dfrac{kV^2}{g}\right)\left(1 - \dfrac{kV_1^{\,2}}{g}\right) = 1$, which leads to

the required result

8 Let tractive force of engine $= F$ N

$\therefore F - 10v^2 = 1000 \dfrac{v\,dv}{dx}$ and $Fv = 12000$

Eliminate F to get $dx = \dfrac{100 \, v^2 \, dv}{1200 - v^3}$

$\Rightarrow [x]_0^x = -\dfrac{100}{3} \left[\ln(1200 - v^3) \right]_5^{10}$

$\Rightarrow x = 56.1 \Rightarrow$ distance covered ≈ 56 m.

9 $\dfrac{m\,dv}{dt} = -mkv - mg$

$\Rightarrow \dfrac{dv}{dt} = -kv - g$

$\Rightarrow \dfrac{1}{k} \ln(kv + g) = -t + \dfrac{1}{k} \ln(ku + g)$

$\Rightarrow t = \dfrac{1}{k} \ln\left(\dfrac{ku + g}{kv + g}\right)$

$\therefore \quad v = 0 \Rightarrow$ required time $= \dfrac{1}{k} \ln\left(\dfrac{ku + g}{g}\right)$

10 $mg - mkv^2 = mv \dfrac{dv}{dx} \Rightarrow g - kv^2 = v \dfrac{dv}{dx}$

$\Rightarrow x = -\dfrac{1}{2k} \ln(g - kv^2) + \dfrac{1}{2k} \ln(g - kU^2)$

$\Rightarrow x = \dfrac{1}{2k} \ln\left(\dfrac{g - kU^2}{g - kv^2}\right)$

11 $mv \dfrac{dv}{dx} = mg - mkv^2 \Rightarrow \dfrac{v\,dv}{g - kv^2} = dx$

$\Rightarrow \dfrac{-1}{2k} \ln(g - kv^2) = x - \dfrac{1}{2k} \ln g$

$\Rightarrow kv^2 = g(1 - e^{-2kx})$

Hits ground with speed V having fallen a
distance h

$\therefore kV^2 = g(1 - e^{-2kh})$ ... ①

Rebounds with speed eV or $\dfrac{V}{\sqrt{2}}$

Then $-m v \dfrac{dv}{dx} = mg + mkv^2 \Rightarrow \dfrac{-v\,dv}{g + kv^2} = dx$

$\Rightarrow -\dfrac{1}{2k} \ln(g + kv^2) = x - \dfrac{1}{2k} \ln\left(g + \dfrac{kV^2}{2}\right)$

and $v = 0 \Rightarrow$ maximum height $H = \dfrac{1}{2k} \ln\left(\dfrac{g + \dfrac{kV^2}{2}}{g}\right)$

Now substitute for V from equation ①

$\Rightarrow$ maximum height $= \dfrac{1}{2k} \ln\left(\dfrac{3 - e^{-2kh}}{2}\right)$

12 Auxiliary equation has repeated roots of -2

$\therefore x = (At + B) e^{-2t}$

$t = 0, x = a \qquad \Rightarrow B = a$

$t = 0, \dfrac{dx}{dt} = 0 \Rightarrow A - 2B = 0 \Rightarrow A = 2a$

$\therefore x = a(2t + 1) e^{-2t}$

$\therefore \dfrac{dx}{dt} = -4at \, e^{-2t}$ (Differentiate x as a product)

$\therefore \dfrac{d^2x}{dt^2} = 4a(2t - 1) e^{-2t}$

(Differentiate $\dfrac{dx}{dt}$ as a product)

$\therefore \dfrac{d^2x}{dt^2} = 0 \Rightarrow t = \dfrac{1}{2} \Rightarrow \dfrac{dx}{dt} = -2ae^{-1}$

$\therefore$ greatest speed is $2ae^{-1}$

$\Big[$To check that it is the greatest, a sketch of the
graph of $\dfrac{dx}{dt}$ against t is helpful.

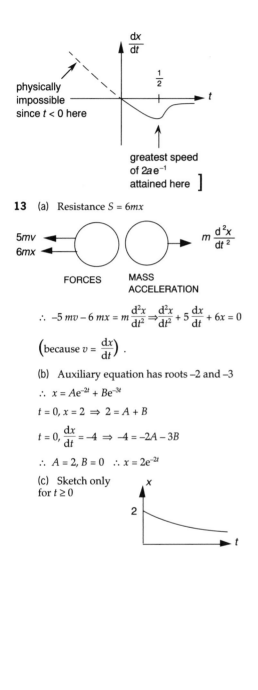

physically impossible since $t < 0$ here

$\dfrac{1}{2}$

greatest speed of $2ae^{-1}$ attained here]

13 (a) Resistance $S = 6mx$

$5mv$

$6mx$

$m\dfrac{d^2x}{dt^2}$

FORCES   MASS ACCELERATION

$\therefore \; -5\,mv - 6\,mx = m\dfrac{d^2x}{dt^2} \Rightarrow \dfrac{d^2x}{dt^2} + 5\dfrac{dx}{dt} + 6x = 0$

$\left(\text{because } v = \dfrac{dx}{dt}\right)$.

(b) Auxiliary equation has roots -2 and -3

$\therefore \; x = Ae^{-2t} + Be^{-3t}$

$t = 0,\ x = 2 \Rightarrow 2 = A + B$

$t = 0,\ \dfrac{dx}{dt} = -4 \Rightarrow -4 = -2A - 3B$

$\therefore \; A = 2,\ B = 0 \quad \therefore \; x = 2e^{-2t}$

(c) Sketch only for $t \geq 0$

x

2

t

14 (a) Extension is $\dfrac{2L}{3}$ when in equilibrium

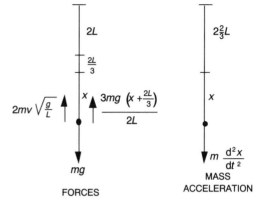

$2L$

$\dfrac{2L}{3}$

$2mv\sqrt{\dfrac{g}{L}}$

x

$3mg\left(x + \dfrac{2L}{3}\right)$ over $2L$

mg

FORCES

$2\tfrac{2}{3}L$

x

$m\dfrac{d^2x}{dt^2}$

MASS ACCELERATION

$\left[\text{Tension} = \dfrac{3\,mg\left(x + \dfrac{2L}{3}\right)}{2L}\right.$

Mass acceleration must be in the direction of x increasing. The resistance of $2mv\sqrt{\dfrac{g}{L}}$ acts in the opposite direction.]

$\therefore \; mg - 2mv\sqrt{\dfrac{g}{L}} - \dfrac{3mg\left(x + \dfrac{2L}{3}\right)}{2L} = m\dfrac{d^2x}{dt^2}$

$\therefore \; \dfrac{d^2x}{dt^2} + 2\sqrt{\left(\dfrac{g}{L}\right)}\dfrac{dx}{dt} + \dfrac{3}{2}\left(\dfrac{g}{L}\right)x = 0$

(b) The equation ① is of the form

$\dfrac{d^2x}{dt^2} + \omega^2 x + 2\lambda\dfrac{dx}{dt} = 0$

with $\lambda = \sqrt{\dfrac{g}{L}}$ and $\omega^2 = \dfrac{3}{2}\left(\dfrac{g}{L}\right)$ and therefore represents damped harmonic motion.

(c) The auxiliary equation has roots

$-\sqrt{\dfrac{g}{L}} \pm i\sqrt{\dfrac{g}{2L}}$

$\therefore \; x =$

$e^{-\left(\sqrt{\tfrac{g}{L}}\right)t}\left(A\cos\left(\sqrt{\dfrac{g}{2L}}\right)t + B\sin\left(\sqrt{\dfrac{g}{2L}}\right)t\right)$

$\Rightarrow a = \sqrt{\dfrac{g}{L}}$ and $b = \sqrt{\dfrac{g}{2L}}$

(d) $t = 0,\ x = L,\ \dfrac{dx}{dt} = 0$

$\Rightarrow x = Le^{-at}\left(\cos bt + \sqrt{2}\sin bt\right)$

195

or $L\sqrt{3}e^{-at}\cos{(bt-0.96)}$

Minimum x when $bt-0.96 = \pi$ or $t = \dfrac{4.10}{b}$

$\Rightarrow$ minimum $x = -0.005\,L$

$\therefore \ x + \dfrac{2L}{3} > 0$

$\therefore$ Tension > 0

$\therefore$ String never goes slack.

15

2 sin t 1 y

$\vdash - - - - \vdash \hspace{2em} \vdash \hspace{2em} \vdash$
O A B P

Let $OP = x \ \therefore \ x = 2\sin t + 1 + y$

$\therefore \ \dfrac{d^2x}{dt^2} = -2\sin t + \dfrac{d^2y}{dt^2}$

Only force acting is the resisting tension of $2y$

$\therefore \ -2y = 0.5\,\dfrac{d^2x}{dt^2}$

$\therefore \ -2y = 0.5\left(-2\sin t + \dfrac{d^2y}{dt^2}\right)$

$\therefore \ \dfrac{d^2y}{dt^2} + 4y = 2\sin t.$

(a) The auxiliary equation has roots $\pm 2i$

$\therefore$ Complementary function is
$$A\cos 2t + B\sin 2t$$

A particular solution is $\dfrac{2}{3}\sin t$

$\therefore$ General solution
$$y = A\cos 2t + B\sin 2t + \dfrac{2}{3}\sin t$$

$t = 0,\ y = 0 \Rightarrow 0 = A$

$t = 0,\ \dfrac{dy}{dt} = -2 \Rightarrow -2 = 2B + \dfrac{2}{3} \Rightarrow B = -\dfrac{4}{3}$

$\therefore \ y = -\dfrac{4}{3}\sin 2t + \dfrac{2}{3}\sin t,$ as required.

(b) $y = 0 \Rightarrow \sin t = 2\sin 2t$

$\Rightarrow \sin t = 4\sin t\cos t \Rightarrow \cos t = \dfrac{1}{4}$

$\Rightarrow t = 1.32$

$\therefore$ Returns to natural length after 1.32 seconds.

16 (a)

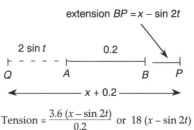

extension $BP = x - \sin 2t$

Tension $= \dfrac{3.6\,(x - \sin 2t)}{0.2}$ or $18\,(x - \sin 2t)$

This is the only force acting. It is against the motion.

$\therefore \ -18\,(x - \sin 2t) = 2\,\dfrac{d^2x}{dt^2}$

$\therefore \ \dfrac{d^2x}{dt^2} + 9x = 9\sin 2t$

(b) Auxiliary equation has roots $\pm 3i$

$\therefore$ Complementary function is $A\cos 3t + B\sin 3t$

A particular solution is $1.8\sin 2t$

$\therefore$ General solution is
$$x = A\cos 3t + B\sin 3t + 1.8\sin 2t$$

$t = 0,\ x = 0 \quad \Rightarrow 0 = A$

$t = 0,\ \dfrac{dx}{dt} = 0 \ \Rightarrow 0 = 3B + 3.6 \ \Rightarrow B = -1.2$

$\therefore \ x = -1.2\sin 3t + 1.8\sin 2t$

$\therefore$ Instantaneous rest $\Rightarrow \dfrac{dx}{dt} = 0$

$\Rightarrow -3.6\cos 3t + 3.6\cos 2t = 0$

$\Rightarrow \cos 3t = \cos 2t$

$\Rightarrow 3t = 2\pi - 2t$

$\Rightarrow t = \dfrac{2\pi}{5}$

$\therefore$ Instantaneous rest again after $\dfrac{2\pi}{5}$ seconds.

17 (a) The auxiliary equation has roots $\pm 2i$

$\therefore$ Complementary function is
$$A\cos 2t + B\sin 2t$$

For the particular solution try $x = at\sin 2t$.
This gives $a = \dfrac{3}{2}$

$\therefore$ General solution is
$$x = A\cos 2t + B\sin 2t + \dfrac{3}{2}t\sin 2t.$$

(b) In 'normal' SHM, the particle will oscillate symmetrically about the centre. In this case the oscillations will get bigger.

18 (a) $\dfrac{dr}{dt} = \lambda \Rightarrow r = \lambda t + c$.

But $r = a$ when $t = 0 \Rightarrow r = \lambda t + a$.

(b)

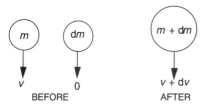

BEFORE   AFTER

$\therefore (m + dm)(v + dv) - mv = (m + dm) g \times dt$

This reduces to $m \dfrac{dv}{dt} + v \dfrac{dm}{dt} = mg$

$\therefore \dfrac{d}{dt}(mv) = mg$

If k is the density of the spherical raindrop then

$m = \dfrac{4}{3}\pi r^3 k \Rightarrow m = \dfrac{4}{3}\pi (\lambda t + a)^3 \, k$

Substitute in the differential equation to get

$\dfrac{d}{dt}\left(\dfrac{4}{3}\pi (\lambda t + a)^3 k \times v\right) = \dfrac{4}{3}\pi (\lambda t + a)^3 \, kg$

$\Rightarrow \dfrac{d}{dt}\left((\lambda t + a)^3 v\right) = (\lambda t + a)^3 g$, as required

$\Rightarrow (\lambda t + a)^3 v = \dfrac{(\lambda t + a)^4 g}{4\lambda} + c$

But $v = 0$ when $t = 0$

$\Rightarrow (\lambda t + a)^3 v = \dfrac{(\lambda t + a)^4 g}{4\lambda} - \dfrac{a^4 g}{4\lambda}$

$\Rightarrow v = \dfrac{(\lambda t + a)g}{4\lambda} - \dfrac{a^4 g}{4\lambda}(\lambda t + a)^{-3}$

19 (a) $\dfrac{dm}{dt} = -\lambda \Rightarrow m = -\lambda t + c$.

But $m = M$ when $t = 0$

$\therefore m = M - \lambda t$

(b)

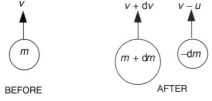

BEFORE   AFTER

$\therefore (m + dm)(v + dv) - dm (v - u) - mv$
$= -(m + dm) \times g \, dt$

$\Rightarrow m\dfrac{dv}{dt} + u\dfrac{dm}{dt} = -mg$

Now replace m by $M - \lambda t$

$\therefore (M - \lambda t)\dfrac{dv}{dt} - \lambda u = -(M - \lambda t) g$

$\Rightarrow \dfrac{dv}{dt} = \dfrac{\lambda u}{M - \lambda t} - g$, as required.

Initially $\dfrac{dv}{dt} = \dfrac{\lambda u}{M} - g$ and this must be positive in order to leave the ground $\therefore \lambda u > Mg$.

Integrate the differential equation to give

$v = -u \ln (M - \lambda t) - gt + c$

But $v = 0$ when $t = 0$

$\therefore v = -u \ln (M - \lambda t) - gt + u \ln M$

$\Rightarrow v = -u \ln \left(1 - \dfrac{\lambda t}{M}\right) - gt$, as required.

Now replace v by $\dfrac{dx}{dt}$

$\therefore \dfrac{dx}{dt} = -u \ln \left(1 - \dfrac{\lambda t}{M}\right) - gt$

$\Rightarrow x = -u\left[t \times \ln\left(1 - \dfrac{\lambda t}{M}\right) - t - \dfrac{M}{\lambda}\ln\left(1 - \dfrac{\lambda t}{M}\right)\right]$
$\qquad - \dfrac{gt^2}{2} + c$

(Using integration by parts.)

But $x = 0$ when $t = 0 \Rightarrow c = 0$

When $m = \dfrac{M}{2} \Rightarrow t = \dfrac{M}{2\lambda}$

$\Rightarrow x = -u\left[\dfrac{M}{2\lambda}\ln\dfrac{1}{2} - \dfrac{M}{2\lambda} - \dfrac{M}{\lambda}\ln\dfrac{1}{2}\right] - \dfrac{gM^2}{8\lambda^2}$

$\Rightarrow x = \dfrac{uM}{2\lambda}\left[1 - \ln 2 - \dfrac{Mg}{4\lambda u}\right]$, as required.

20

$$
\begin{array}{ccc}
\uparrow v & \uparrow v + dv & \uparrow v - u \\
\bigcirc m & \bigcirc m + dm & \bigcirc -dm \\
\text{BEFORE} & \text{AFTER} &
\end{array}
$$

$\therefore (m + dm)(v + dv) - dm (v - u) - mv$
$\qquad\qquad = -(m + dm) g \times dt$

$\Rightarrow m\dfrac{dv}{dt} + u\dfrac{dm}{dt} = -mg$

But $m = M(1 - kt)$ and $\dfrac{dm}{dt} = - Mk$

$\therefore \ M(1 - kt) \dfrac{dv}{dt} - Mku = - M(1 - kt)\,g$

$\Rightarrow (1 - kt) \dfrac{dv}{dt} = ku - g(1 - kt)$, as required

$\Rightarrow \dfrac{dv}{dt} = \dfrac{ku}{1 - kt} - g$

$\Rightarrow v = - u \ln \,(1 - kt) - gt$

$\qquad$ (when $t = 0,\ v = 0$)

21 $\quad m\dfrac{dv}{dt} + v\dfrac{dm}{dt} = mg$ $\ $ (See question 18(b))

$\therefore \ \dfrac{d}{dt}(mv) = \ mg$

Now put $m = \dfrac{4}{3}\pi r^3 k$

$\therefore \ \dfrac{d}{dt}(r^3 v) = + r^3 g$

But $\dfrac{dr}{dt} = \lambda r \ \Rightarrow \ \ln r = \lambda t + c \ \Rightarrow \ r = Ae^{\lambda t}$

$\therefore \ \dfrac{d}{dt}\left(A^3 e^{3\lambda t} v\right) = + A^3 e^{3\lambda t}\, g$

$\therefore \ \dfrac{d}{dt}\left(e^{3\lambda t} v\right) = e^{3\lambda t}\, g$

$\therefore \ e^{3\lambda t} v = \dfrac{e^{3\lambda t} g}{3\lambda} + c$

But $v = 0$ when $t = 0$

$\therefore \ e^{3\lambda t} v = \dfrac{e^{3\lambda t} g}{3\lambda} - \dfrac{g}{3\lambda}$

$\therefore \ v = \dfrac{g}{3\lambda}\left(1 - e^{-3\lambda t}\right)$

$\therefore \ v \rightarrow \dfrac{g}{3\lambda}$ as $t \rightarrow \infty$

22 $\quad$ Let mass at time t be n

$\qquad$ BEFORE $\qquad\qquad\qquad$ AFTER

$\therefore \ (n + dn)(v + dv) - dn\,(v - V) - nv = - kv \times dt$

$\Rightarrow \ n\dfrac{dv}{dt} + V\dfrac{dn}{dt} = - kv$

But $\dfrac{dn}{dt} = -m \ \Rightarrow \ n = - mt + M$

$\therefore \ (- mt + M)\dfrac{dv}{dt} + V\,(-m) = - kv$

$\Rightarrow \dfrac{dv}{dt} = \dfrac{Vm - kv}{M - mt}$, as required

$\therefore \ \dfrac{dv}{Vm - kv} = \dfrac{dt}{M - mt}$

$\Rightarrow \dfrac{-1}{k}\ln(Vm - kv) = \dfrac{-1}{m}\ln(M - mt) + c$

But $v = 0$ when $t = 0$

$\therefore \ -\dfrac{1}{k}\ln(Vm - kv)$

$\qquad = \dfrac{-1}{m}\ln(M - mt) - \dfrac{1}{k}\ln Vm + \dfrac{1}{m}\ln M$

$\Rightarrow \dfrac{1}{k}\ln\left(1 - \dfrac{kv}{Vm}\right) = \dfrac{1}{m}\ln\left(1 - \dfrac{mt}{M}\right)$

$\Rightarrow 1 - \dfrac{kv}{Vm} = \left(1 - \dfrac{mt}{M}\right)^{\frac{k}{m}}$

$\Rightarrow v = \dfrac{Vm}{k}\left[1 - \left(1 - \dfrac{mt}{M}\right)^{\frac{k}{m}}\right]$, as required.

Section 4

1 Before impact:

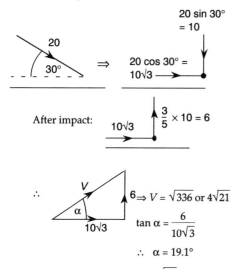

20 sin 30°
= 10

20

30° ⟹ 20 cos 30° =
10√3 →

After impact:

10√3 ↑ $\frac{3}{5} \times 10 = 6$

∴ V
6 ⟹ $V = \sqrt{336}$ or $4\sqrt{21}$

α

10√3 $\tan \alpha = \frac{6}{10\sqrt{3}}$

∴ $\alpha = 19.1°$

∴ Velocity after impact is $4\sqrt{21}$ m s⁻¹ at 19.1° to the plane.

2 Before impact:

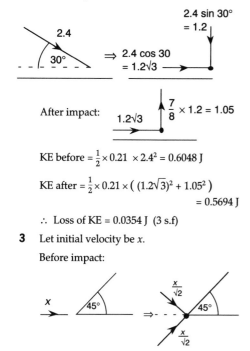

2.4 sin 30°
= 1.2

2.4

30° ⟹ 2.4 cos 30
= 1.2√3 →

After impact:

1.2√3 ↑ $\frac{7}{8} \times 1.2 = 1.05$

KE before $= \frac{1}{2} \times 0.21 \times 2.4^2 = 0.6048$ J

KE after $= \frac{1}{2} \times 0.21 \times \left((1.2\sqrt{3})^2 + 1.05^2 \right)$
$= 0.5694$ J

∴ Loss of KE = 0.0354 J (3 s.f)

3 Let initial velocity be x.

Before impact:

x 45° ⟹ $\frac{x}{\sqrt{2}}$ ╱ 45°
$\frac{x}{\sqrt{2}}$

After impact $\frac{1}{2} \times \frac{x}{\sqrt{2}} = \frac{x}{2\sqrt{2}}$

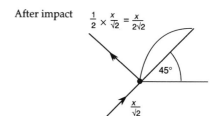

45°

$\frac{x}{\sqrt{2}}$

Now we have the flight of a projectile. Time to reach 'maximum height' (furthest distance from the plane) is given by:

$$u = \frac{x}{2\sqrt{2}}, \ v = 0, \ a = -\frac{g}{\sqrt{2}}$$

$$\Rightarrow 0 = \frac{x}{2\sqrt{2}} - \frac{gt}{\sqrt{2}} \Rightarrow t = \frac{x}{2g}$$

∴ Time before it hits plane again is

$$2 \times \frac{x}{2g} \ \text{ i.e. } \ \frac{x}{g}.$$

Now parallel to the plane:

$$u = \frac{x}{\sqrt{2}}, \ a = \frac{-g}{\sqrt{2}}, \ t = \frac{x}{g} \Rightarrow v = \frac{x}{\sqrt{2}} - \frac{g}{\sqrt{2}} \times \frac{x}{g}$$
$$\Rightarrow v = 0$$

∴ No parallel component of velocity when the particle hits the plane.

∴ Particle hits the plane at right angles.

4

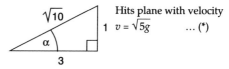

√10

1 α

3

Hits plane with velocity
$v = \sqrt{5g}$ ... (*)

Before impact

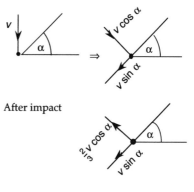

v ↓ α ⟹ $v \cos \alpha$ α
$v \sin \alpha$

After impact

$\frac{2}{3} v \cos \alpha$ α
$v \sin \alpha$

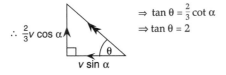

$\Rightarrow \tan\theta = \frac{2}{3}\cot\alpha$

$\Rightarrow \tan\theta = 2$

$\therefore \frac{2}{3}v\cos\alpha$

$v\sin\alpha$

$\therefore$ Angle with horizontal $= \theta - \alpha$

$= \tan^{-1} 2 - \tan^{-1}\frac{1}{3} = 45°.$

In order to cope with the projectile, find the vertical and horizontal component of the initial velocity first of all.

Vertical component $= \frac{2}{3}v\cos^2\alpha - v\sin^2\alpha$

$= \frac{2}{3}v\times\frac{9}{10} - v\times\frac{1}{10} = \frac{v}{2}.$

Horizontal component

$= \frac{2}{3}v\cos\alpha\sin\alpha + v\sin\alpha\cos\alpha$

$= \frac{5}{3}v\sin\alpha\cos\alpha = \frac{v}{2}.$

$\therefore$ We have

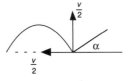

Reaches maximum height at time t where

$0 = \frac{v}{2} - gt$ i.e. $t = \frac{v}{2g}$

$\therefore$ time before it lands again $= 2\times\frac{v}{2g}$ i.e. $\frac{v}{g}$

$\therefore$ Range of first bounce $= \frac{v}{2}\times\frac{v}{g} = \frac{v^2}{2g} = 2.5.$

(Using *)

$\therefore$ Required distance is 2.5 m.

5

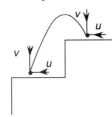

Let the components of velocity before the first impact be u and v. In order that each bounce is the same, the separate components before impact at the next bounce must also be u and v.

After the first bounce we have

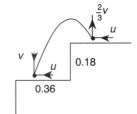

Let the time of flight between bounces be t.

For the motion considered vertically we have:

$-v = \frac{2}{3}v - gt \Rightarrow v = \frac{3gt}{5}$ ... ①

$-0.18 = \frac{2}{3}v\times t - \frac{1}{2}gt^2$ ... ②

For the motion considered horizontally we have

$0.36 = ut$ ... ③

Equations ① and ② give $t = \frac{3}{7}$

$\therefore$ $v = 2.52$ and $u = 0.84$

$\therefore$ Horizontal and vertical components required are 0.84 m s⁻¹ and 2.52 m s⁻¹

6   First consider a general bounce.

Before impact:

After impact:

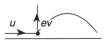

Time of flight of first bounce is $\frac{2ev}{g}$

Hits plane again with downwards component of velocity of ev

$\therefore$ Time of flight of second bounce is $\frac{2e^2v}{g}$

Similarly time of flight of third bounce is $\frac{2e^3v}{g}$,

etc.

$\therefore$ Total time of flight

$= \frac{2ev}{g} + \frac{2e^2v}{g} + \frac{2e^3v}{g} + ...$

But this is an infinite G.P.

$\therefore$ Total time $= \dfrac{\frac{2ev}{g}}{1-e} = \frac{2ev}{g(1-e)}$

In our case $v = 7\sin30° = 3.5$ and $e = 0.8$

$\therefore$ Total time $= \frac{2\times0.8\times3.5}{9.8\times0.2} = 2\frac{6}{7}$

∴ Total time of bouncing is $2\frac{6}{7}$ seconds

∴ Total distance $= u \times 2\frac{6}{7} = \frac{7\sqrt{3}}{2} \times 2\frac{6}{7} = 10\sqrt{3}$

∴ Total distance covered when bouncing is $10\sqrt{3}$ m

7 Before:

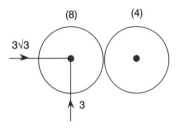

After

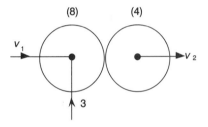

∴ $8 \times 3\sqrt{3} = 8v_1 + 4v_2 \Rightarrow 2v_1 + v_2 = 6\sqrt{3}$

and $v_2 - v_1 = -\frac{3}{4}(0 - 3\sqrt{3}) \Rightarrow v_2 - v_1 = \frac{9}{4}\sqrt{3}$

Solve to get $v_1 = \frac{5\sqrt{3}}{4}$ and $v_2 = \frac{7\sqrt{3}}{2}$

And

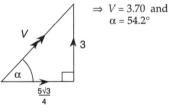

$\Rightarrow V = 3.70$ and $\alpha = 54.2°$

∴ The 8 kg sphere has a velocity of 3.70 m s^{-1} (2 d.p.) inclined at 54.2° (1 d.p.) to the line of the centres.

The 4 kg sphere has a velocity of $\frac{7\sqrt{3}}{2}$ m s^{-1} along the line of centres.

8 Given

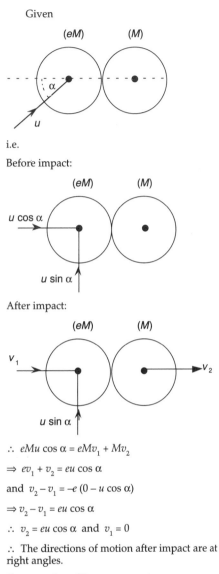

i.e.

Before impact:

After impact:

∴ $eMu \cos \alpha = eMv_1 + Mv_2$

$\Rightarrow ev_1 + v_2 = eu \cos \alpha$

and $v_2 - v_1 = -e(0 - u \cos \alpha)$

$\Rightarrow v_2 - v_1 = eu \cos \alpha$

∴ $v_2 = eu \cos \alpha$ and $v_1 = 0$

∴ The directions of motion after impact are at right angles.

9 Conservation of linear momentum

$0.5 \times 9 \cos 60° = 37.5 v \Rightarrow v = 0.06$

∴ moves backwards at 0.06 m s^{-1} after catching the ball.

10   Given

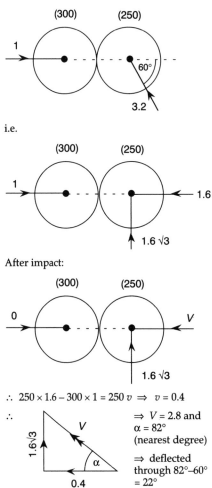

i.e.

After impact:

$\therefore$ $250 \times 1.6 - 300 \times 1 = 250v \Rightarrow v = 0.4$

$\therefore$

$\Rightarrow V = 2.8$ and
$\alpha = 82°$
(nearest degree)

$\Rightarrow$ deflected
through $82°-60°$
$= 22°$

$\therefore$ The angle of deflection is $22°$ and the speed after collision is 2.8 ms^{-1}.

11

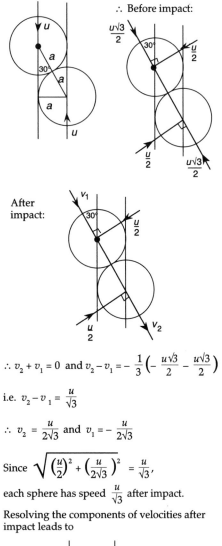

$\therefore$ Before impact:

After impact:

$\therefore$ $v_2 + v_1 = 0$ and $v_2 - v_1 = -\dfrac{1}{3}\left(-\dfrac{u\sqrt{3}}{2} - \dfrac{u\sqrt{3}}{2}\right)$

i.e. $v_2 - v_1 = \dfrac{u}{\sqrt{3}}$

$\therefore$ $v_2 = \dfrac{u}{2\sqrt{3}}$ and $v_1 = -\dfrac{u}{2\sqrt{3}}$

Since $\sqrt{\left(\dfrac{u}{2}\right)^2 + \left(\dfrac{u}{2\sqrt{3}}\right)^2} = \dfrac{u}{\sqrt{3}}$,

each sphere has speed $\dfrac{u}{\sqrt{3}}$ after impact.

Resolving the components of velocities after impact leads to

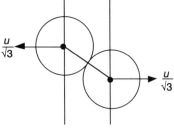

$\therefore$ The velocities are $\dfrac{u}{\sqrt{3}}$ perpendicular to the original direction.

12 Given:

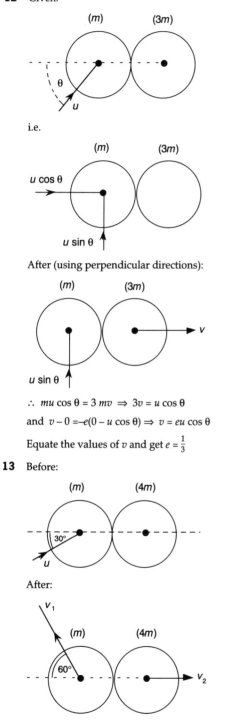

i.e.

After (using perpendicular directions):

$\therefore \ mu \cos \theta = 3 \ mv \Rightarrow 3v = u \cos \theta$

and $v - 0 = -e(0 - u \cos \theta) \Rightarrow v = eu \cos \theta$

Equate the values of v and get $e = \frac{1}{3}$

13 Before:

After:

(Using the given information of the 90° turn.)

$\therefore \ mu \cos 30° = -mv_1 \cos 60° + 4mv_2$

$\Rightarrow 4v_2 - \frac{v_1}{2} = \frac{u\sqrt{3}}{2}$

and $v_1 \sin 60° = u \sin 30° \Rightarrow v_1 = \frac{u\sqrt{3}}{3}$

and $v_2 + v_1 \cos 60° = -e \ (0 - u \cos 30°)$

$\Rightarrow v_2 + \frac{v_1}{2} = \frac{eu\sqrt{3}}{2}$

$\therefore \ v_1 = \frac{u\sqrt{3}}{3}, \ v_2 = \frac{u\sqrt{3}}{6}$ and $e = \frac{2}{3}$.

The coefficient of restitution is $\frac{2}{3}$

14 Before:

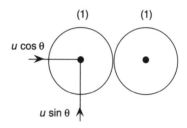

After:

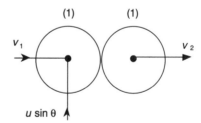

$\therefore \ u \cos \theta = v_1 + v_2$

and $v_2 - v_1 = \frac{-1}{8} (0 - u \cos \theta) \Rightarrow v_2 - v_1 = \frac{u}{8} \cos \theta$

$\therefore \ v_1 = \frac{7u}{16} \cos \theta$

$\therefore$ Velocity of A after impact is given by

$\Rightarrow V^2 = u^2 \times \frac{9}{13} + u^2 \times \left(\frac{7}{16}\right)^2 \times \frac{4}{13}$

$\Rightarrow V = \frac{25u}{8\sqrt{13}}$ and

$\tan \alpha = \frac{16}{7} \tan \theta$

$\Rightarrow \tan \alpha = \frac{24}{7}$

203

But $\cos A = \dfrac{5^2 + 5^2 - 6^2}{(2 \times 5 \times 5)} \Rightarrow \cos A = \dfrac{7}{25}$

$\Rightarrow \tan A = \dfrac{24}{7} \Rightarrow A = \alpha$

$\therefore$ The velocity of A after impact is $\dfrac{25u}{8\sqrt{13}}$ and it

moves off in the direction AQ.

15 Before:

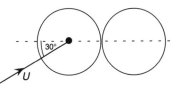

After:

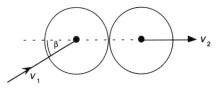

$\therefore \quad U \cos 30 = v_1 \cos \beta + v_2$

$\Rightarrow v_1 \cos \beta + v_2 = \dfrac{U\sqrt{3}}{2}$ ... ①

and $U \sin 30 = v_1 \sin \beta \Rightarrow v_1 \sin \beta = \dfrac{U}{2}$ ... ②

and $v_2 - v_1 \cos \beta = -e\,(0 - U \cos 30°)$

$\Rightarrow v_2 - v_1 \cos \beta = \dfrac{eU\sqrt{3}}{2}$ ... ③

(a) Add equations ① and ③ to give

$v_2 = \dfrac{U\sqrt{3}}{4}(1 + e)$, as required.

(b) Substitute back into ① and get

$v_1 \cos \beta = \dfrac{U\sqrt{3}}{4}(1 - e)$.

$\therefore$ The velocity component of S along the line

of centres is $\dfrac{U\sqrt{3}}{4}(1 - e)$ and the velocity

component perpendicular to this line is $\dfrac{U}{2}$

(i.e. $v_1 \sin \beta$)

(c) $e = \dfrac{2}{3} \Rightarrow v_1 \cos \beta = \dfrac{U}{4\sqrt{3}}$

Now use ② to get $\tan \beta = 2\sqrt{3}$

$\therefore \ \beta = 73.9°$ (1 d.p.)

16 Momentum: $u\,(-2\mathbf{i} + 11\mathbf{j})$

$= \lambda\,(-3\mathbf{i} + 4\mathbf{j}) + \mu\,(2\mathbf{i} + 4\mathbf{j})$

$\therefore \ \lambda = 1.5u, \mu = 1.25u$

$\therefore$ Velocity vectors after impact are

$u\,(-4.5\mathbf{i} + 6\mathbf{j})$ and $u\,(2.5\mathbf{i} + 5\mathbf{j})$

$\therefore$

The red ball moves off along
the line of centres with
direction α given by

$\tan \alpha = \dfrac{6}{4.5} \Rightarrow$

$\therefore$ Along the line of centres afterwards:

Red ball velocity $= 4.5 \cos \alpha + 6 \sin \alpha = 7.5$

White ball velocity $= 5 \sin \alpha - 2.5 \cos \alpha = 2.5$

$\therefore$ Along the line of centres before:

White ball velocity $= 2 \cos \alpha + 11 \sin \alpha = 10$

$\therefore$ Newton gives $7.5 - 2.5 = -e(0 - 10) \Rightarrow e = \dfrac{1}{2}$

as required

M4

Solutions

Section 5

1 (a)

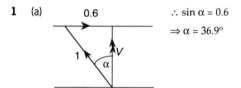

$\therefore \sin \alpha = 0.6$

$\Rightarrow \alpha = 36.9°$

$\therefore$ Direction of swing makes an angle of 53.1° with the bank

(b) $V = \sqrt{1 - 0.6^2} \Rightarrow V = 0.8$

$\Rightarrow$ time $= \dfrac{336}{0.8} = 420$

$\therefore$ Time is 420 seconds, i.e. 7 mins

2 (a) $(t - 2)\mathbf{i} + (3t - 1)\mathbf{j}$

(b) $(t - 2)^2 + (3t - 1)^2 = 10t^2 - 10t + 5$

Differentiate and and put equal to zero

$\therefore 20t - 10 = 0 \Rightarrow t = 0.5$

(c) $t = 0.5$ in (a) gives $-1.5\mathbf{i} + 0.5\mathbf{j}$

and $|-1.5\mathbf{i} + 0.5\mathbf{j}| = \sqrt{(-1.5)^2 + (0.5)^2} = 1.58$

$\therefore$ shortest distance is 1.58 m.

3 (a)

$\therefore V = \sqrt{150^2 - 10^2}$

$= 10\sqrt{224}$

$\therefore$ Time $= \dfrac{200}{10\sqrt{224}}$

$= 1.34$ (2 d.p.)

$\therefore$ Distance in front of target $= 10 \times 1.34$ i.e. 13.4 m.

4 $\mathbf{v}_A = -10\mathbf{i} + 8\mathbf{j}$. Integrate to get

$\mathbf{r}_B = (-10\mathbf{i} + 8\mathbf{j})t + \mathbf{c} \Rightarrow \mathbf{r}_A = (-10\mathbf{i} + 8\mathbf{j})t + 6\mathbf{i} + 4\mathbf{j}$

Similarly $\mathbf{r}_B = (15\mathbf{i} + 6\mathbf{j})t - 3\mathbf{i} + 6\mathbf{j}$

(a) Put $t = 0.75$

$\therefore \mathbf{r}_A = -1.5\mathbf{i} + 10\mathbf{j}, \ \mathbf{r}_B = 8\tfrac{1}{4}\mathbf{i} + 10\tfrac{1}{2}\mathbf{j}$

(b) $\mathbf{r}_B - \mathbf{r}_A = 9\tfrac{3}{4}\mathbf{i} + \tfrac{1}{2}\mathbf{j}$

$\therefore |\mathbf{r}_B - \mathbf{r}_A| = \sqrt{\left(9\tfrac{3}{4}\right)^2 + \left(\tfrac{1}{2}\right)^2}$

$= 9.76$ (2 d.p.)

$\therefore$ Distance apart is 9.76 m.

(c) At time t, $\mathbf{r}_B - \mathbf{r}_A = (25t - 9)\mathbf{i} + (-2t + 2)\mathbf{j}$

But $(25t - 9)^2 + (-2t + 2)^2 = 629t^2 - 458t + 85$

Differentiate and and put equal to zero

$\therefore 1258t - 458 = 0 \Rightarrow t = 0.364$

But 0.364 hrs $\approx$ 22 min

$\therefore$ nearest together at 10 22 hours.

5 $\dot{\mathbf{r}} = (-\mathbf{i} + 5\mathbf{j}) - (2\mathbf{i} + \mathbf{j}) = -3\mathbf{i} + 4\mathbf{j}$

$\therefore \mathbf{r} = (-3\mathbf{i} + 4\mathbf{j})t + \mathbf{c}$

$\therefore \mathbf{r} = (-3\mathbf{i} + 4\mathbf{j})t + (4\mathbf{i} - 2\mathbf{j})$, as required

$\therefore |\mathbf{r}| = \sqrt{(4 - 3t)^2 + (4t - 2)^2}$

But $(4 - 3t)^2 + (4t - 2)^2$ is least when
$-6(4 - 3t) + 8(4t - 2) = 0$, i.e. when $t = 0.8$, as required.

6 $\dfrac{d\mathbf{v}}{dt} = -\mathbf{v} \Rightarrow \mathbf{v} = \mathbf{c}\,e^{-t} \Rightarrow \mathbf{v} = (12\mathbf{i} + 6\mathbf{j})e^{-t}$

$\therefore t = \ln 3 \Rightarrow \mathbf{v} = 4\mathbf{i} + 2\mathbf{j}$

7 $\mathbf{v} = \mathbf{c}e^{3t} \Rightarrow \mathbf{v} = (\mathbf{i} - \mathbf{j})e^{3t}$

Now integrate $\therefore \mathbf{r} = (\mathbf{i} - \mathbf{j})\dfrac{e^{3t}}{3} + \mathbf{d}$

But $\mathbf{r} = 3\mathbf{i}$ where $t = 0 \Rightarrow \mathbf{d} = \dfrac{1}{3}(8\mathbf{i} + \mathbf{j})$

$\therefore \mathbf{r} = (\mathbf{i} - \mathbf{j})\dfrac{e^{3t}}{3} + \dfrac{1}{3}(8\mathbf{i} + \mathbf{j})$

8 (a) $\mathbf{v} = (4\mathbf{i} + 2\mathbf{j})e^{6t} \Rightarrow \mathbf{r} = (4\mathbf{i} + 2\mathbf{j})\dfrac{e^{6t}}{6} + \mathbf{d}$

But $\mathbf{r} = \mathbf{i} + \mathbf{j}$ when $t = 0 \Rightarrow \mathbf{d} = \dfrac{1}{3}(\mathbf{i} + 2\mathbf{j})$

$\therefore \mathbf{r} = (2\mathbf{i} + \mathbf{j})\dfrac{e^{6t}}{3} + \dfrac{1}{3}(\mathbf{i} + 2\mathbf{j})$

(b) $\dfrac{d\mathbf{v}}{dt} = (4\mathbf{i} + 2\mathbf{j})\, 6e^{6t} \Rightarrow$

$\left|\dfrac{d\mathbf{v}}{dt}\right| = 6e^{6t}\sqrt{4^2 + 2^2}$ i.e. $6\sqrt{20}\, e^{6t}$

$\therefore\ 6\sqrt{20}\, e^{6t} \geq 100 \Rightarrow t \geq 0.22$

$\therefore$ Time required in 0.22 seconds

9 Auxiliary equation $m^2 + 4m + 8 = 0$

$\Rightarrow m = -2 \pm 2i$

$\therefore\ \mathbf{r} = e^{-2t}\,(\mathbf{c}\cos 2t + \mathbf{d}\sin 2t)$

$t = 0, \mathbf{r} = \mathbf{i} + \mathbf{j} \Rightarrow \mathbf{i} + \mathbf{j} = \mathbf{c}$

$t = 0,\ \dfrac{d\mathbf{r}}{dt} = 2\mathbf{i} - 4\mathbf{j} \Rightarrow 2\mathbf{i} - 4\mathbf{j} = 2\mathbf{d} - 2\mathbf{c}$

$\therefore\ \mathbf{c} = \mathbf{i} + \mathbf{j}$ and $\mathbf{d} = 2\mathbf{i} - \mathbf{j}$

$\therefore\ \mathbf{r} = e^{-2t}\left[(\mathbf{i} + \mathbf{j})\cos 2t + (2\mathbf{i} - \mathbf{j})\sin 2t\right]$

10 Auxiliary equation $m^2 + 3m + 2 = 0$

$\Rightarrow m = -1$ or -2

$\therefore\ \mathbf{r} = \mathbf{c}e^{-t} + \mathbf{d}e^{-2t}$

$t = 0, \mathbf{r} = 2\mathbf{j} \Rightarrow 2\mathbf{j} = \mathbf{c} + \mathbf{d}$

$t = 0,\ \dfrac{d\mathbf{r}}{dt} = \mathbf{i} + \mathbf{j} \Rightarrow \mathbf{i} + \mathbf{j} = -\mathbf{c} - 2\mathbf{d}$

$\therefore\ \mathbf{c} = \mathbf{i} + 5\mathbf{j}$ and $\mathbf{d} = -\mathbf{i} - 3\mathbf{j}$

$\therefore\ \mathbf{r} = (\mathbf{i} + 5\mathbf{j})\,e^{-t} - (\mathbf{i} + 3\mathbf{j})\,e^{-2t}$

11 Auxiliary equation $m^2 - 2m + 1 = 0$

$\Rightarrow m = 1$, repeated

$\therefore\ \mathbf{r} = e^{t}\,(\mathbf{c}t + \mathbf{d})$

$t = 0, \mathbf{r} = \mathbf{i} \Rightarrow \mathbf{i} = \mathbf{d}$

$t = 0,\ \dfrac{d\mathbf{r}}{dt} = \mathbf{j} \Rightarrow \mathbf{j} = \mathbf{c} + \mathbf{d}$

$\therefore\ \mathbf{c} = \mathbf{j} - \mathbf{i}$ and $\mathbf{d} = \mathbf{i}$

$\therefore\ \mathbf{r} = e^{t}\left[(\mathbf{j} - \mathbf{i})\,t + \mathbf{i}\right]$

$\therefore\ t = 2 \Rightarrow \mathbf{v} = e^2\,(-\mathbf{i} + 2\mathbf{j})$

$\Rightarrow |\mathbf{r}| = e^2\sqrt{5}$ or 16.5

$\therefore$ Distance OP is 16.5 m (1 d.p.)

12 Displacement $\mathbf{d} = 2\mathbf{i} + 3\mathbf{j} + 2\mathbf{k}$ and $\mathbf{F} = \lambda\mathbf{d}$

But $\mathbf{F} \cdot \mathbf{d} = 34$

$\therefore\ \lambda\begin{pmatrix}2\\3\\2\end{pmatrix} \cdot \begin{pmatrix}2\\3\\2\end{pmatrix} = 34 \Rightarrow \lambda = 2$

$\therefore$ Force $\mathbf{F} = (4\mathbf{i} + 6\mathbf{j} + 4\mathbf{k})$ newtons

13 Contact force $= 5\mathbf{k}$

$\therefore$ Total force acting $= 3\mathbf{i} + \mathbf{j} + 7\mathbf{k}$

Displacement $\mathbf{d} = 4\mathbf{i} + 5\mathbf{j} + 2\mathbf{k}$

$\therefore$ Increase in KE = Work done

$= \begin{pmatrix}3\\1\\7\end{pmatrix} \cdot \begin{pmatrix}4\\5\\2\end{pmatrix} = 31$ J

14 Displacement $\mathbf{d} = 12\mathbf{i} + 3\mathbf{j} + 21\mathbf{k}$.

Force $\mathbf{F} = (4\mathbf{i} + \mathbf{j} + 7\mathbf{k})$ newtons

(a) Work done $= \mathbf{F} \cdot \mathbf{d} = \begin{pmatrix}4\\1\\7\end{pmatrix} \cdot \begin{pmatrix}12\\3\\21\end{pmatrix} = 198$

$\therefore$ Work done is 198 J

(b) Work done = gain in KE

$\therefore\ 198 = \frac{1}{2} \times 0.1 \times v^2 \Rightarrow v = 62.9$ (1 d.p.)

$\therefore$ Speed at B is 62.9 m s^{-1}

15 $\overrightarrow{PQ} \times \mathbf{F} = (\mathbf{q} - \mathbf{p}) \times \mathbf{F}$

(a) $(-2\mathbf{i} - 2\mathbf{k}) \times (2\mathbf{i} + \mathbf{j}) = 2\mathbf{i} - 4\mathbf{j} - 2\mathbf{k}$

(b) $(-3\mathbf{i} + \mathbf{j} - \mathbf{k}) \times (3\mathbf{i} + 2\mathbf{j} + \mathbf{k}) = 3\mathbf{i} - 9\mathbf{k}$

16 $2\mathbf{i} \times (\mathbf{i} + \mathbf{j}) = 2\mathbf{k},\ 3\mathbf{j} \times (2\mathbf{j} + \mathbf{k}) = 3\mathbf{i}$

$(\mathbf{i} + \mathbf{k}) \times (\mathbf{j} - 2\mathbf{k}) = -\mathbf{i} + 2\mathbf{j} + \mathbf{k}$

$\therefore$ Total moment $= (2\mathbf{i} + 2\mathbf{j} + 3\mathbf{k})$ Nm

17 $9\mathbf{i} + 6\mathbf{j} - 2\mathbf{k}$ has magnitude

$= \sqrt{9^2 + 6^2 + (-2)^2} = 11$

$\therefore$ Force $= \dfrac{6}{11}\,(9\mathbf{i} + 6\mathbf{j} - 2\mathbf{k})$ newtons

Also $(4\mathbf{i} - \mathbf{j} + 7\mathbf{k}) - (\mathbf{i} - 3\mathbf{j} + 2\mathbf{k}) = 3\mathbf{i} + 2\mathbf{j} + 5\mathbf{k}$

$\therefore$ Moment $= (3\mathbf{i} + 2\mathbf{j} + 5\mathbf{k}) \times \dfrac{6}{11}\,(9\mathbf{i} + 6\mathbf{j} - 2\mathbf{k})$

$= \dfrac{6}{11}\,(-34\mathbf{i} + 51\mathbf{j})$

$\therefore$ Moment required is $\dfrac{6}{11}\,(-34\mathbf{i} + 51\mathbf{j})$ Nm

18 (a) $(-\mathbf{i} + \mathbf{j}) + (2\mathbf{j} - 2\mathbf{k}) + \mathbf{F} = 0$

$\therefore\ \mathbf{F} = (\mathbf{i} - 3\mathbf{j} + 2\mathbf{k})$ newtons

(b) Moments about the origin give

$\mathbf{G} = -17\mathbf{i} \times (-\mathbf{i} + \mathbf{j}) + \dfrac{9}{2}\mathbf{i} \times (2\mathbf{j} - 2\mathbf{k}) + 4\mathbf{j} \times (\mathbf{i} - 3\mathbf{j} + 2\mathbf{k})$

$= (-17\mathbf{k}) + (9\mathbf{j} + 9\mathbf{k}) + (8\mathbf{i} - 4\mathbf{k})$

$= 8\mathbf{i} + 9\mathbf{j} - 12\mathbf{k}$

$\therefore\ |\mathbf{G}| = \sqrt{8^2 + 9^2 + (-12)^2} = 17$ Nm

19 $\mathbf{R} = 2\mathbf{j} - \mathbf{i} - 4\mathbf{j} + 3\mathbf{i} = 2\mathbf{i} - 2\mathbf{j}$

$\Rightarrow |\mathbf{R}| = \sqrt{8}$ or $2\sqrt{2}$N

Moments about O give

$2\mathbf{j} \times (-3.5\mathbf{i}) - \mathbf{i} \times (-2.5\mathbf{i}) - 4\mathbf{j} \times (-2.5\mathbf{i} + \mathbf{j})$
$\qquad\qquad\qquad\qquad + 3\mathbf{i} \times (-3.5\mathbf{i} + \mathbf{j})$

$= 7\mathbf{k} \qquad + 0 \qquad - 10\mathbf{k} \qquad + 3\mathbf{k}$

$= 0 \quad \therefore \ \mathbf{R}$ acts through O

20 (a) $(3\mathbf{i} - 4\mathbf{j} + \mathbf{k}) \times (27\mathbf{i} + 16\mathbf{j} - 17\mathbf{k})$

$\qquad = 52\mathbf{i} + 78\mathbf{j} + 156\mathbf{k}$

$\therefore$ Magnitude of couple $= \sqrt{52^2 + 78^2 + 156^2}$

$\qquad = 182$

$\therefore$ Couple has magnitude 182 Nm.

(b) $I\ddot{\theta} = 182 \Rightarrow I \times 4 = 182 \Rightarrow I = 45.5$

21 (a) Direction of the line given by $\begin{pmatrix} 2 \\ 1 \\ -5 \end{pmatrix}$

We need the coordinates of a point on this line before we can find the equation required.

Let the line meet the plane $z = 0$ at $(x, y, 0)$

$\therefore (x\mathbf{i} + y\mathbf{j}) \times (2\mathbf{i} + \mathbf{j} - 5\mathbf{k}) = 3\mathbf{i} - \mathbf{j} + \mathbf{k}$

$\Rightarrow -5y\mathbf{i} + 5x\mathbf{j} + (x - 2y)\mathbf{k} = 3\mathbf{i} - \mathbf{j} + \mathbf{k}$

$\Rightarrow x = -\dfrac{1}{5}$ and $y = -\dfrac{3}{5}$

$\therefore$ Equation of line is: $\mathbf{r} = \begin{pmatrix} -1/5 \\ -3/5 \\ 0 \end{pmatrix} + \lambda \begin{pmatrix} 2 \\ 1 \\ -5 \end{pmatrix}$

(b) The lines meet where

$\begin{pmatrix} -1/5 \\ -3/5 \\ 0 \end{pmatrix} + \lambda \begin{pmatrix} 2 \\ 1 \\ -5 \end{pmatrix} = \begin{pmatrix} k \\ k \\ -k \end{pmatrix} + \mu \begin{pmatrix} 2 \\ 1 \\ -1 \end{pmatrix}$

$\therefore -\dfrac{1}{5} + 2\lambda = k + 2\mu$

$-\dfrac{3}{5} + \lambda = k + \mu$

$-5\lambda = -k - \mu$

This gives $\lambda = -0.15$, $\mu = 0.25$ and $k = -1$

(c) Taking $k = -1$, $\mu = 0.25$

$\qquad$ gives $\mathbf{r} = \begin{pmatrix} -1 \\ -1 \\ 1 \end{pmatrix} + 0.25 \begin{pmatrix} 2 \\ 1 \\ -1 \end{pmatrix}$

$\therefore$ The position vector of P is $\begin{pmatrix} -0.5 \\ -0.75 \\ 0.75 \end{pmatrix}$

22 (a) $\mathbf{R} = 5\mathbf{i} + \mathbf{j} + 2\mathbf{k} \Rightarrow |\mathbf{R}| = \sqrt{30}$ newtons

(b) Let the line of action of $\mathbf{R}$ cut the plane $z = 0$ at $x\mathbf{i} + y\mathbf{j}$

Moments about the origin give

$0.5\mathbf{j} \times 4\mathbf{i} + (\mathbf{j} + \mathbf{k}) \times (\mathbf{i} + \mathbf{j} + 2\mathbf{k})$

$\qquad = (x\mathbf{i} + y\mathbf{j}) \times (5\mathbf{i} + \mathbf{j} + 2\mathbf{k})$

$\therefore -2\mathbf{k} + \mathbf{i} + \mathbf{j} - \mathbf{k} = 2y\mathbf{i} - 2x\mathbf{j} + (x - 5y)\mathbf{k}$

$y = \dfrac{1}{2}$, and $x = -\dfrac{1}{2}$

$\therefore \ \mathbf{r} = \begin{pmatrix} -1/2 \\ 1/2 \\ 0 \end{pmatrix} + t \begin{pmatrix} 5 \\ 1 \\ 2 \end{pmatrix}$.

23 $\mathbf{R} = (2\mathbf{i} - \mathbf{j})$ newtons

Moments about the origin give

$(2\mathbf{j} + \mathbf{k}) \times (2\mathbf{i} - \mathbf{j}) = 3\mathbf{i} \times \mathbf{R} + \mathbf{G}$

$\therefore \ \mathbf{i} + 2\mathbf{j} - 4\mathbf{k} = -3\mathbf{k} + \mathbf{G}$

$\therefore \ \mathbf{G} = (\mathbf{i} + 2\mathbf{j} - \mathbf{k})$ newton metres

24 $\mathbf{R} = (3\mathbf{j} + 4\mathbf{k})$ newtons

Moments about the origin give

$(\mathbf{i} + \mathbf{k}) \times (3\mathbf{j} + 4\mathbf{k}) + (\mathbf{i} + 4\mathbf{j}) = (3\mathbf{j} + \mathbf{k}) \times \mathbf{R} + \mathbf{G}$

$\therefore \ -3\mathbf{i} - 4\mathbf{j} + 3\mathbf{k} + \mathbf{i} + 4\mathbf{j} = 9\mathbf{i} + \mathbf{G}$

$\therefore \ \mathbf{G} = (-11\mathbf{i} + 3\mathbf{k})$ newton metres

25 (a) $\mathbf{F} = 2\mathbf{i} + \mathbf{k} \Rightarrow |\mathbf{F}| = \sqrt{5}$ newtons

(b) Moments about the origin give

$3\mathbf{j} \times (2\mathbf{i} + \mathbf{k}) = 3\mathbf{k} \times \mathbf{F} + \mathbf{G}$

$\therefore 3\mathbf{i} - 6\mathbf{k} = 6\mathbf{j} + \mathbf{G}$

$\therefore \ \mathbf{G} = 3\mathbf{i} - 6\mathbf{j} - 6\mathbf{k} \Rightarrow |\mathbf{G}| = 9$ newtons

(c) $\mathbf{r} = \begin{pmatrix} 0 \\ 3 \\ 0 \end{pmatrix} + t \begin{pmatrix} 2 \\ 0 \\ 1 \end{pmatrix}$

26 $\mathbf{F} = (7\mathbf{i} + 2\mathbf{j} - 4\mathbf{k})$ newtons.

$\mathbf{d} = (4\mathbf{i} + 2\mathbf{j} - 2\mathbf{k})$ metres

$\therefore \ \mathbf{F} . \mathbf{d} = 28 + 4 + 8 = 40$

$\therefore$ Work done $= 40$ Nm

Also $40 = \dfrac{1}{2} \times 5 \times v^2 \Rightarrow v = 4$

$\therefore$ final speed is 4 m s^{-1}

27 $(\mathbf{i} + 3\mathbf{j}) + (-2\mathbf{i} - \mathbf{j}) + (\mathbf{i} - 2\mathbf{j}) = 0 \ \therefore$ A couple

$\begin{pmatrix} 2 \\ 5 \\ 0 \end{pmatrix} \times \begin{pmatrix} 1 \\ 3 \\ 0 \end{pmatrix} + \begin{pmatrix} 0 \\ 4 \\ 0 \end{pmatrix} \times \begin{pmatrix} -2 \\ -1 \\ 0 \end{pmatrix} + \begin{pmatrix} -1 \\ 1 \\ 0 \end{pmatrix} \times \begin{pmatrix} 1 \\ -2 \\ 0 \end{pmatrix}$

$= \begin{pmatrix} 0 \\ 0 \\ 1 \end{pmatrix} + \begin{pmatrix} 0 \\ 0 \\ 8 \end{pmatrix} + \begin{pmatrix} 0 \\ 0 \\ 1 \end{pmatrix} \ \therefore$ Couple is $\begin{pmatrix} 0 \\ 0 \\ 10 \end{pmatrix}$

$\therefore$ Moment of couple is 10 units anti-clockwise

28 (a) $\ddot{\mathbf{r}} = -k^2\mathbf{r} \ \therefore$ period $= \dfrac{2\pi}{k}$

(b) $|\ddot{\mathbf{r}}| = k^2 |\mathbf{r}| = k^2 \sqrt{16 \cos^2 kt + 9 \sin^2 kt}$

$\qquad = k^2 \sqrt{9 + 7 \cos^2 kt} \ \leqslant 4k^2$

$\therefore$ Greatest magnitude of $\mathbf{F}$ is $4mk^2$

(c) $t = \dfrac{\pi}{3k}$

$\Rightarrow \mathbf{r} = 2\mathbf{i} + \dfrac{3\sqrt{3}}{2}\mathbf{j}$, $\dot{\mathbf{r}} = -2\sqrt{3}\,k\mathbf{i} + \dfrac{3}{2}k\mathbf{j}$

Now moves at this constant speed for a time of $\dfrac{\pi}{k}$

$\therefore$ $\mathbf{r} = (-2\sqrt{3}\,k\mathbf{i} + \dfrac{3}{2}k\mathbf{j})\dfrac{\pi}{k} + \left(2\mathbf{i} + \dfrac{3\sqrt{3}}{2}\mathbf{j}\right)$

$= 2(1 - \pi\sqrt{3})\,\mathbf{i} + \dfrac{3}{2}(\pi + \sqrt{3})\mathbf{j}$

29 (a) $\begin{pmatrix}3\\2\\1\end{pmatrix} + \begin{pmatrix}4\\5\\6\end{pmatrix} + \mathbf{F} = 0 \Rightarrow \mathbf{F} = -7\begin{pmatrix}1\\1\\1\end{pmatrix}$

$\Rightarrow |\mathbf{F}| = 7\sqrt{3}$

(b)

$C\ (6, 4, 9)$ $\overrightarrow{BC} = \begin{pmatrix}-2\\1\\4\end{pmatrix}$

B $\mathbf{F}$ Let $\overrightarrow{BA} = \begin{pmatrix}a\\b\\c\end{pmatrix}$

$(8, 3, 5)$ A

$\therefore\ \overrightarrow{B}\,:\ \begin{pmatrix}-2\\1\\4\end{pmatrix} \times \begin{pmatrix}4\\5\\6\end{pmatrix} + \begin{pmatrix}a\\b\\c\end{pmatrix} \times (-7)\begin{pmatrix}1\\1\\1\end{pmatrix} = 0$

$\Rightarrow \begin{pmatrix}-14\\28\\-14\end{pmatrix} + (-7)\begin{pmatrix}b-c\\c-a\\a-b\end{pmatrix} = 0$

$\Rightarrow \overrightarrow{BA} = \begin{pmatrix}a\\a+2\\a+4\end{pmatrix}$

But $\overrightarrow{BA} = \lambda\begin{pmatrix}3\\2\\1\end{pmatrix}$

$\Rightarrow a = -6,\ b = -4,\ c = -2 \Rightarrow A\ (2, -1, 3)$

(c) $\mathbf{r} = \begin{pmatrix}2\\-1\\3\end{pmatrix} + \lambda\begin{pmatrix}1\\1\\1\end{pmatrix}$

30 $\mathbf{F} = \begin{pmatrix}3\\6\\6\end{pmatrix} = 3\mathbf{a} \Rightarrow \mathbf{a} = \begin{pmatrix}1\\2\\2\end{pmatrix} \Rightarrow \mathbf{v} = \begin{pmatrix}1\\2\\2\end{pmatrix}t$

$\Rightarrow \mathbf{r} = \begin{pmatrix}1\\2\\2\end{pmatrix}\dfrac{t^2}{2} + \begin{pmatrix}1\\-1\\-1\end{pmatrix}$

$\therefore\ t = 2 \Rightarrow \mathbf{r} = \begin{pmatrix}3\\3\\3\end{pmatrix},\ m\mathbf{v} = \begin{pmatrix}6\\12\\12\end{pmatrix}$

Work done $= \begin{pmatrix}3\\6\\6\end{pmatrix} \cdot \begin{pmatrix}2\\4\\4\end{pmatrix} = 6 + 24 + 24 = 54\ \mathrm{J}$

31 $\begin{pmatrix}-11\\17\\-14\end{pmatrix} + t\begin{pmatrix}6\\-7\\8\end{pmatrix} = \begin{pmatrix}-9\\9\\-32\end{pmatrix} + t\begin{pmatrix}5\\-3\\17\end{pmatrix} \Rightarrow t = 2$

$\therefore$ Collide after 2 seconds at $\begin{pmatrix}1\\3\\2\end{pmatrix}$

$\left.\begin{array}{l} \mathbf{V}_c - \mathbf{V}_a = \lambda\begin{pmatrix}2\\3\\4\end{pmatrix} \\[12pt] \mathbf{V}_c - \mathbf{V}_b = \mu\begin{pmatrix}1\\2\\3\end{pmatrix} \end{array}\right\}$ $\therefore \begin{pmatrix}6\\-7\\8\end{pmatrix} + \lambda\begin{pmatrix}2\\3\\4\end{pmatrix}$

$= \begin{pmatrix}5\\-3\\17\end{pmatrix} + \mu\begin{pmatrix}1\\2\\3\end{pmatrix}$

(both equal $\mathbf{v}_c$)

$\Rightarrow \lambda = -6,\ \mu = -11$

$\Rightarrow \mathbf{V}_c = \begin{pmatrix}-6\\-25\\-16\end{pmatrix}$

Then $\begin{pmatrix}a\\b\\c\end{pmatrix} + \begin{pmatrix}-6\\-25\\-16\end{pmatrix}2 = \begin{pmatrix}1\\3\\2\end{pmatrix} \Rightarrow \begin{pmatrix}a\\b\\c\end{pmatrix} = \begin{pmatrix}13\\53\\34\end{pmatrix}$,

its initial position.

32 Meet when $s = -2$ and $t = 1$ $\therefore$ Meet at $\begin{pmatrix}-6\\-1\\-1\end{pmatrix}$

$\mathbf{F} = \begin{pmatrix}1\\1\\2\end{pmatrix} + \begin{pmatrix}1\\2\\-3\end{pmatrix} = \begin{pmatrix}2\\3\\-1\end{pmatrix} \Rightarrow |\mathbf{F}| = \sqrt{14}\ \mathrm{N}$

Line of action of $\mathbf{F}$: $\mathbf{r} = \begin{pmatrix}-6\\-1\\-1\end{pmatrix} + \lambda\begin{pmatrix}2\\3\\-1\end{pmatrix}$

$\begin{pmatrix}2\\3\\-1\end{pmatrix} = 2\mathbf{a} \Rightarrow \mathbf{a} = \begin{pmatrix}1\\1.5\\-0.5\end{pmatrix} \Rightarrow \mathbf{v} = \begin{pmatrix}1\\1.5\\-0.5\end{pmatrix}t$

$\Rightarrow \mathbf{r} = \begin{pmatrix}1\\1.5\\-0.5\end{pmatrix}\dfrac{t^2}{2} + \begin{pmatrix}-6\\-1\\-1\end{pmatrix}$

$\therefore$ At $t = 4$, $\mathbf{v} = \begin{pmatrix}4\\6\\-2\end{pmatrix}$ and $\mathbf{r} = \begin{pmatrix}2\\11\\-5\end{pmatrix}$

Section 6

1 (a) $-15e^{-12t} \sin 5t - 36e^{-12t} \cos 5t = 0$

$\Rightarrow \tan 5t = -2.4$

$\therefore 5t = n\pi - 1.18 \Rightarrow t = \dfrac{n\pi}{5} - 0.24$

(b) $n = 0 \Rightarrow x = 3e^{-12(-0.24)} \cos(-1.2)$

$n = 1 \Rightarrow x = 3e^{-12\left(\frac{\pi}{5} - 0.24\right)} \cos(\pi - 1.2)$

Divide and get $e^{\frac{12\pi}{5}} \times -1$

$\therefore$ Ratio of *distances* is $e^{\frac{12\pi}{5}} : 1$

2 (a) $\ddot{x} = -\lambda^2 x$ and $\ddot{y} = -\lambda^2 y$

$\therefore x = A \cos \lambda t + B \sin \lambda t$ and
$y = C \cos \lambda t + D \sin \lambda t$

But $x = 2a$, $\dot{x} = 0$ when $t = 0 \Rightarrow x = 2a \cos \lambda t$

Also $y = 0$, $\dot{y} = \lambda a$ when $t = 0 \Rightarrow y = a \sin \lambda t$

$\therefore \dfrac{x^2}{4a^2} + \dfrac{y^2}{a^2} = \cos^2 \lambda t + \sin^2 \lambda t = 1$, as required

(b) Returns to A when $x = 2a$, $y = 0$
$\therefore \cos \lambda t = 1$ and $\sin \lambda t = 0$ $\therefore \lambda t = 2\pi$

$\therefore t = \dfrac{2\pi}{\lambda}$

3 (a) $-6Mx\mathbf{j} = M(\ddot{x}\mathbf{i} + \ddot{y}\mathbf{j})$

$\Rightarrow \ddot{x} = 0$ and $\ddot{y} = -6x$

But $\ddot{x} = 0 \Rightarrow \dot{x} = u \Rightarrow x = ut$ § ... ①

$\therefore \ddot{y} = -6ut \Rightarrow \dot{y} = -3ut^2 + u \Rightarrow y = -ut^3 + ut$
  ... ②

Eliminate t between equations ① and ② to get
$yu^2 = x(u^2 - x^2)$

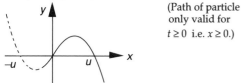

(Path of particle
only valid for
$t \geq 0$ i.e. $x \geq 0$.)

4 $\ddot{x} = ft \Rightarrow \dot{x} = \dfrac{ft^2}{2} + u \Rightarrow x = \dfrac{ft^3}{6} + ut$ ... ①

$\ddot{y} = 0 \Rightarrow \dot{y} = v \Rightarrow y = vt$ ... ②

Eliminate t from equations ① and ② to get
$6xv^3 = fy^3 + 6uv^2y$, as required.

5 $r = e^{-t} \Rightarrow \dot{r} = -e^{-t} \Rightarrow \ddot{r} = e^{-t}$

$\theta = t^2 - 1 \Rightarrow \dot{\theta} = 2t \Rightarrow \ddot{\theta} = 2$

Since $\dot{r} = -e^{-t}$ and $r\dot{\theta} = 2te^{-t} \Rightarrow \mathbf{v} = e^{-t}\begin{pmatrix} -1 \\ 2t \end{pmatrix}$

Since $\ddot{r} - r\dot{\theta}^2 = e^{-t} - e^{-t} \times 4t^2 = e^{-t}(1 - 4t^2)$

and $\dfrac{1}{r}\dfrac{d}{dt}(r^2\dot{\theta}) = 2\dot{r}\dot{\theta} + r\ddot{\theta}$

$\qquad = -2e^{-t} \times 2t + e^{-t} \times 2 = e^{-t}(2 - 4t),$

$\Rightarrow \mathbf{a} = e^{-t}\begin{pmatrix} 1 - 4t^2 \\ 2 - 4t \end{pmatrix}$

$\mathbf{a}$ perpendicular to $\mathbf{v} \Rightarrow \mathbf{a} \cdot \mathbf{v} = 0$

$\Rightarrow e^{-t}\begin{pmatrix} -1 \\ 2t \end{pmatrix} \cdot e^{-t}\begin{pmatrix} 1 - 4t^2 \\ 2 - 4t \end{pmatrix} = 0$

$\Rightarrow e^{-2t}(-1 + 4t^2 + 4t - 8t^2) = 0$

$\Rightarrow 4t^2 - 4t + 1 = 0 \Rightarrow t = 0.5$

The value of t is 0.5

6 $\dot{\theta} = \omega \Rightarrow \ddot{\theta} = 0$

Also $r = ke^{\theta} \Rightarrow \dot{r} = k\omega e^{\theta} \Rightarrow \ddot{r} = k\omega^2 e^{\theta}$

$\therefore \ddot{r} - r\dot{\theta}^2 = k\omega^2 e^{\theta} - k\omega^2 e^{\theta} = 0$

$\therefore$ the radial component of acceleration is zero

$\therefore$ the resultant force can only act at right
angles to OP.

Also $\dfrac{1}{r}\dfrac{d}{dt}(r^2\dot{\theta}) = 2\dot{r}\dot{\theta} + r\ddot{\theta} = 2k\omega^2 e^{\theta} = 2r\omega^2$

$\Rightarrow$ resultant force $= m \times 2r\omega^2$, as required.

7 (a) $\dot{\theta} = \omega \Rightarrow \ddot{\theta} = 0$

Also $r = a(1 + \cos\theta) \Rightarrow \dot{r} = -a\omega \sin\theta$

$\Rightarrow \ddot{r} = -a\omega^2 \cos\theta$

$\therefore \ddot{r} - r\dot{\theta}^2 = -a\omega^2 \cos\theta - a(1 + \cos\theta)\omega^2$

$= -a\omega^2(1 + 2\cos\theta)$, as required.

(b) $\dfrac{1}{r}\dfrac{d}{dt}(r^2\dot{\theta}) = 2\dot{r}\dot{\theta} + r\ddot{\theta} = -2a\omega^2 \sin\theta$

$\therefore f = a\omega^2 \sqrt{(1 + 2\cos\theta)^2 + (-2\sin\theta)^2}$

$= a\omega^2 \sqrt{5 + 4\cos\theta}$

(c) maximum value of $5 + 4\cos\theta$ is $5 + 4 = 9$

$\therefore$ maximum value of $f = a\omega^2 \sqrt{9} = 3a\omega^2$, as
required

8 (a) $\dot{\theta} = \omega \Rightarrow \ddot{\theta} = 0$

Also $r = d(2 + \cos\theta) \Rightarrow \dot{r} = -d\omega \sin\theta$

$\Rightarrow \ddot{r} = -d\omega^2 \cos\theta$

$\therefore \mathbf{v} = \begin{pmatrix} -d\omega \sin\theta \\ d\omega(2 + \cos\theta) \end{pmatrix}$

$\therefore$ At $\theta = \dfrac{\pi}{2}$, $\mathbf{v} = d\omega \begin{pmatrix} -1 \\ 2 \end{pmatrix}$

$\Rightarrow |\mathbf{v}| = d\omega \sqrt{5}$, as required

(b) $\ddot{r} - r\dot{\theta}^2 = -d\omega^2 \cos\theta - d\omega^2 (2 + \cos\theta)$

$\therefore$ At $\theta = \dfrac{\pi}{2}$ this equals $-2\,d\omega^2$

$\therefore$ magnitude of this radial component $= 2\,d\omega^2$

9 (a) Follow the derivation as given in the course (page 114)

Given perpendicular unit vectors $\mathbf{a}$ and $\mathbf{b}$ along and perpendicular to the radius vector $\mathbf{r} = \overrightarrow{OP}$, then

$\mathbf{r} = r\mathbf{a}$ where $\dfrac{d\mathbf{a}}{dt} = \dot{\theta}\mathbf{b}$ and $\dfrac{d\mathbf{b}}{dt} = -\dot{\theta}\mathbf{a}$

$\therefore \dot{\mathbf{r}} = r\dot{\theta}\mathbf{b} + \dot{r}\mathbf{a}$

$\therefore \ddot{\mathbf{r}} = \dot{r}\dot{\theta}\mathbf{b} + r\ddot{\theta}\mathbf{b} - r\dot{\theta}^2\mathbf{a} + \ddot{r}\mathbf{a} + \dot{r}\dot{\theta}\mathbf{b}$

$= (\ddot{r} - r\dot{\theta}^2)\,\mathbf{a} + (r\ddot{\theta} + 2\dot{r}\dot{\theta})\,\mathbf{b}$

$\therefore$ The required acceleration component is $r\ddot{\theta} + 2\dot{r}\dot{\theta}$

(b) Since $r\ddot{\theta} + 2\dot{r}\dot{\theta} = \dfrac{1}{r}\dfrac{d}{dt}(r^2\dot{\theta})$ and since $r^2\dot{\theta}$ is constant $\Rightarrow$ zero transverse acceleration

$\therefore$ The resultant force must act in the direction $\overrightarrow{OP}$.

10 (a) $\tan\alpha = \dfrac{-r\dot{\theta}}{\dot{r}} = -\dfrac{rd\theta}{dr} \Rightarrow \dfrac{dr}{d\theta} = -r\cot\alpha$, as required

(b) $\displaystyle\int \dfrac{dr}{r} = \int -\cot\alpha \times d\theta \Rightarrow \ln r = -\theta\cot\alpha + c$

$\Rightarrow r = Ae^{-\theta\cot\alpha}$

$\Rightarrow r = Re^{-\theta\cot\alpha}$

11 (a) $\dot{\theta} = \omega \Rightarrow \ddot{\theta} = 0$

Radial force $= 3mr\omega^2$.

Radial acceleration $= \ddot{r} - r\omega^2$

$\therefore 3mr\omega^2 = m(\ddot{r} - r\omega^2) \Rightarrow \ddot{r} - 4\omega^2 r = 0$, as required

(b) $r = Ae^{2\omega t} + Be^{-2\omega t}$

$t = 0, r = 2a \Rightarrow 2a = A + B$

$t = 0, \dot{r} = 0 \Rightarrow 0 = 2\omega A - 2\omega B$

$\therefore A = a$ and $B = a$

$\therefore r = ae^{2\omega t} + ae^{-2\omega t}$

(c) $\dot{\theta} = \omega \Rightarrow \theta = \omega t + c$.

But $t = 0$ when $\theta = 0 \Rightarrow \theta = \omega t$

$\therefore r = ae^{2\theta} + ae^{-2\theta}$

12 $s = c\tan\psi \Rightarrow \dfrac{ds}{d\psi} = c\sec^2\psi \Rightarrow \rho = c\sec^2\psi$

Since v is constant, the tangential acceleration $\dfrac{dv}{dt} = 0$

$\therefore$ Transverse acceleration $= \dfrac{v^2}{\rho} = \dfrac{u^2}{c\sec^2\psi}$

$= \dfrac{u^2}{c}\cos^2\psi$

$\therefore$ When $\psi = \dfrac{\pi}{4}$, transverse acceleration

$= \dfrac{u^2}{c}\left(\dfrac{1}{\sqrt{2}}\right)^2 = \dfrac{u^2}{2c}$, as required.

13 $-mg\sin\psi = m\ddot{s} \Rightarrow \ddot{s} + \dfrac{g}{4a}s = 0$

$\Rightarrow s = A\cos\dfrac{1}{2}\left(\sqrt{\dfrac{g}{a}}\right)t + B\sin\dfrac{1}{2}\left(\sqrt{\dfrac{g}{a}}\right)t$

$\therefore t = 0, s = s_0 \Rightarrow A = s_0$

and $t = 0, \dot{s} = 0 \Rightarrow B = 0$

$\therefore s = s_0\cos\dfrac{1}{2}\left(\sqrt{\dfrac{g}{a}}\right)t$

$\therefore$ Reaches 0 when $s = 0 \Rightarrow \cos\dfrac{1}{2}\left(\sqrt{\dfrac{g}{a}}\right)t = 0$

$\Rightarrow \dfrac{1}{2}\left(\sqrt{\dfrac{g}{a}}\right)t = \dfrac{\pi}{2} \Rightarrow t = \pi\sqrt{\dfrac{a}{g}}$

$\therefore$ The time taken to read 0 is $\pi\sqrt{\dfrac{a}{g}}$, and this is independent of s_0.

14 (a) $\sin\psi = \dfrac{dy}{ds} \Rightarrow \dfrac{s}{4a} = \dfrac{dy}{ds}$

$\Rightarrow \displaystyle\int \dfrac{s\,ds}{4a} = \int dy$

$\Rightarrow \dfrac{s^2}{8a} = y + c \Rightarrow \dfrac{s^2}{8a} = y$

$\therefore \psi = \dfrac{\pi}{4} \Rightarrow s = 4a \times \dfrac{1}{\sqrt{2}} = 2a\sqrt{2} \Rightarrow y = a$

Conservation of energy:

$\dfrac{1}{2}m(3ag) + 0 = \dfrac{1}{2}mv^2 + mga \Rightarrow v = \sqrt{ga}$

The required speed is $\sqrt{ga}$

(b) $\rho = \dfrac{ds}{d\psi} = 4a \cos \psi$

$\therefore$ At $\psi = \dfrac{\pi}{4}$, $\rho = 2a\sqrt{2}$

$\therefore$ Normal contact force R is given by

$R - mg \cos \psi = \dfrac{mv^2}{\rho} \Rightarrow R = mg \times \dfrac{1}{\sqrt{2}} + \dfrac{m \times ga}{2a \sqrt{2}}$

$\Rightarrow R = \dfrac{3}{4} mg \sqrt{2}$, as required

15 (a)

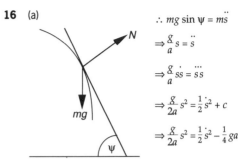

$\therefore mg \sin \psi = m\ddot{s}$

$\Rightarrow \ddot{s} = \dfrac{gs}{k}$

(b) $\ddot{s} = \dfrac{g}{k} s \Rightarrow \dot{s}\,\ddot{s} = \dfrac{g}{k} s\dot{s}$

$\Rightarrow \dfrac{1}{2}\dot{s}^2 = \dfrac{g}{2k} s^2 + c$

$\Rightarrow \dfrac{1}{2}\dot{s}^2 = \dfrac{gs^2}{2k} + \dfrac{1}{2}u^2$

$\therefore v^2 = gk \sin^2 \psi + u^2$

Also $\rho = \dfrac{ds}{d\psi} = k \cos \psi$

Since $R - mg \cos \psi = -\dfrac{mv^2}{\rho}$ and the particle

leaves the surface when $R = 0 \Rightarrow g \cos \psi = \dfrac{v^2}{\rho}$

$\Rightarrow g \cos \psi = \dfrac{gk \sin^2\psi + u^2}{k \cos \psi}$

$\therefore u^2 = \dfrac{1}{2} gk \Rightarrow \cos \psi = \dfrac{\sin^2\psi + \dfrac{1}{2}}{\cos \psi}$

$\Rightarrow \cos^2 \psi = \sin^2\psi + \dfrac{1}{2}$

$\Rightarrow \cos 2\psi = \dfrac{1}{2}$

$\Rightarrow 2\psi = \dfrac{\pi}{3} \Rightarrow \psi = \dfrac{\pi}{6}$

The particle leaves the surface when $\psi = \dfrac{\pi}{6}$

16 (a)

$\therefore mg \sin \psi = m\ddot{s}$

$\Rightarrow \dfrac{g}{a} s = \ddot{s}$

$\Rightarrow \dfrac{g}{a} s\dot{s} = \dot{s}\,\ddot{s}$

$\Rightarrow \dfrac{g}{2a} s^2 = \dfrac{1}{2}\dot{s}^2 + c$

$\Rightarrow \dfrac{g}{2a} s^2 = \dfrac{1}{2}\dot{s}^2 - \dfrac{1}{4} ga$

$\Rightarrow v^2 = \dfrac{g}{2a} (2s^2 + a^2)$, as required

(b) $mg \cos \psi - N = \dfrac{mv^2}{\rho}$ and $\rho = \dfrac{ds}{d\psi} = a \cos \psi$

$\therefore N = mg \cos \psi - \dfrac{mg}{2a} \times \dfrac{(2a^2 \sin^2 \psi + a^2)}{a \cos \psi}$

$\Rightarrow N = mg \cos \psi - \dfrac{mg}{2 \cos \psi} (2 \sin^2 \psi + 1)$

$\Rightarrow N = \dfrac{mg}{2 \cos \psi} \left[2 \cos^2\psi - 2 \sin^2\psi - 1\right]$

$\Rightarrow N = \dfrac{mg}{2 \cos \psi} \left[1 - 4 \sin^2 \psi\right]$, as required.

(c) $N = 0 \Rightarrow \sin \psi = \dfrac{1}{2} \Rightarrow \psi = \dfrac{\pi}{6} \Rightarrow s = \dfrac{a}{2}$

$\therefore$ distance travelled $= \dfrac{a}{2}$

Section 7

1 (a) Resolving along the normal:

$$mg \cos \psi = \frac{mv^2}{\rho} \Rightarrow g \cos \psi = \frac{v^2}{\rho} \qquad \dots \text{①}$$

Resolving along the tangent:

$$mg \sin \psi - mR = m \frac{dv}{dt}$$

$$\Rightarrow g \sin \psi - R = v \frac{dv}{ds} \qquad \dots \text{②}$$

Dividing equation ② by $g \cos \psi$ we get

$$\tan \psi - \frac{R}{g \cos \psi} = \frac{v}{g \cos \psi} \times \frac{dv}{ds} = \frac{\rho}{v} \times \frac{dv}{ds}$$

(Using equation ①)

$$= \frac{1}{v} \times \frac{ds}{d\psi} \times \frac{dv}{ds} = \frac{1}{v} \frac{dv}{d\psi} \text{ , as required}$$

2

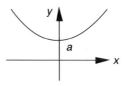

$$\therefore \quad mg \sin \psi = -m \frac{dv}{dt}$$

$$\Rightarrow \frac{gs}{4a} = -v \frac{dv}{ds}$$

$$\Rightarrow \int \frac{g}{4a} s \, ds = \int -v \, dv \Rightarrow \frac{g}{8a} s^2 = -\frac{1}{2} v^2 + \frac{g}{8a} c^2$$

$$\Rightarrow v^2 = \frac{g}{4a} (c^2 - s^2)$$

At the vertex $s = 0 \Rightarrow v^2 = \frac{gc^2}{4a} \Rightarrow v = c \sqrt{\frac{g}{4a}}$

as required.

At the vertex $R - mg = \frac{mv^2}{\rho} \qquad \dots \text{①}$

Since $\rho = \frac{ds}{d\psi} \Rightarrow \rho = 4a \cos \psi \;\therefore\; \rho$ at vertex $= 4a$

$\therefore$ Equation ① gives

$$R = mg + \frac{m \times c^2 \frac{g}{4a}}{4a} = mg \left(1 + \frac{c^2}{16a^2}\right),$$

as required

3 $s = 4b \sin \psi \Rightarrow s = 4b \frac{dy}{ds} \Rightarrow s^2 = 8by$

$$\Rightarrow \sin \psi = \sqrt{\frac{y}{2b}} \Rightarrow \cos \psi = \sqrt{\frac{2b-y}{2b}}$$

Energy: $\frac{1}{2} mv^2 + mgy = mgh \Rightarrow v^2 = 2g(h-y)$

Resolving: $R - mg \cos \psi = \frac{mv^2}{\rho}$ and

$$\rho = \frac{ds}{d\psi} = 4b \cos \psi$$

$$\therefore\; R = mg \cos \psi + \frac{2mg(h-y)}{4b \cos \psi}$$

$\therefore$ Vertical component of total force acting on the particle

$$= R \cos \psi - mg$$

$$= mg \cos^2 \psi + \frac{2mg(h-y)}{4b} - mg$$

which eventually simplifies to give

$$-\frac{mg}{b}\left(y - \frac{h}{2}\right)$$

$$\therefore\; \ddot{y} = -\frac{g}{b}\left(y - \frac{h}{2}\right)$$

$$\Rightarrow \text{period of SHM} = 2\pi \sqrt{\frac{b}{g}}$$

and the amplitude is $\frac{h}{2}$.

4

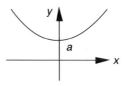

$$y^2 = x^2 + a^2 \Rightarrow \frac{dy}{dx} = \frac{x}{y} \Rightarrow \frac{d^2y}{dx^2} = \frac{a^2}{y^3}$$

$$\therefore\; \rho = \frac{\left[1 + \left(\frac{x}{y}\right)^2\right]^{\frac{3}{2}}}{\frac{a^2}{y^3}} \Rightarrow \rho = a \text{ at } (0, a)$$

Energy: $\frac{1}{2} mv^2 + mga = mg \frac{3a}{2} \Rightarrow v^2 = ga$

Resolving $\uparrow$ at vertex: $R - mg = \frac{mv^2}{\rho}$

$$\Rightarrow R = mg + \frac{m \times ga}{a} = 2mg, \text{ as required}$$

5

Energy: $\frac{1}{2}mv^2 = mg$

$\Rightarrow v = \sqrt{2g}$

at $x = \frac{\pi}{2}$,

At $x = \frac{\pi}{2}$, ρ is

infinite so $\frac{v^2}{\rho}$ is

zero. Also $\psi = \frac{3\pi}{4}$

since $\frac{dy}{dx} = -1$ at $x = \frac{\pi}{2}$

$\therefore R + mg \cos \psi = \frac{-mv^2}{\rho} \Rightarrow R = \frac{mg}{\sqrt{2}}$

6 $\rho = \dfrac{[\dot{x}^2 + \dot{y}^2]^{\frac{3}{2}}}{\ddot{x}\,\dot{y} - \dot{y}\,\ddot{x}} = \dfrac{[(2a)^2 + (2at)^2]^{\frac{3}{2}}}{2a \times 2a - 0}$

$= \dfrac{8a^3 (1 + t^2)^{\frac{3}{2}}}{4a^2} = 2a(1 + t^2)^{\frac{3}{2}}$

Energy: $\frac{1}{2}mv^2 + mg\,(at_1^2) = mg(at_0^2)$

$\Rightarrow v^2 = 2\,ga(t_0^2 - t_1^2)$, as required

$\tan \psi = \dfrac{dy}{dx} = t \Rightarrow \cos \psi = \dfrac{1}{\sqrt{1 + t^2}}$

$\therefore R - mg \cos \psi = \dfrac{mv^2}{\rho} \Rightarrow$

$R = \dfrac{mg}{\sqrt{1 + t_1^2}} + \dfrac{2\,mga\,(t_0^2 - t_1^2)}{2a(1 + t_1^2)^{\frac{3}{2}}}$

$\Rightarrow R = \dfrac{mg}{(1 + t_1^2)^{\frac{3}{2}}}\left[(1 + t_1^2) + (t_0^2 - t_1^2) \right]$

$\Rightarrow R = \dfrac{mg(1 + t_0^2)}{(1 + t_1^2)^{\frac{3}{2}}}$, as required

7

θ :	0	$\frac{\pi}{8}$	$\frac{\pi}{4}$	$\frac{3\pi}{8}$	$\frac{\pi}{2}$	$\frac{5\pi}{8}$	$\frac{3\pi}{4}$	$\frac{7\pi}{8}$
r :	4	5	4	3	4	5	4	3

(continued)

π	$\frac{9\pi}{8}$	$\frac{5\pi}{4}$	$\frac{11\pi}{8}$	$\frac{3\pi}{2}$	$\frac{13\pi}{8}$	$\frac{7\pi}{4}$	$\frac{15\pi}{8}$	2π
4	5	4	3	4	5	4	3	4

$r = 4 + \sin 4\theta$

$r^2 \dot{\theta} = h \Rightarrow \int r^2 \, d\theta = \int h \, dt$

$\Rightarrow \displaystyle\int_0^{2\pi} (4 + \sin 4\theta)^2 d\theta = [ht]_0^{20}$

$\Rightarrow \displaystyle\int_0^{2\pi} (16 + 8 \sin 4\theta + \sin^2 4\theta) \, d\theta = 20h$

$\Rightarrow \displaystyle\int_0^{2\pi} (16\tfrac{1}{2} + 8 \sin 4\theta - \tfrac{1}{2} \cos 8\theta) \, d\theta = 20h$

$\left(\text{using } \sin^2 A = \tfrac{1}{2} - \tfrac{1}{2} \cos 2A\right)$

$\Rightarrow \left[16\tfrac{1}{2}\,\theta - 2 \cos 4\theta - \tfrac{1}{16} \sin 8\theta \right]_0^{2\pi} = 20h$

$\Rightarrow 103.67 = 20h \Rightarrow h = 5.18$

$\therefore r^2\dot{\theta} = 5.18$ at all points.

$\therefore \left[16\tfrac{1}{2}\,\theta - 2 \cos 4\theta - \tfrac{1}{16} \sin 8\theta \right]_0^{\pi/4}$

$= \left[5.18t \right]_0^t$

$\Rightarrow 16.96 = 5.18t \Rightarrow t = 3.27$

$\therefore$ The required time is 3.27 seconds

8 $r = t \Rightarrow \dot{r} = 1 \Rightarrow \ddot{r} = 0$ and $\theta = \dfrac{6\pi}{t} \Rightarrow \dot{\theta} = \dfrac{-6\pi}{t^2}$

$\Rightarrow \ddot{\theta} = \dfrac{12\pi}{t^3}$

$\therefore \quad \dot{\mathbf{r}} = \begin{pmatrix} \dot{r} \\ r\dot{\theta} \end{pmatrix} \Rightarrow \dot{\mathbf{r}} = \begin{pmatrix} 1 \\ \frac{-6\pi}{t^2} \end{pmatrix}$

the velocity vector

and $\ddot{\mathbf{r}} = \begin{pmatrix} \ddot{r} - r\dot{\theta}^2 \\ \frac{1}{2}\frac{d}{dt}(r^2\dot{\theta}) \end{pmatrix} \Rightarrow \ddot{\mathbf{r}} = \begin{pmatrix} \frac{-36\pi^2}{t^3} \\ 0 \end{pmatrix}$

the acceleration vector

$\therefore$ zero transverse acceleration

$\therefore$ consistent with a central force.

When $t = 2$, $\ddot{\mathbf{r}} = \begin{pmatrix} -4.5\,\pi^2 \\ 0 \end{pmatrix}$

$\therefore$ The central force is $4.5\pi^2$ towards the origin O.

9 $-\int_{5}^{r} \dfrac{5m}{r^2}\, dr = \dfrac{1}{2} mv^2 - \dfrac{1}{2} m 1^2 \Rightarrow \dfrac{5}{r} = \dfrac{1}{2} v^2 + \dfrac{1}{2} \dots$ ①

Initially $r = 5$ and $r\dot\theta = 0.8$ ∴ $r^2\dot\theta = 5 \times 0.8 = 4$

∴ $r^2\dot\theta = 4$ at all points.   ... ②

Direction of motion at right angles to central

force when $\dot r = 0 \Rightarrow v = r\dot\theta \Rightarrow v = \dfrac{4}{r}$ (use

equation ②).

Substitute in ① to get $\dfrac{5}{r} = \dfrac{8}{r^2} + \dfrac{1}{2}$

$\Rightarrow r = 2$ or $8 \Rightarrow v = 2$ or 0.5

∴ The required speeds are 2 m s^{-1} and 0.5 m s^{-1}

10   (a) $\int -mk^2 r\, dr = \dfrac{1}{2} mv^2 + \text{constant}$

$\Rightarrow \dfrac{-mk^2 r^2}{2} = \dfrac{1}{2} mv^2 + \text{constant}$

$\Rightarrow v^2 + k^2 r^2 = \text{constant}$, as required

(b) Initially $r = 2k$ and $r\dot\theta = V$ ∴ $r^2\dot\theta = 2 kV$

∴ $r^2\dot\theta = 2kV$ at all points   ... ①

But $r = 2k \cos\theta$ ∴ equation ① gives

$\int 4k^2 \cos^2\theta\, d\theta = \int 2kV\, dt$

$\Rightarrow \int_{0}^{\theta} k(1 + \cos 2\theta)\, d\theta = \int_{0}^{t} V dt$

$\Rightarrow k\left(\theta + \dfrac{1}{2}\sin 2\theta\right) = Vt$

$\Rightarrow k(\theta + \sin\theta \cos\theta) = Vt$, as required

Reaches O when $\theta = \dfrac{\pi}{2} \Rightarrow t = \dfrac{k\pi}{2V}$

$ON = OM + MN$
$= k \cos 2\theta + CP$
$= k(\cos 2\theta + 1)$, as
required.

Angular momentum about O gives

$v \times ON = r\dot\theta \times OP \Rightarrow v = \dfrac{r^2\dot\theta}{k(\cos 2\theta + 1)}$

$\Rightarrow v = \dfrac{2kV}{k(\cos 2\theta + 1)}$ (Using ①)

$\Rightarrow v = 2V(\cos 2\theta + 1)^{-1}$, as required.

Energy: $-\int F(r)\, dr = \dfrac{1}{2} m \left(\dfrac{4k^2V}{r^2}\right)^2 - \dfrac{1}{2} mV^2$

$\Rightarrow -\int F(r)\, dr = \dfrac{8mk^4V^2}{r^4} - \dfrac{1}{2} mV^2$

Now differentiate both sides with respect to r

∴ $-F(r) = \dfrac{-32\, mk^4V^2}{r^5} \Rightarrow F(r) = \dfrac{32\, mk^4V^2}{r^5}$,

as required.

11   No forces perpendicular to the plane of polar
coordinates. ∴ P stays in the plane of polar
coordinates.

Radial: $-mf(r) = m(\ddot r - r\dot\theta^2)$

Tangential: $0 = \dfrac{m}{r} \dfrac{d}{dt}(r^2\dot\theta)$

∴ $r^2\dot\theta = h$, a constant and $\ddot r = \dfrac{h^2}{r^3} - f(r)$, as

required

Now $\dfrac{d}{d\theta}\left(\dfrac{1}{r}\right) = \dfrac{-1}{r^2} \dfrac{dr}{d\theta} = -\dfrac{1}{r^2} \times \dfrac{dr}{dt} \times \dfrac{dt}{d\theta}$

$= -\dfrac{1}{r^2} \times \dfrac{\dot r}{\dot\theta} = -\dfrac{\dot r}{h}$

∴ $\dot r = -h \dfrac{d}{d\theta}\left(\dfrac{1}{r}\right)$

Also $\ddot r = \dfrac{d}{dt}(\dot r) = -h \dfrac{d}{dt}\left[\dfrac{d}{d\theta}\left(\dfrac{1}{r}\right)\right]$

$= -h \dfrac{d^2}{d\theta^2}\left(\dfrac{1}{r}\right) \times \dot\theta$

$= \dfrac{-h^2}{r^2} \dfrac{d^2}{d\theta^2}\left(\dfrac{1}{r}\right)$, as required

Substitute for $\ddot r$ in the equation $\ddot r = \dfrac{h^2}{r^3} - f(r)$

to get

$-\dfrac{h^2}{r^2} \dfrac{d^2}{d\theta^2}\left(\dfrac{1}{r}\right) = \dfrac{h^2}{r^3} - f(r)$

∴ $\dfrac{d^2}{d\theta^2}\left(\dfrac{1}{r}\right) + \dfrac{1}{r} = \dfrac{r^2}{h^2} f(r)$. But $\dfrac{1}{r} = u$

∴ $\dfrac{d^2u}{d\theta^2} + u = \dfrac{1}{h^2 u^2} f\left(\dfrac{1}{u}\right)$, as required

Using $f\left(\dfrac{1}{u}\right) = \mu u^3$ and $av = h$, we get

$\dfrac{d^2u}{d\theta^2} + u = \dfrac{\mu u}{a^2 v^2}$

Now put $k^2 = 1 - \dfrac{\mu}{a^2 v^2}$ to get

$\dfrac{d^2u}{d\theta^2} + k^2 u = 0$

At last something we recognise!

$\therefore u = A \cos k\theta + B \sin k\theta$

$\therefore r = \dfrac{1}{A \cos k\theta + B \sin k\theta}$

$\therefore \theta = 0, r = a \Rightarrow A = \dfrac{1}{a}$

and $\theta = 0, \dot{r} = 0 \Rightarrow B = 0$

$\therefore r = \dfrac{1}{\frac{1}{a} \cos k\theta} \Rightarrow r = a \sec k\theta$, as required.

12 Perpendicular to the radius we have:

$\dfrac{1}{r} \dfrac{d}{dt} (r^2 \dot{\theta}) = 0 \Rightarrow r^2 \dot{\theta} = h \Rightarrow r \times r\dot{\theta} = h$

$\Rightarrow a \times U = h$

$\Rightarrow r^2 \dot{\theta} = aU$, as required

Also $-\dfrac{2maU^2}{r^2} = m \left(\ddot{r} - \dfrac{h^2}{r^3} \right)$

Putting $h = aU$, this gives $\ddot{r} = \dfrac{a^2 U^2}{r^3} - \dfrac{2aU^2}{r^2}$, as required

Multiplying by $\dot{r}$ and integrating we get

$\dfrac{1}{2} \dot{r}^2 = -\dfrac{a^2 U^2}{2r^2} + \dfrac{2aU^2}{r} + \text{constant}$

$\therefore t = 0, r = a, \dot{r} = 0$

$\Rightarrow \dfrac{1}{2} \dot{r}^2 = -\dfrac{a^2 U^2}{2r^2} + \dfrac{2aU^2}{r} - \dfrac{3U^2}{2}$

$\Rightarrow \dot{r}^2 = \dfrac{U^2}{r^2} (-a^2 + 4ar - 3r^2)$, as required

13 $r^2 \dot{\theta} = h \Rightarrow c^2 \dot{\theta} = h \cos 2\theta \Rightarrow$

$\displaystyle\int c^2 \sec 2\theta \, d\theta = \int h \, dt$

$\Rightarrow \dfrac{c^2}{2} \ln \tan \left(\theta + \dfrac{\pi}{4} \right) = ht$

$\Rightarrow \theta + \dfrac{\pi}{4} = \tan^{-1} \left(e^{\frac{2ht}{c^2}} \right)$

$\Rightarrow \dot{\theta} = \dfrac{h}{c^2} \operatorname{sech} \left(\dfrac{2ht}{c^2} \right)$

$\therefore r^2 \dot{\theta} = h \Rightarrow r^2 = c^2 \cosh \left(\dfrac{2ht}{c^2} \right)$

$\Rightarrow r = c \sqrt{\cosh \left(\dfrac{2ht}{c^2} \right)}$

$\Rightarrow \dot{r} = \dfrac{\frac{h}{c} \sinh \left(\frac{2ht}{c^2} \right)}{\sqrt{\cosh \left(\frac{2ht}{c^2} \right)}}$

$\Rightarrow \dot{r}^2 = \dfrac{h^2 r^2}{c^4} - \dfrac{h^2}{r^2}$

$\therefore$ Differentiating with respecct to t

$\Rightarrow 2\dot{r}\ddot{r} = \dfrac{2h^2 r \dot{r}}{c^4} + \dfrac{2h^2}{r^3} \dot{r}$

$\Rightarrow \ddot{r} = \dfrac{h^2 r}{c^4} + \dfrac{h^2}{r^3}$

$\therefore -f(r) = m \left(\ddot{r} - \dfrac{h^2}{r^3} \right) \Rightarrow -f(r) = \dfrac{mh^2}{c^4} r.$

$\therefore$ The central force is proportional to r.

Clearly that is too long a question for your 'A' level. However, the mathematics is interesting because it shows that, given a curve, it is possible to work out the corresponding central force. In theory, then, if we know the path traced out by a planet, we ought to be able to work out the corresponding central force. We'll leave that to somebody else!

14 $\rightarrow : a = u \cos \alpha t \therefore$ time to hit the wall is

$\dfrac{a}{u \cos \alpha}.$

Rebounds with its horizontal velocity component now $eu \cos \alpha$

$\therefore$ time taken to return is $\dfrac{a}{eu \cos \alpha}$

$\therefore$ Total time of flight $= \dfrac{a}{u \cos \alpha} + \dfrac{a}{eu \cos \alpha}$

Vertically the wall doesn't affect the velocity.

$\therefore$ the time of flight is as though the wall wasn't there!

$\uparrow: \ddot{y} = -g, \ \dot{y} = -gt + u \sin \alpha, \ y = -\dfrac{1}{2}gt^2 + ut \sin \alpha$

$\therefore y = 0 \Rightarrow t = \dfrac{2 u \sin \alpha}{g}$, the time of flight

$\therefore \dfrac{a}{u \cos \alpha} + \dfrac{a}{eu \cos \alpha} = \dfrac{2u \sin \alpha}{g}$

$\therefore ag \left(1 + \dfrac{1}{e} \right) = u^2 \times 2 \sin \alpha \cos \alpha$, the required result.

15

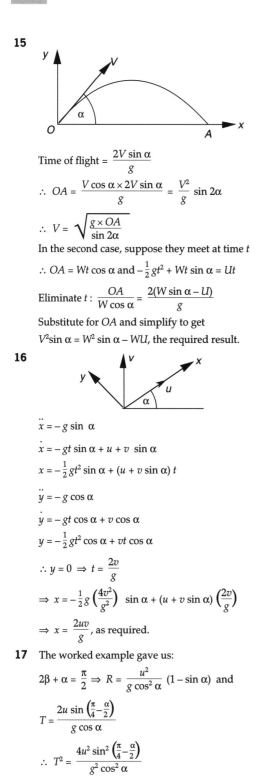

Time of flight $= \dfrac{2V \sin \alpha}{g}$

$\therefore OA = \dfrac{V \cos \alpha \times 2V \sin \alpha}{g} = \dfrac{V^2}{g} \sin 2\alpha$

$\therefore V = \sqrt{\dfrac{g \times OA}{\sin 2\alpha}}$

In the second case, suppose they meet at time t

$\therefore OA = Wt \cos \alpha$ and $-\dfrac{1}{2} gt^2 + Wt \sin \alpha = Ut$

Eliminate t: $\dfrac{OA}{W \cos \alpha} = \dfrac{2(W \sin \alpha - U)}{g}$

Substitute for OA and simplify to get

$V^2 \sin \alpha = W^2 \sin \alpha - WU$, the required result.

16

$\ddot{x} = -g \sin \alpha$

$\dot{x} = -gt \sin \alpha + u + v \sin \alpha$

$x = -\dfrac{1}{2} gt^2 \sin \alpha + (u + v \sin \alpha) t$

$\ddot{y} = -g \cos \alpha$

$\dot{y} = -gt \cos \alpha + v \cos \alpha$

$y = -\dfrac{1}{2} gt^2 \cos \alpha + vt \cos \alpha$

$\therefore y = 0 \Rightarrow t = \dfrac{2v}{g}$

$\Rightarrow x = -\dfrac{1}{2} g \left(\dfrac{4v^2}{g^2}\right) \sin \alpha + (u + v \sin \alpha) \left(\dfrac{2v}{g}\right)$

$\Rightarrow x = \dfrac{2uv}{g}$, as required.

17 The worked example gave us:

$2\beta + \alpha = \dfrac{\pi}{2} \Rightarrow R = \dfrac{u^2}{g \cos^2 \alpha} (1 - \sin \alpha)$ and

$T = \dfrac{2u \sin \left(\frac{\pi}{4} - \frac{\alpha}{2}\right)}{g \cos \alpha}$

$\therefore T^2 = \dfrac{4u^2 \sin^2 \left(\frac{\pi}{4} - \frac{\alpha}{2}\right)}{g^2 \cos^2 \alpha}$

$= \dfrac{2u^2}{g^2 \cos^2 \alpha} \left(1 - \cos \left(\dfrac{\pi}{2} - \alpha\right)\right)$

$= \dfrac{2u^2}{g^2 \cos^2 \alpha} (1 - \sin \alpha)$

$\therefore gT^2 = 2R$, as required.

(I hope that *you* worked the problem through from scratch.)

18

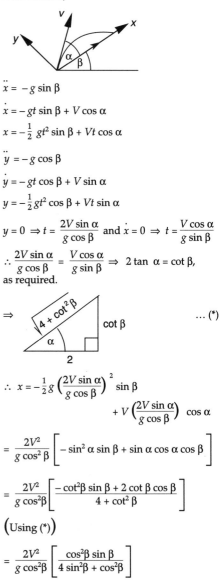

$\ddot{x} = -g \sin \beta$

$\dot{x} = -gt \sin \beta + V \cos \alpha$

$x = -\dfrac{1}{2} gt^2 \sin \beta + Vt \cos \alpha$

$\ddot{y} = -g \cos \beta$

$\dot{y} = -gt \cos \beta + V \sin \alpha$

$y = -\dfrac{1}{2} gt^2 \cos \beta + Vt \sin \alpha$

$y = 0 \Rightarrow t = \dfrac{2V \sin \alpha}{g \cos \beta}$ and $\dot{x} = 0 \Rightarrow t = \dfrac{V \cos \alpha}{g \sin \beta}$

$\therefore \dfrac{2V \sin \alpha}{g \cos \beta} = \dfrac{V \cos \alpha}{g \sin \beta} \Rightarrow 2 \tan \alpha = \cot \beta,$ as required.

$\Rightarrow$

$\qquad\qquad \dots (*)$

$\therefore x = -\dfrac{1}{2} g \left(\dfrac{2V \sin \alpha}{g \cos \beta}\right)^2 \sin \beta$

$\qquad\qquad + V \left(\dfrac{2V \sin \alpha}{g \cos \beta}\right) \cos \alpha$

$= \dfrac{2V^2}{g \cos^2 \beta} \left[-\sin^2 \alpha \sin \beta + \sin \alpha \cos \alpha \cos \beta \right]$

$= \dfrac{2V^2}{g \cos^2 \beta} \left[\dfrac{-\cot^2\beta \sin \beta + 2 \cot \beta \cos \beta}{4 + \cot^2 \beta} \right]$

$\left(\text{Using } (*) \right)$

$= \dfrac{2V^2}{g \cos^2 \beta} \left[\dfrac{\cos^2\beta \sin \beta}{4 \sin^2\beta + \cos^2\beta} \right]$

$$= \frac{2V^2}{g}\left[\frac{\sin\beta}{1+3\sin^2\beta}\right]$$

But the expression $\dfrac{X}{1+3X^2}$ is greatest when its derivative is zero

$$\therefore\ \frac{(1+3X^2)-6X^2}{(1+3X^2)^2}=0\ \Rightarrow X=\frac{1}{\sqrt{3}}$$

$$\therefore\ \text{greatest } X = \frac{2V^2}{g}\left[\frac{1/\sqrt{3}}{1+1}\right]=\frac{V^2}{g\sqrt{3}}$$

as required.

19

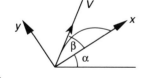

$$y=0\ \Rightarrow\ t=\frac{2u\sin(\psi-\alpha)}{g\cos\alpha}$$

$$\dot{x}=0\ \Rightarrow\ t=\frac{u\cos(\psi-\alpha)}{g\sin\alpha}$$

Equate these times and get $2\tan\alpha = \cot(\psi-\alpha)$, as required.

$$\therefore\ x=\frac{2u^2}{g\cos^2\alpha}\left[-\sin^2(\psi-\alpha)\sin\alpha\right.$$
$$\left.+\sin(\psi-\alpha)\cos(\psi-\alpha)\cos\alpha\right]$$

(See question 18)

$$=\frac{u^2}{g\cos^2\alpha}\left[\left(\cos 2(\psi-\alpha)-1\right)\sin\alpha\right.$$
$$\left.+\sin 2(\psi-\alpha)\cos\alpha\right]$$

$$=\frac{u^2}{g\cos^2\alpha}\left[\cos 2(\psi-\alpha)\sin\alpha\right.$$
$$\left.+\sin 2(\psi-\alpha)\cos\alpha-\sin\alpha\right]$$

$$=\frac{u^2}{g\cos^2\alpha}\left[\sin(2\psi-\alpha)-\sin\alpha\right],\text{ as required}$$

20

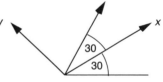

$$\ddot{y}=-g\cos\alpha$$

$$\dot{y}=-gt\cos\alpha+V\sin\beta$$

$$y=-\frac{1}{2}gt^2\cos\alpha+Vt\sin\beta$$

$$\therefore\ y=0\ \Rightarrow\ t=\frac{2V\sin\beta}{g\cos\alpha}$$

Rebounds from plane with $\dot{y}=eV\sin\beta$

$\therefore$ Time of second bounce is $\dfrac{2eV\sin\beta}{g\cos\alpha}$

$\therefore$ Time of third bounce is $\dfrac{2e^2V\sin\beta}{g\cos\alpha}$ etc

$\therefore$ Time for n bounces

$$=\frac{2V\sin\beta}{g\cos\alpha}\left(1+e+e^2+\ldots+e^{n-1}\right)$$

$$=\frac{2V\sin\beta\,(1-e^n)}{g\cos\alpha\,(1-e)}\quad\text{(a geometric progression)}$$

Then $\quad\ddot{x}=-g\sin\alpha$

$$\dot{x}=-gt\sin\alpha+V\cos\beta$$

$$x=-\frac{1}{2}gt^2\sin\alpha+Vt\cos\beta$$

After n bounces, the total distance up the plane must be zero $\therefore\ x=0\ \Rightarrow\ t=\dfrac{2V\cos\beta}{g\sin\alpha}$.

Equate these times to get:

$$\frac{2V\sin\beta\,(1-e^n)}{g\cos\alpha\,(1-e)}=\frac{2V\cos\beta}{g\sin\alpha}$$

$\therefore\ (1-e^n)\tan\alpha\tan\beta=(1-e)$, as required.

21

Equations of motion are:

$$\ddot{x}=-\frac{g}{2}\qquad\text{and}\qquad\ddot{y}=-\frac{g\sqrt{3}}{2}$$

$$\dot{x}=-\frac{gt}{2}+45\sqrt{3}\qquad\qquad\dot{y}=-\frac{g\sqrt{3}t}{2}+45$$

$$x=-\frac{gt^2}{4}+45\sqrt{3}.t\qquad\quad y=-\frac{g\sqrt{3}t^2}{4}+45t$$

Lands again when $y=0$

$$\Rightarrow\quad t=\frac{180}{g\sqrt{3}}=10.6$$

$$\Rightarrow\quad x=\frac{-g}{4}\left(\frac{180}{g\sqrt{3}}\right)^2+45\sqrt{3}\left(\frac{180}{g\sqrt{3}}\right)=551$$

$\therefore$ Lands again after 10.6 sec with a range of 551 m

Section 8

1

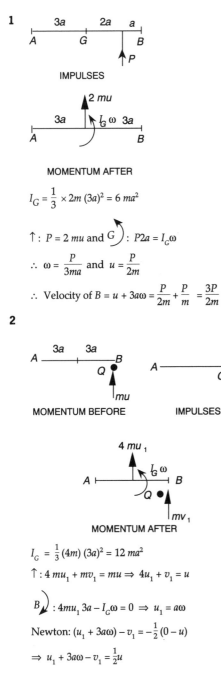

$I_G = \frac{1}{3} \times 2m \, (3a)^2 = 6 \, ma^2$

$\uparrow: P = 2 \, mu$ and $\left(G\right.\!\!\curvearrowleft$: $P2a = I_G\omega$

$\therefore \omega = \dfrac{P}{3ma}$ and $u = \dfrac{P}{2m}$

$\therefore$ Velocity of $B = u + 3a\omega = \dfrac{P}{2m} + \dfrac{P}{m} = \dfrac{3P}{2m}$

2

$I_G = \frac{1}{3}(4m)\,(3a)^2 = 12 \, ma^2$

$\uparrow: 4mu_1 + mv_1 = mu \Rightarrow 4u_1 + v_1 = u$

$\left(B\right.\!\!\curvearrowright$: $4mu_1 \, 3a - I_G\omega = 0 \Rightarrow u_1 = a\omega$

Newton: $(u_1 + 3a\omega) - v_1 = -\frac{1}{2}(0 - u)$

$\Rightarrow u_1 + 3a\omega - v_1 = \frac{1}{2}u$

Solve these equations to get $u_1 = \dfrac{3u}{16}$, $v_1 = \dfrac{u}{4}$ and $\omega = \dfrac{3u}{16a}$

3

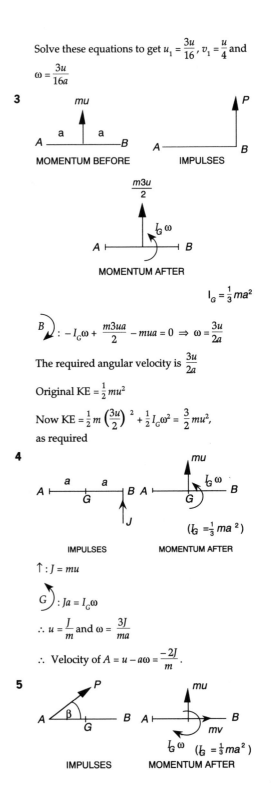

$I_G = \frac{1}{3} ma^2$

$\left(B\right.\!\!\curvearrowright$: $-I_G\omega + \dfrac{m3ua}{2} - mua = 0 \Rightarrow \omega = \dfrac{3u}{2a}$

The required angular velocity is $\dfrac{3u}{2a}$

Original KE $= \frac{1}{2} mu^2$

Now KE $= \frac{1}{2} m \left(\dfrac{3u}{2}\right)^2 + \frac{1}{2} I_G\omega^2 = \dfrac{3}{2} mu^2$, as required

4

$\uparrow: J = mu$

$\left(G\right.\!\!\curvearrowright$: $Ja = I_G\omega$

$\therefore u = \dfrac{J}{m}$ and $\omega = \dfrac{3J}{ma}$

$\therefore$ Velocity of $A = u - a\omega = \dfrac{-2J}{m}$.

5

$\rightarrow P \cos \beta = mv$

$\uparrow : P \sin \beta = mu$

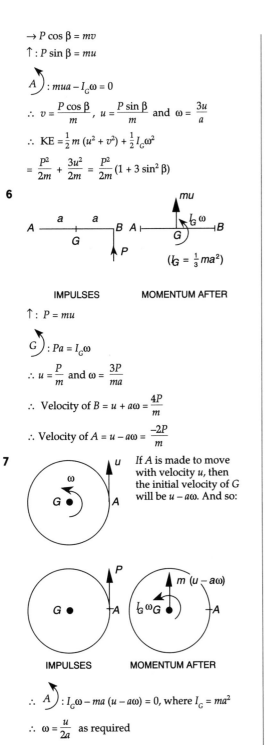

$A \!\!\bigg)\!\! : mua - I_G \omega = 0$

$\therefore v = \dfrac{P \cos \beta}{m}$, $u = \dfrac{P \sin \beta}{m}$ and $\omega = \dfrac{3u}{a}$

$\therefore KE = \dfrac{1}{2} m (u^2 + v^2) + \dfrac{1}{2} I_G \omega^2$

$= \dfrac{P^2}{2m} + \dfrac{3u^2}{2m} = \dfrac{P^2}{2m} (1 + 3 \sin^2 \beta)$

6

$A \underset{G}{\overline{a a}} B$ $A \vdash \overset{I_G \omega}{\underset{G}{}} \dashv B$

$\qquad\qquad\uparrow P \qquad\qquad \uparrow mu$

$\qquad\qquad\qquad\qquad (I_G = \tfrac{1}{3} ma^2)$

IMPULSES   **MOMENTUM AFTER**

$\uparrow : P = mu$

$G \!\!\bigg)\!\! : Pa = I_G \omega$

$\therefore u = \dfrac{P}{m}$ and $\omega = \dfrac{3P}{ma}$

$\therefore$ Velocity of $B = u + a\omega = \dfrac{4P}{m}$

$\therefore$ Velocity of $A = u - a\omega = \dfrac{-2P}{m}$

7

If A is made to move with velocity u, then the initial velocity of G will be $u - a\omega$. And so:

IMPULSES   **MOMENTUM AFTER**

$\therefore A \!\!\bigg)\!\! : I_G \omega - ma (u - a\omega) = 0$, where $I_G = ma^2$

$\therefore \omega = \dfrac{u}{2a}$ as required

8 As in question 7, the velocity of G will initially be $u - a\omega$.

$\therefore A \!\!\bigg)\!\! : I_G \omega = ma (u - a\omega) = 0$, where $I_G = \dfrac{1}{2} ma^2$

$\therefore \omega = \dfrac{2u}{3a}$, as required

9

If A is made to move with velocity u, then the velocity of G will be made up of two parts (as shown in the diagram)

Since $AG = a\sqrt{2}$ we have:

IMPULSES $ma\omega \sqrt{2}$ **MOMENTUM AFTER**

$\qquad\qquad\qquad\qquad (I_G = \tfrac{2}{3} ma^2)$

$\therefore A \!\!\bigg)\!\! : ma\omega \sqrt{2} \times a\sqrt{2} + I_G \omega - mu \times a = 0$

$\therefore \omega = \dfrac{3u}{8a}$, as required

10 (a) First find the position of G. Let it be $\bar{x}$ from A

$\therefore A \!\!\bigg)\!\! : m \times L + m \times \dfrac{4L}{3} = 2m \, \bar{x} \Rightarrow \bar{x} = \dfrac{7L}{6}$

$\therefore M.I. = \underbrace{\dfrac{1}{3} mL^2 + m \left(\dfrac{L}{6}\right)^2}_{\text{rod}}$

$\underbrace{+ \, m \left(\dfrac{L}{6}\right)^2}_{\text{particle}} = \dfrac{7}{18} mL^2$

(b) Set up the three separate diagrams

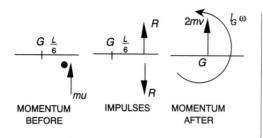

MOMENTUM BEFORE   IMPULSES   MOMENTUM AFTER

(R is the impulse on the rod and the equal and opposite impulse on the particle. v is the velocity of G immediately after impact.)

$\uparrow \therefore \ 2mv - mu = 0 \Rightarrow v = \dfrac{u}{2}$ ... ①

Moments about G for the whole system:

$\overset{\curvearrowright}{G} : \left(\dfrac{7}{18}mL^2\right)\omega - mu\dfrac{L}{6} = 0 \Rightarrow \omega = \dfrac{3u}{7L}$ ... ②

(c) KE before $= \dfrac{1}{2}mu^2$

KE after $= \dfrac{1}{2}\left(\dfrac{7}{18}mL^2\right)\omega^2 + \dfrac{1}{2}\times 2m \times v^2$

Now use equations ① and ② above

$\therefore$ KE after $= \dfrac{2}{7}mu^2$

$\therefore$ Loss of KE $= \dfrac{3}{7}$ of the original KE

11 Set up the three separate diagrams

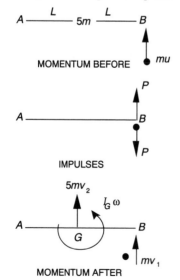

MOMENTUM BEFORE

IMPULSES

MOMENTUM AFTER

(P is the impulse on the rod and the equal and opposite impulse on the particle. v_2 is the

velocity of G, the centre of mass of AB. ω is the angular velocity and v_1 the velocity of the particle after impact.)

Conservation of linear momentum for the whole system:

$\therefore \ 5mv_2 + mv_1 = mu$ ... ①

The velocity of B is $v_2 + L\omega$

$\therefore$ Newton's law gives: $v_2 + L\omega - v_1 = -\dfrac{1}{3}(0-u)$

$\Rightarrow v_2 + L\omega - v_1 = \dfrac{u}{3}$.   ... ②

Moments about B for the whole system:

$\overset{\curvearrowright}{B} : \left(\dfrac{1}{3}\times 5m \times L^2\right)\omega - 5m\,Lv_2 - 0 = 0$

$\Rightarrow v_2 = \dfrac{L\omega}{3}$ ... ③

Solve equations ①, ② and ③ to give $\omega = \dfrac{4u}{9L}$

and $v_1 = \dfrac{7u}{27}$

$\therefore$ the speed of P after impact is $\dfrac{7u}{27}$.

12

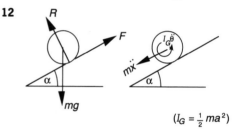

$(I_G = \tfrac{1}{2}ma^2)$

$\therefore \ R - mg\cos\alpha = 0,\ mg\sin\alpha - F = m\ddot{x},\ Fa = I_G\ddot{\theta}$

And rolling implies $\dot{x} - a\dot{\theta} = 0$

Eliminating F gives $g\sin\alpha - \dfrac{1}{2}a\ddot{\theta} = \ddot{x}$

$\Rightarrow g t \sin\alpha - \dfrac{1}{2}a\dot{\theta} = \dot{x}$

$\Rightarrow \dot{x} = \dfrac{2}{3}gt\sin\alpha$

$\Rightarrow \ddot{x} = \dfrac{2}{3}g\sin\alpha$

$\therefore \ F = \dfrac{1}{3}mg\sin\alpha \ \therefore F \le \mu R \ \Rightarrow \mu \ge \dfrac{1}{3}\tan\alpha$

The acceleration is $\dfrac{2}{3}g\sin\alpha$ and the least value of the coefficient of friction is $\dfrac{1}{3}\tan\alpha$

13

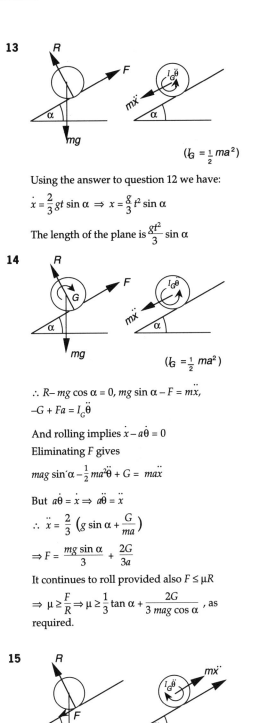

$$(I_G = \tfrac{1}{2}ma^2)$$

Using the answer to question 12 we have:

$$\dot{x} = \tfrac{2}{3}gt\sin\alpha \;\Rightarrow\; x = \tfrac{g}{3}t^2\sin\alpha$$

The length of the plane is $\dfrac{gt^2}{3}\sin\alpha$

14

$$(I_G = \tfrac{1}{2}ma^2)$$

$$\therefore\; R - mg\cos\alpha = 0,\; mg\sin\alpha - F = m\ddot{x},$$
$$-G + Fa = I_G\ddot{\theta}$$

And rolling implies $\dot{x} - a\dot{\theta} = 0$

Eliminating F gives

$$mag\sin'\alpha - \tfrac{1}{2}ma^2\ddot{\theta} + G = ma\ddot{x}$$

But $a\dot{\theta} = \dot{x} \Rightarrow a\ddot{\theta} = \ddot{x}$

$$\therefore\; \ddot{x} = \tfrac{2}{3}\left(g\sin\alpha + \frac{G}{ma}\right)$$

$$\Rightarrow F = \frac{mg\sin\alpha}{3} + \frac{2G}{3a}$$

It continues to roll provided also $F \le \mu R$

$$\Rightarrow \mu \ge \frac{F}{R} \Rightarrow \mu \ge \tfrac{1}{3}\tan\alpha + \frac{2G}{3\,mag\cos\alpha}\,,\text{ as}$$
required.

15

$$(I_G = \tfrac{1}{2}ma^2)$$

$$\therefore\; R - mg\cos\alpha = 0,\; -mg\sin\alpha - F = m\ddot{x},$$

$$Fa = I_G\ddot{\theta}$$

And rolling implies $\dot{x} - a\dot{\theta} = 0$

Eliminating F gives $-g\sin\alpha - \tfrac{1}{2}a\ddot{\theta} = \ddot{x}$

$$\Rightarrow -g\sin\alpha - \tfrac{1}{2}\ddot{x} = \ddot{x}$$

$$\Rightarrow \ddot{x} = -\tfrac{2}{3}g\sin\alpha$$

$$\Rightarrow \dot{x} = -\tfrac{2}{3}gt\sin\alpha + \text{constant} \qquad \dots\,①$$

Initially the angular velocity was ω and the velocity of the point of contact was zero (because this disc began rolling).

$\therefore$ Initially

$\therefore$ Velocity of A is zero

$$\Rightarrow u - a\omega = 0$$

$\therefore$ Initially $\dot{x} = a\omega$

$\therefore$ Equation ① gives $\dot{x} = -\tfrac{2}{3}gt\sin\alpha + a\omega$

$$\Rightarrow x = -\frac{gt^2}{3}\sin\alpha + a\omega t$$

And $\dot{x} = 0 \Rightarrow t = \dfrac{3a\omega}{2g\sin\alpha} \Rightarrow x = \dfrac{3a^2\omega^2}{4g\sin\alpha}$, as required.

16

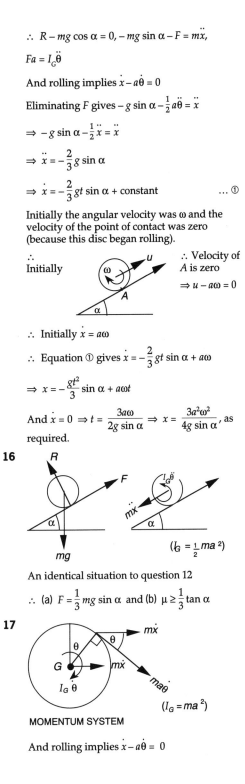

$$(I_G = \tfrac{1}{2}ma^2)$$

An identical situation to question 12

$$\therefore\; \text{(a)}\; F = \tfrac{1}{3}mg\sin\alpha \;\text{ and (b) } \mu \ge \tfrac{1}{3}\tan\alpha$$

17

$$(I_G = ma^2)$$

MOMENTUM SYSTEM

And rolling implies $\dot{x} - a\dot{\theta} = 0$

We *could* take moments about G and integrate but this question is ideally tackled by conservation of energy. (We are not interested in any forces, we just want $\dot{\theta}$.)

Taking the horizontal as zero potential energy, we get:

$$3\,mga = mga + mga\,(1 + \cos\theta) + \tfrac{1}{2}I_G\dot{\theta}^2 + \tfrac{1}{2}m\dot{x}^2$$

$$+ \tfrac{1}{2}m\left\{(\dot{x} + a\dot{\theta}\cos\theta)^2 + (a\dot{\theta}\sin\theta)^2\right\}$$

$$\Rightarrow mga = mga\cos\theta + \tfrac{1}{2}ma^2\dot{\theta}^2 + \tfrac{1}{2}ma^2\dot{\theta}^2$$

$$+ \tfrac{1}{2}m\left\{\dot{x}^2 + 2a\dot{x}\dot{\theta}\cos\theta + a^2\dot{\theta}^2\right\}$$

$$\Rightarrow g\,(1 - \cos\theta) = a\dot{\theta}^2 + \tfrac{1}{2}\left\{a\dot{\theta}^2 + 2a\dot{\theta}^2\cos\theta + a\dot{\theta}^2\right\}$$

$$\Rightarrow g(1 - \cos\theta) = a\dot{\theta}^2\,(2 + \cos\theta)$$

$$\Rightarrow \dot{\theta}^2 = \frac{g}{a} \times \frac{(1 - \cos\theta)}{(2 + \cos\theta)}, \text{ as required.}$$

18

The velocity of the point of contact A is initially $a\,\Omega$ to the right.

∴ the frictional force **F** will be to the left. And so:

INITIAL SITUATION

$(I_G = ma^2)$

$$\therefore \uparrow: R - mg = 0 \qquad\qquad \dots ①$$

$$\leftarrow: F = m\ddot{x} \qquad\qquad \dots ②$$

$$G \,\rotatebox{0}{$\circlearrowright$}: Fa = -I_G\ddot{\theta} \qquad\qquad \dots ③$$

It slips ∴ $F = \mu R \qquad\qquad \dots ④$

Equations ①, ② and ④ give $\ddot{x} = \mu g \Rightarrow \dot{x} = \mu g t$

$$\dots ⑤$$

Equations ② and ③ give $\ddot{x} = -a\ddot{\theta}$

$$\Rightarrow \dot{x} = -a\dot{\theta} + a\Omega \text{ (since } \dot{x} = 0 \text{ when } \dot{\theta} = \Omega)$$

$$\Rightarrow a\dot{\theta} = a\Omega - \mu g t \text{ (Use equation ⑤)} \qquad \dots ⑥$$

The hoop begins to roll when $\dot{x} - a\dot{\theta} = 0$

∴ Equations ⑤ and ⑥ give $\mu g t = a\Omega - \mu g t$

$$\Rightarrow t = \frac{a\Omega}{2\mu g}, \text{ as required.}$$

19 The same diagrams and equations as in question 18 except that, here, $I_G = \tfrac{1}{2}ma^2$

We still get $\ddot{x} = \mu g t$ but, this time, $\ddot{x} = -\tfrac{1}{2}a\ddot{\theta}$

$$\Rightarrow \dot{x} = -\tfrac{1}{2}a\dot{\theta} + \tfrac{1}{2}a\Omega \Rightarrow a\dot{\theta} = a\Omega - 2\mu g t.$$

The disc begins to roll when $\dot{x} - a\dot{\theta} = 0$

$$\therefore \mu g t = a\Omega - 2\mu g t \Rightarrow t = \frac{a\Omega}{3\mu g}, \text{ as required.}$$

Hence $\dot{\theta} = \frac{1}{3}\Omega$ as required.

20 The same diagrams and equations as in question 18 except that, here, $I_G = \tfrac{2}{5}ma^2$

We still get $\ddot{x} = \mu g t$ but, this time, $\ddot{x} = -\tfrac{2}{5}a\ddot{\theta}$

$$\Rightarrow \dot{x} = -\tfrac{2}{5}a\dot{\theta} + \tfrac{2}{5}a\Omega \Rightarrow a\dot{\theta} = a\Omega - \tfrac{5}{2}\mu g t$$

The sphere begins to roll when $\dot{x} - a\dot{\theta} = 0$

$$\therefore \mu g t = a\Omega - \frac{5\mu g t}{2} \Rightarrow t = \frac{2a\Omega}{7\mu g}, \text{ as required}$$

21

$(I_G = \tfrac{1}{3}ma^2)$

$$\uparrow: R - mg = -ma\ddot{\theta}\sin\theta \qquad\qquad \dots ①$$

$$\rightarrow: F = ma\ddot{\theta}\cos\theta \qquad\qquad \dots ②$$

$$A\,\rotatebox{0}{$\circlearrowright$}: mga\sin\theta = I_G\ddot{\theta} + ma^2\ddot{\theta} \qquad\qquad \dots ③$$

Equation ③ gives $a\ddot{\theta} = \tfrac{3}{4}g\sin\theta$

∴ Equation ② gives $F = \tfrac{3}{4}mg\sin\theta\cos\theta$

and equation ① gives $R = mg - \dfrac{3\,mg\sin^2\theta}{4}$

∴ Initially (when θ = 30°)

$$F = \frac{3}{4} mg \times \frac{\sqrt{3}}{4} = \frac{3\sqrt{3}\, mg}{16}$$

and $R = mg - \frac{3}{4} mg \times \frac{1}{4} = \frac{13\, mg}{16}$

∴ will not immediately slip providing $\mu > \dfrac{F}{R}$

i.e. $\mu > \dfrac{3\sqrt{3}}{13}$, as required

In that case, the reaction on the plane is $\dfrac{13\, mg}{16}$

22

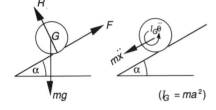

Rolls ∴ $\dot{x} = a\dot{\theta}$

Down the plane : $mg \sin \alpha - F = m\ddot{x}$

Perpendicular to plane: $mg \cos \alpha = R$

$\overset{\frown}{G}$: $Fa = I_G \ddot{\theta}$

Now use $\ddot{x} = a\ddot{\theta}$ and substitute for F to get

$mg \sin \alpha - m\ddot{x} = m\ddot{x}$

∴ $\ddot{x} = \dfrac{1}{2} g \sin \alpha$, as required.

23

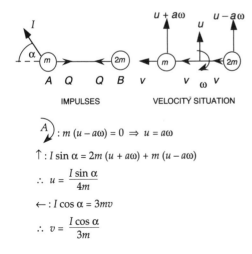

IMPULSES VELOCITY SITUATION

$\overset{\frown}{A}$: $m(u - a\omega) = 0 \Rightarrow u = a\omega$

↑ : $I \sin \alpha = 2m(u + a\omega) + m(u - a\omega)$

∴ $u = \dfrac{I \sin \alpha}{4m}$

← : $I \cos \alpha = 3mv$

∴ $v = \dfrac{I \cos \alpha}{3m}$

∴ Initial speed of A

$$= \sqrt{v^2 + (2u)^2} = \frac{I}{6m} \sqrt{4 + 5 \sin^2\alpha}$$

and

initial speed of B

$$= v = \frac{I \cos \alpha}{3m}$$

KE generated $= \dfrac{1}{2} . 2m . \dfrac{I^2}{36m^2} (4 + 5 \sin^2\alpha)$

$$+ \frac{1}{2} . m . \frac{I^2 \cos^2\alpha}{9m^2}$$

$$= \frac{I^2}{12m} (2 + \sin^2\alpha)$$

24

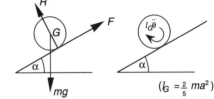

When placed on the plane, the sphere will skid on the spot until it eventually comes to a halt. Then it will roll. While it is spinning and skidding, we have:

$\overset{\frown}{G}$: $Fa = -I_G \ddot{\theta}$ ∴ $F = -\dfrac{2ma}{5} \ddot{\theta}$ ... ①

Up the plane: $F - mg \sin \alpha = 0$

Perpendicular to the plane : $R - mg \cos \alpha = 0$

(These last two equations give $\dfrac{F}{R} = \tan \alpha$.

But $\mu = \tan \alpha$ ∴ This confirms skidding on the spot.)

Now substitute for F in ① to get

$$g \sin \alpha = -\frac{2a\ddot{\theta}}{5}$$

$\Rightarrow gt \sin \alpha = -\dfrac{2a\dot{\theta}}{5} + \dfrac{2a\Omega}{5}$ ($t = 0$ when $\dot{\theta} = \Omega$)

Sphere stops skidding when

$\dot{\theta} = 0 \Rightarrow t = \dfrac{2a\Omega}{5g \sin \alpha}$, as required.

Section 9

1 $PE = -mga \sin 2\theta + \dfrac{\dfrac{mg}{2\sqrt{3}}(4a \sin \theta - a)^2}{2a}$

(taking zero level as A0)

$= -mga \sin 2\theta + \dfrac{mga}{4\sqrt{3}}(16 \sin^2\theta - 8 \sin \theta + 1)$

$= -mga \sin 2\theta + \dfrac{mga}{4\sqrt{3}}(8 - 8 \cos 2\theta - 8 \sin \theta + 1)$

$= -\dfrac{mga}{\sqrt{3}}(\sqrt{3} \sin 2\theta + 2 \cos 2\theta + 2 \sin \theta) + \text{const.}$

$\dfrac{dV}{d\theta} = 0 \Rightarrow 2\sqrt{3} \cos 2\theta - 4 \sin 2\theta + 2 \cos \theta = 0$

and $\theta = 30°$ satisfies this equation

$\dfrac{d^2V}{d\theta^2} = -4\sqrt{3} \sin 2\theta - 8 \cos 2\theta - 2 \sin \theta$

At $\theta = 30°$, $\dfrac{d^2V}{d\theta^2} < 0$ ∴ unstable equilibrium

At $\theta = 90°$, $\dfrac{dV}{d\theta} < 0$ and at $\theta = 120°$, $\dfrac{dV}{d\theta} > 0$

∴ there is a solution to the equation $\dfrac{dV}{d\theta} = 0$

for $90° < \theta < 120°$.

∴ there is a position of equilibrium in this range.

2

$AB^2 = 16a^2 + 4a^2 - 16a^2 \cos \theta$ (cosine rule)

∴ $AB = 2a \sqrt{5 - 4 \cos \theta}$

If length of string is l then

$OP = 4a - BP$

$= 4a - (l - 2a \sqrt{5 - 4 \cos \theta}$

$= 2a \sqrt{5 - 4 \cos \theta} + \text{const.}$

∴ $PE = -Wa \cos (\pi - \theta) +$

$\qquad kW \left[\text{constant} + 2a \sqrt{5 - 4 \cos \theta} \right]$

(zero level horizontally through O)

∴ $V = Wa \cos \theta + 2 kWa \sqrt{5 - 4 \cos \theta} + \text{const.}$

$\dfrac{dV}{d\theta} = 0 \Rightarrow -\sin \theta + \dfrac{4 k \sin \theta}{\sqrt{5 - 4 \cos \theta}} = 0$

$\Rightarrow \sin \theta = 0$ or $\sqrt{5 - 4 \cos \theta} = 4k$

$\Rightarrow \sin \theta = 0$ or $\cos \theta = \dfrac{5 - 16 k^2}{4}$

If $\dfrac{1}{4} < k < \dfrac{3}{4}$, then a position of equilibrium is obtained from $\cos \theta = \dfrac{5 - 16 k^2}{4}$

Then $k = \dfrac{1}{4}\sqrt{3} \Rightarrow \sin \theta = 0$ or $\cos \theta = \dfrac{1}{2}$

$\Rightarrow \theta = 0°, 180°$ or $60°$

also $\dfrac{d^2V}{d\theta^2} = -\cos \theta +$

$\dfrac{\sqrt{3} \cos \theta \sqrt{5 - 4 \cos \theta} - 2\sqrt{3}(5 - 4 \cos \theta)^{-\frac{1}{2}} \sin^2\theta}{5 - 4 \cos \theta}$

And $\theta = 0°$ or $180° \Rightarrow \dfrac{d^2V}{d\theta^2} > 0$ ∴ minimum

Also $\theta = 60° \Rightarrow \dfrac{d^2V}{d\theta^2} < 0$ ∴ maximum

∴Stable at $\theta = 0°$ and $\theta = 180°$ but unstable at $\theta = 60°$

3 $AB^2 = 4a^2 + a^2 - 4a^2 \cos \theta$ (cosine rule)

∴ $AB = a \sqrt{5 - 4 \cos \theta}$

If length of string is l, then $BC = l - a \sqrt{5 - 4 \cos \theta}$

∴ $V = -\dfrac{mga}{2} \sin \theta - \dfrac{1}{4} mg (l - a \sqrt{5 - 4 \cos \theta})$

$\qquad\qquad\qquad\qquad\qquad + \text{constant}$

$= \dfrac{mga}{4}(-2 \sin \theta + \sqrt{5 - 4 \cos \theta}) + \text{constant}$

∴ $\dfrac{dV}{d\theta} = 0 \Rightarrow -2 \cos \theta + \dfrac{2 \sin \theta}{\sqrt{5 - 4 \cos \theta}} = 0$

$\Rightarrow \cos^2\theta (5 - 4 \cos \theta) = \sin^2\theta$

$\Rightarrow \cos^2\theta (5 - 4 \cos \theta) = 1 - \cos^2\theta$

$\Rightarrow 4 \cos^3\theta - 6 \cos^2\theta + 1 = 0$

∴ $x = 2 \cos \theta \Rightarrow x^3 - 3x^2 + 2 = 0$

$\Rightarrow (x - 1)(x^2 - 2x - 2) = 0$

$\Rightarrow x = 1$ or $1 \pm \sqrt{3}$

$\Rightarrow \cos \theta = \dfrac{1}{2}$ or $\dfrac{1 - \sqrt{3}}{2}$

$\Rightarrow \theta = 60°$ or $248.5°$

At $\theta = 60°$, $\dfrac{d^2V}{d\theta^2} > 0$ ∴ minimum

At $\theta = 248.5°$, $\dfrac{d^2V}{d\theta^2} < 0$ ∴ maximum

∴ Stable at $\theta = 60°$ but unstable at $\theta = 248.5°$

4 Elastic PE = work done in stretching it a length e

$$= \int_0^e \frac{\lambda x}{l} \, dx$$

$$= \left[\frac{\lambda x^2}{2l} \right]_0^e$$

$$= \frac{\lambda e^2}{2l}$$

$BC^2 = 4a^2 + a^2 - 4a^2 \cos \theta$
(cosine rule)

$\therefore BC = a \sqrt{5 - 4 \cos \theta}$

$\therefore$ Extension in string

$$= a \left(\sqrt{5 - 4 \cos \theta} - 1 \right)$$

$$\therefore V = - \frac{Wa}{2} \cos (\pi - \theta) +$$

$$\frac{\frac{1}{2} Wa^2 \left(\sqrt{5 - 4 \cos \theta} - 1 \right)^2}{2a} + \text{constant}$$

$$= \frac{Wa}{2} \cos \theta + \frac{Wa}{2} \left[3 - 2 \cos \theta - \sqrt{5 - 4 \cos \theta} \right]$$
$$+ \text{constant}$$

$$= - \frac{Wa}{2} \cos \theta - \frac{Wa}{2} \sqrt{5 - 4 \cos \theta} + \text{constant}$$

$$\therefore \frac{dV}{d\theta} = 0 \Rightarrow \frac{1}{2} \sin \theta - \frac{\sin \theta}{\sqrt{5 - 4 \cos \theta}} = 0$$

$\Rightarrow \sin \theta = 0$ or $\sqrt{5 - 4 \cos \theta} = 2$

$\Rightarrow \sin \theta = 0$ or $\cos \theta = \frac{1}{4}$

$\Rightarrow \cos \theta = 1$ or -1 or $\frac{1}{4}$

$\Rightarrow \theta = 0°, 180°$ or $75.5°$

At $\theta = 0°$ and $180°$, $\frac{d^2V}{d\theta^2} < 0 \therefore$ maximum

At $\theta = 75.5°$, $\frac{d^2V}{d\theta^2} > 0 \therefore$ minimum

$\therefore$ Unstable at $\theta = 0°$ and $\theta = 180°$ but stable at $\theta = 75.5°$.

5 $AP^2 = 2a^2 - 2a^2 \cos \left(\frac{\pi}{3} + \theta \right)$ (cosine rule in triangle AOP)

$$= 2a^2 \left(1 - \cos \left(\frac{\pi}{3} + \theta \right) \right)$$

$$= 4a^2 \sin^2 \frac{1}{2} \left(\frac{\pi}{3} + \theta \right)$$

$$\therefore AP = 2a \sin \left(\frac{\pi}{6} + \frac{\theta}{2} \right)$$

$BP^2 = 2a^2 - 2a^2 \cos^2 \left(\frac{\pi}{3} - \theta \right)$ (cosine rule in triangle POB)

$\therefore$ Similarly $BP = 2a \sin \left(\frac{\pi}{6} - \frac{\theta}{2} \right)$.

The depth of P below the level of AB is

$a \cos \theta - a \cos \frac{\pi}{3}$.

Let string PAQ have length l_1 and string PBR length l_2

$$\therefore V = - kmg \left[l_1 - 2a \sin \left(\frac{\pi}{6} + \frac{\theta}{2} \right) \right]$$

$$- kmg \left[l_2 - 2a \sin \left(\frac{\pi}{6} - \frac{\theta}{2} \right) \right]$$

$$- mg \left(a \cos \theta - a \cos \frac{\pi}{3} \right)$$

$$= 2 kmga \left[\sin \left(\frac{\pi}{6} + \frac{\theta}{2} \right) + \sin \left(\frac{\pi}{6} - \frac{\theta}{2} \right) \right]$$

$$- mga \cos \theta + \text{constant}$$

$$= 2 kmga \times 2 \sin \frac{\pi}{6} \cos \frac{1}{2} \theta - mga \cos \theta$$
$$+ \text{constant}$$

$$= 2 kmga \cos \frac{1}{2} \theta - mga \cos \theta + \text{constant},$$
$$\text{as required}$$

$$\therefore \frac{dV}{d\theta} = mag \left(-k \sin \frac{1}{2} \theta + \sin \theta \right)$$

$$\text{and} \frac{d^2V}{d\theta^2} = mag \left(-\frac{k}{2} \cos \frac{1}{2} \theta + \cos \theta \right)$$

$$\therefore \frac{dV}{d\theta} = 0 \Rightarrow -k \sin \frac{1}{2} \theta + \sin \theta = 0$$

$$\Rightarrow -k \sin \frac{1}{2} \theta + 2 \sin \frac{1}{2} \theta \cos \frac{1}{2} \theta = 0$$

$$\Rightarrow \sin \frac{1}{2} \theta = 0 \text{ or } \cos \frac{1}{2} \theta = \frac{k}{2}$$

When $k = 1.8 \Rightarrow \sin \frac{1}{2} \theta = 0$ and $\cos \frac{1}{2} \theta = 0.9$

$\Rightarrow \theta = 0°$ or $\theta = \pm 51.7°$

At $\theta = 0°$, $\frac{d^2V}{d\theta^2} > 0 \therefore$ minimum

At $\theta = \pm 51.7°$ $\frac{d^2V}{d\theta^2} < 0 \therefore$ maximum

$\therefore$ Stable at $\theta = 0°$ but unstable at $\theta = \pm 51.7°$

6

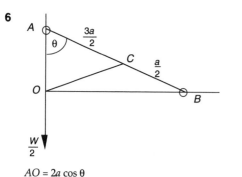

$AO = 2a \cos \theta$

$\therefore OC^2 = (2a \cos \theta)^2 + \left(\dfrac{3a}{2}\right)^2 - 2.2\,a \cos \theta \times \dfrac{3a}{2} \times \cos \theta$

(cosine rule)

$= \dfrac{9a^2}{4} - 2a^2 \cos^2 \theta$

$= \dfrac{9a^2}{4} - 2a^2 (1 - \sin^2 \theta)$

$\therefore OC = \dfrac{a}{2}\sqrt{1 + 8 \sin^2 \theta}$

If the string has length l, the potential energy of the hanging weight is $-\dfrac{W}{2}\left[l - \dfrac{a}{2}\sqrt{1 + 8 \sin^2 \theta}\right]$

(zero level OB)

$\therefore V = -\dfrac{W}{2}\left[(l - \dfrac{a}{2}\sqrt{1 + 8 \sin^2 \theta}\right] + Wa \cos \theta$

$= \dfrac{Wa}{4}\left[4 \cos \theta + \sqrt{1 + 8 \sin^2 \theta}\right] + \text{constant}$

$\therefore \dfrac{dV}{d\theta} = 0 \Rightarrow -4 \sin \theta + \dfrac{8 \sin \theta \cos \theta}{\sqrt{1 + 8 \sin^2 \theta}} = 0$

$\Rightarrow \sin \theta = 0$ or $\sqrt{1 + 8 \sin^2 \theta} = 2 \cos \theta$

$\Rightarrow \sin \theta = 0$ or $1 + 8 \sin^2 \theta = 4 (1 - \sin^2 \theta)$

$\Rightarrow \sin \theta = 0$ or $\sin \theta = \dfrac{1}{2}$

$\Rightarrow \theta = 30°$ only in this case

At $\theta = 30°$, $\dfrac{d^2V}{d\theta^2} < 0$ $\therefore$ maximum

$\therefore$ Unstable equilibrim at $\theta = 30°$

7

$AC = 4a \sin \theta$

$\therefore$ Velocity of C is $4a \cos \theta\,\dot\theta$

$\therefore$ KE of particle $= \dfrac{1}{2}\left(\dfrac{m}{12}\right)\left(4a \cos \theta\,\dot\theta\right)^2$

$= \dfrac{2}{3} ma^2 \cos^2 \theta\,\dot\theta^2$

KE of rod $AB = \dfrac{1}{2}\left(\dfrac{4}{3} ma^2\right)\dot\theta^2 = \dfrac{2}{3} ma^2\dot\theta^2$

PE of rod $AB = -mga \cos \theta$ (AC the zero level)

Total energy is constant

$\therefore \dfrac{2}{3} ma^2 \cos^2 \theta\,\dot\theta^2 + \dfrac{2}{3} ma^2\dot\theta^2 - mga \cos \theta = \text{const.}$

$\therefore 2a\dot\theta^2 (1 + \cos^2 \theta) - 3g \cos \theta = \text{constant}$

(a) Velocity of C is initially $\sqrt{6ag}$

$\Rightarrow 4a \cos \theta \times \dot\theta_0 = \sqrt{6ag}$ (and $\theta = 0$)

$\Rightarrow \dot\theta_0 = \sqrt{\dfrac{3g}{8a}}$

$\therefore 2a\dot\theta^2 (1 + \cos^2\theta) - 3g \cos \theta$

$= 2a \left(\sqrt{\dfrac{3g}{8a}}\right)^2 (1 + 1) - 3g \times 1 = \dfrac{-3g}{2}$

$\therefore 2a\,\dot\theta^2 (1 + \cos^2 \theta) - 3g \cos \theta = -\dfrac{3g}{2}$

$\therefore \dot\theta = 0 \Rightarrow \cos \theta = \dfrac{1}{2} \Rightarrow \theta = 60°$

(b) Differentiate the energy equation

$\therefore 4a\,\dot\theta\ddot\theta (1 + \cos^2\theta) + 2a\dot\theta^2 (-2 \cos \theta \sin \theta\,\dot\theta)$

$\hspace{3cm} + 3g \sin \theta\,\dot\theta = 0$

$\Rightarrow 4a\ddot\theta (1 + \cos^2\theta) - 4a \cos \theta \sin \theta\,\dot\theta^2 + 3g \sin \theta = 0$

Now let $\theta = \psi$ where ψ is small

$\therefore \cos \psi \approx 1$, $\sin \psi \approx \psi$ and $\dot\theta = \dot\psi$

$\therefore 4a\ddot\psi (1 + 1) - 4a \times 1 \times \psi + \dot\psi^2 + 3g\psi \approx 0$

∴ $8a\ddot{\psi} \approx -3g\ \psi$ (ignore $\psi \times \dot{\psi}^2$ as being too small)

∴ $\ddot{\psi} \approx -\left(\frac{3g}{8a}\right)\psi$

∴ period of small oscillations is approximately

$2\pi\sqrt{\dfrac{8a}{3g}}$ or $4\pi\sqrt{\dfrac{2a}{3g}}$

8

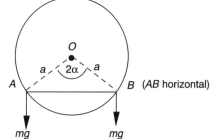

$AC = 4a\cos\theta$

∴ Velocity of $C = -4a\sin\theta\dot{\theta}$

∴ KE of $C = \frac{1}{2}\left(\frac{m}{2}\right)\left(-4a\sin\theta\dot{\theta}\right)^2$

$= 4ma^2\sin^2\theta\dot{\theta}^2$

PE of $C = -\frac{mg}{2}\times 4a\cos\theta = -2mga\cos\theta$

(line through A is zero level)

KE of rod $= \frac{1}{2}\left(\frac{4}{3}ma^2\right)\dot{\theta}^2$ i.e. $\frac{2}{3}ma^2\dot{\theta}^2$

PE of rod $= -mga\cos\theta$

Total energy is constant

∴ $4ma^2\sin^2\theta\dot{\theta}^2 - 2mga\cos\theta$

$\qquad + \frac{2}{3}ma^2\dot{\theta}^2 - mga\ \cos\theta = $ constant

$\Rightarrow 2a\dot{\theta}^2(1+6\sin^2\theta) - 9g\ \cos\theta = $ constant

(a) When $\theta = \alpha, \dot{\theta} = 0$

$\Rightarrow 2a\dot{\theta}^2(1+6\sin^2\theta) - 9g\cos\theta = -9g\cos\alpha$

∴ $\theta = 0 \Rightarrow \dot{\theta}^2 = \frac{9g}{2a}(1-\cos\alpha)$

∴ Acceleration of C along $CA = 4a\dot{\theta}^2$

$= 18g(1-\cos\alpha)$

∴ $\frac{m}{2}\times 18g(1-\cos\alpha) = T - \frac{mg}{2}$

$\Rightarrow T = \frac{mg}{2}(19-18\cos\alpha)$

(b) Differentiate the energy equation

∴ $4a\dot{\theta}\ddot{\theta}(1+6\sin^2\theta) + 2a\dot{\theta}^2(12\sin\theta\cos\theta\dot{\theta})$
$\qquad + 9g\sin\theta\dot{\theta} = 0$

∴ $4a\ddot{\theta}(1+6\sin^2\theta) + 24a\sin\theta\cos\theta\dot{\theta}^2$
$\qquad + 9g\sin\theta = 0$

Let $\theta = \alpha$ so $\sin\alpha \approx \alpha, \cos\alpha \approx 1, \dot{\theta} = \dot{\alpha}$

and $\ddot{\theta} = \ddot{\alpha}$

∴ $4a\ddot{\alpha}(1+6\alpha^2) + 24a\alpha \times 1 \times \dot{\alpha}^2 + 9\alpha g \approx 0$

$\Rightarrow 4a\ddot{\alpha} + 9\alpha g \approx 0$ (ignoring small terms)

$\Rightarrow \ddot{\alpha} \approx -\left(\frac{9y}{4a}\right)\alpha$

∴ Period of small oscillations is approximately

$2\pi\sqrt{\dfrac{4a}{9g}}$ or $\dfrac{4\pi}{3}\sqrt{\dfrac{a}{g}}$.

∴ One quarter of the period is approximately

$\dfrac{\pi}{3}\sqrt{\dfrac{a}{g}}$

9 The position of stable equilibrium is given by

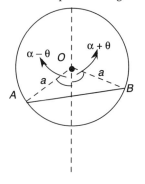

A small displacement θ gives

Velocity of A and B are both equal to $a\dot{\theta}$

∴ KE of system $= \frac{1}{2}m(a\dot{\theta})^2 \times 2$ i.e. $ma^2\dot{\theta}^2$

Depth of A below the horizontal through O is

$a \cos(\alpha - \theta)$

The corresponding depth of B is

$a \cos(\alpha + \theta)$

Total energy is a constant

$\therefore \ ma^2\dot{\theta}^2 - mga \cos(\alpha - \theta) - mga \cos(\alpha + \theta)$
$= \text{constant}$

$\Rightarrow ma^2\dot{\theta}^2 - mga \left[\cos(\alpha - \theta) + \cos(\alpha + \theta)\right]$
$= \text{constant}$

$\Rightarrow ma^2\dot{\theta}^2 - 2\,mga \cos\alpha \cos\theta = \text{constant}$

$\Rightarrow a\dot{\theta}^2 - 2\,g \cos\alpha \cos\theta = \text{constant}$

Differentiation $\Rightarrow 2a\dot{\theta}\,\ddot{\theta} + 2g \cos\alpha \sin\theta\,\dot{\theta} = 0$

$\Rightarrow \ddot{\theta} \approx -\dfrac{g \cos\alpha}{a}\,\theta \ \ (\text{since } \sin\theta \approx \theta)$

$\therefore$ Period of small oscillations is approximately

$2\pi \sqrt{\dfrac{a}{g \cos\alpha}}$

10 In the horizontal position:

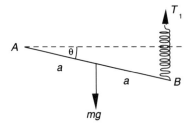

$\therefore \ A\!\curvearrowright : \ mga = T \times 2a$

$\Rightarrow T = \dfrac{mg}{2}$

If extension in spring in that position is x, then

$T = \dfrac{\lambda x}{l} \Rightarrow \dfrac{mg}{2} = \dfrac{\lambda x}{l} \Rightarrow x = \dfrac{mgl}{2\lambda}.$

given a small displacement θ:

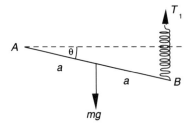

$\therefore$ Extension in spring is now $\dfrac{mgl}{2\lambda} + 2a \sin\theta$

Total energy is constant

$\therefore \ \dfrac{1}{2}\left(\dfrac{4}{3}ma^2\right)\dot{\theta}^2 + \dfrac{\lambda \left(\dfrac{mgl}{2\lambda} + 2a \sin\theta\right)^2}{2l}$
$\qquad\qquad - mga \sin\theta = \text{constant}$

Now differentiate

$\therefore \ \dfrac{4}{3}ma^2\dot{\theta}\,\ddot{\theta} + \dfrac{\lambda}{l}\left(\dfrac{mgl}{2\lambda} + 2a \sin\theta\right)\times 2a \cos\theta\,\dot{\theta}$

$\qquad\qquad - mga \cos\theta\,\dot{\theta} = 0$

$\Rightarrow \dfrac{4}{3}ma\ddot{\theta} + \dfrac{\lambda}{l}\left(\dfrac{mgl}{2\lambda} + 2a \sin\theta\right)2 \cos\theta$

$\qquad\qquad - mg \cos\theta = 0$

Since θ is small, $\sin\theta \approx \theta$ and $\cos\theta \approx 1$

$\therefore \ \dfrac{4}{3}ma\,\ddot{\theta} + \dfrac{\lambda}{l}\left(\dfrac{mgl}{2\lambda} + 2a\theta\right)2 \times 1 - mg \times 1 \approx 0$

$\Rightarrow \dfrac{4}{3}ma\,\ddot{\theta} \approx -\dfrac{4\lambda a}{l}\theta \ \Rightarrow \ \ddot{\theta} \approx -\left(\dfrac{3\lambda}{lm}\right)\theta$

$\Rightarrow$ period of small oscillations is

approximately $2\pi\sqrt{\dfrac{lm}{3\lambda}}$